THE OFFICIAL HANDBOOK OF THE MARVEL UNIVERSE

X-MEN
Part One

BEAST

REAL NAME: Henry "Hank" P. McCoy
KNOWN ALIASES: Formerly Kreature, Mutate #666
IDENTITY: Publicly known
OCCUPATION: Adventurer, former biochemist, college lecturer
PLACE OF BIRTH: Dunfee, Illinois
CITIZENSHIP: United States of America with no criminal record
MARITAL STATUS: Single
KNOWN RELATIVES: Sadie McCoy (grandmother), Edna McCoy (mother), Norton McCoy (father), Robert McCoy (uncle)
GROUP AFFILIATION: X-Men, formerly X-Treme X-Men, X-Factor, Defenders, Avengers, Rejects
EDUCATION: Ph. D. Biochemistry

HISTORY: While working at a nuclear power plant, Norton McCoy was exposed to massive amounts of radiation that affected his genes. As a result, Norton's son, Henry "Hank" McCoy, was born a mutant who showed the signs of his being different from birth with his unusually large hands and feet.

As a youth, Hank's freakish appearance was the subject of much ridicule from his classmates, earning him the nickname of "beast". However, one classmate, Jennifer Nyles, came to know the real Hank after he began tutoring her in biology. On the night of the junior prom, Jennifer insisted that Hank accompany her as her date, and stood up for him after he was teased.

In his senior year, Hank's superhuman agility and athletic prowess earned him recognition as a star football player. During one game, Hank easily stopped a trio of robbers who were attempting to escape across the football field. The villain named the Conquistador noticed his efforts, kidnapping Hank's parents in an attempt to coerce the young mutant into working for him. The X-Men soon arrived and defeated the villain, and Hank was invited by Professor Charles Xavier to join the team of teenage mutant heroes and enroll in the Xavier School for Gifted Youngsters. Unable to resist the temptation of a private institution that could offer him limitless academic opportunities, Hank accepted.

A brilliant student, Hank completed his doctoral studies under Xavier's tutelage, and finally graduated from the Xavier School to take a position at the Brand Corporation as a genetic researcher under Doctor Carl Maddicks. During one of his experiments, Hank discovered the hormonal extract that causes genetic mutation and went to inform Maddicks of his findings. However, Maddicks was secretly plotting to steal top-secret government documents, and Hank took it upon himself to stop Maddicks. In order to disguise his appearance, Hank took the hormonal extract and underwent radical physical changes that enhanced his agility and strength – as well as causing him to grow fangs, pointed ears, and fur all over his body. When he stayed too long in this state, Hank found he could not return to his original form. He was now a beast in fact as well as in name. At first, he tried to hide his mutation with a latex mask and gloves, but later learned to accept his new appearance.

After receiving his doctorate in genetics and being considered one of the world's experts on mutations and evolutionary human biology, despite never having earned a Nobel Prize or been invited to join the National Academy of Sciences, Hank left Brand and applied to join the ranks of Earth's Mightiest Heroes in the Avengers. Initially accepted as a probationary member, Hank soon proved his worth and was granted full membership. During his time with the team he revealed his identity to the public in the hope that his status as an Avenger would help ease human/mutant tensions.

Following a restructuring of the Avengers, Hank left and became involved with the team of adventurers known as the Defenders which he soon reorganized into a more formal and cohesive unit, bringing in his former X-Men teammates Iceman and Angel. Following the apparent death of several of the Defenders, Hank reunited with the other four original X-Men to form X-Factor, an organization that intended to seek out and aid other mutants under the pretense of hunting down those perceived menaces to society. Shortly after the formation of X-Factor, Hank was captured by Maddicks, who sought to experiment on Hank in an attempt to find a "cure" for his son's own mutancy. However, the serum Hank was given caused him to revert to his original human appearance. Soon after, Hank first met television anchorwoman Trish Tilby, who was investigating X-Factor.

During an attack on New York by the eternal mutant Apocalypse and his Four Horsemen, Hank was stricken with a virus that sapped his intellect and increased his strength every time he exerted himself physically. The more Hank used his strength, the stronger he got, but the less intelligent he became. Finally, to save his friend Iceman from the deadly kiss of the mutant named Infectia, Hank intervened and was himself affected, the result of which returned him to his blue-furred form and restored his intellect. Soon after, Hank and Trish began seeing each other romantically; however her work often intruded on their relationship and the pair ultimately called it off.

After X-Factor disbanded, Hank returned to the ranks of the X-Men and became the team's resident technological and medical genius, working on everything from advanced alien technology to the deadly mutant-killing Legacy Virus. Hank also continued his on/off relationship with Trish until she released information on the Virus to the public, which caused hysteria that culminated in the beating to death of a young mutant.

During his tenure with the X-Men, Beast was lured into a trap and replaced in the ranks of the X-Men by the Dark Beast, an alternate-reality version of himself. Sealed behind a brick wall, Hank was nearly about to give up when his water tube broke and spurted, revealing the grooves of a trap door in his cell. Energized by hope, Beast broke his restraints and escaped with the aid of the new government-sponsored X-Factor team.

Hank returned to the X-Men in time to aid the team against the threat of the powerful psionic creature known as Onslaught. After the battle, Hank met with Trish and apologized for his previous harsh treatment of her. She forgave him and the pair renewed their relationship.

Hank eventually took an extended leave of absence from the X-Men to work on a cure for the Legacy Virus, which he ultimately found thanks to his implementing the work of his former colleague, the late Moira MacTaggart. Soon after, Hank joined Storm's team of X-Treme X-Men in their quest for the diaries of the late mutant seer Destiny. Almost killed in the team's first battle with the enhanced human named Vargas, Hank's life was saved by his teammate Tessa who used a heretofore-unseen power to accelerate his mutation to a new level.

Hank returned to Xavier's mansion to recuperate and mutated further, becoming bulkier, heavier, and taking on a more lionesque appearance. Forced to relearn fine motor control over his body, Hank once again served as the team's resident genius, as well as an active teacher of dozens of young mutants at the renamed Xavier Institute of Higher Learning.

Unable to deal with his latest mutation, Trish called Hank and ended their relationship over the phone. Soon after, Hank was beaten into a coma by a student possessed by Professor Xavier's malevolent twin Cassandra Nova, who herself had possessed Xavier's body. Hank recovered in time to expose her plans and Cassandra was ultimately defeated, but not before she had exposed her brother Charles to the world as a mutant, forever changing life at the Xavier mansion for the X-Men.

PHYSICAL DESCRIPTION:

HEIGHT: 5'11"
WEIGHT: 402 lbs
EYES: Blue
HAIR: Brown (originally), Bluish-black (currently)

DISTINGUISHING FEATURES: Covered with fur, unusually large hands and feet, pointed ears, fang-like teeth, lionesque appearance

POWERS & ABILITIES:

STRENGTH LEVEL: The Beast possesses superhuman strength enabling him to lift/press approximately 2 tons under optimal conditions.

SUPERHUMAN POWERS: In addition to his superhuman strength, the Beast possesses superhuman agility, endurance, and speed, despite his bulk. He possesses the agility of a great ape and the acrobatic prowess of an accomplished circus aerialist. His physiology is durable enough to allow him to survive a three-story fall by landing on his feet without suffering any broken bones or sprains.

The Beast's legs are powerful enough to enable him to leap approximately 15 feet high in a standing high jump, and around 25 feet in a standing broad jump. He can also run on all fours at approximately 40 miles per hour for short sprints.

The Beast can crawl up brick walls by wedging his fingers and toes into the smallest cracks and applying a vise-like grip on them, as well as walk a tightrope with minimal effort. He is adept in performing complicated sequences of gymnastics such as flips, rolls, and springs, and can also walk on his hands for many hours. Further, his manual and pedal dexterity are so great that he can perform multiple tasks such as writing with both hands at once or tying knots in rope with his toes.

The Beast possesses enhanced senses, the ability to secrete pheromones to attract members of the opposite sex, as well as a slight healing factor that allows him to regenerate minor wounds and recover quickly from minor ailments such as colds. The Beast also possesses cat-like night vision as well as razor-sharp claws on his hands and feet.

SPECIAL SKILLS: Hank is considered one of the world's experts on mutations and evolutionary human biology. He has extensive knowledge of genetics, biochemistry, and a variety of other scientific fields. Hank is also an accomplished keyboard player.

POWER GRID

	1	2	3	4	5	6	7
INTELLIGENCE							
STRENGTH							
SPEED							
DURABILITY							
ENERGY PROJECTION							
FIGHTING SKILLS							

REAL NAME: Lucas Bishop
KNOWN ALIASES: None
IDENTITY: No dual identity; the general public is unaware that Bishop comes from the future of an alternate timeline
OCCUPATION: Adventurer, police officer, former Commander in the Xavier Security Enforcers (X.S.E.)
PLACE OF BIRTH: Mutant relocation camp in Brooklyn, New York on an alternate 21st Century Earth
CITIZENSHIP: United States of America in an alternate 21st Century future with no criminal record

MARITAL STATUS: Single
KNOWN RELATIVES: Gateway (great-grandfather), unnamed grandmother, unnamed parents, Shard (sister, deceased)
GROUP AFFILIATION: X-Men, formerly X-Treme Sanctions Executive, X-Treme X-Men, The Twelve, M-Faces (leader), Xavier Security Enforcers
EDUCATION: Unrevealed

HISTORY: Lucas Bishop was born in the 21st Century A.D. of an alternate future timeline in which the mutant-hunting robot Sentinels had taken control of North America. In this timeline, Professor Charles Xavier and most of the members of the mutant team he founded, the X-Men, had been killed. Surviving mutants were hunted down and either killed or imprisoned within relocation camps.

Bishop's parents escaped to America shortly before the island nation of Australia was destroyed in a tactical nuclear strike. They were soon captured and interred in a mutant relocation camp in Sheep's Head Bay in Brooklyn, New York. There, Bishop and his sister Shard were born and, like other mutants, they were branded with "M" tattoos over their right eyes for identification.

Eventually, humans and mutants joined forces and overthrew the Sentinels in what became known as the Summers Rebellion. However, humans still resisted coexistence with mutants, and radical terrorist groups of mutants, such as the Exhumes, made war on humans. One of the veterans of the Summers Rebellion, a mutant named Hecat'e, stated that it was unacceptable for humans to hunt down criminal mutants, believing mutants should police themselves. Hence, Hecat'e formed the Xavier Security Enforcers, named after Charles Xavier in honor of his dream of peaceful coexistence between mutants and normal humans.

After the death of their parents, Bishop and Shard lived with their grandmother, who was herself a mutant. She told them stories about the heroism of the X-Men and instructed them to follow Xavier's dream of peace between mutants and the rest of humanity. One day, when Bishop and Shard were both still children, two X.S.E. members were pursuing Virago, a member of the Exhumes. Virago was about to murder Bishop when one X.S.E. member shot her dead. Until then, Bishop had regarded the X.S.E. as his enemies and the Exhumes as heroes, but from then on he wanted to join the X.S.E.

Later, criminal mutants attacked Bishop and Shard. Bishop attempted to save his sister from them, but it was two members of the X.S.E. who stopped the criminals. Impressed by Bishop, the X.S.E. members offered him a position in the organization. Bishop accepted on the condition that Shard be accepted into the X.S.E. as well. Thus Bishop and Shard became cadets at the X.S.E. Academy under Hecate's supervision. Among the other members of their class was a mutant named Trevor Fitzroy.

Bishop and Shard eventually graduated from the Academy and became officers of the X.S.E. Shard, however, became Bishop's commanding officer. Bishop contented himself with a lower rank so that he could work the streets as a homicide policeman alongside his friends and fellow X.S.E. officers, Malcolm and Randall.

Fitzroy eventually turned criminal and was imprisoned, but escaped with other mutant criminals through a portal to the X-Men's own time. Bishop, Malcolm, and Randall followed, even though they were aware they had no means to return to their own time. Stranded in the past, the trio tracked their mark into the midst of a fray between the X-Men and the Sentinels. Confronted with the legends of his youth, Bishop's first reaction was one of disbelief. Ultimately, Bishop's troops were slain by Fitzroy's forces during a deadly firefight. Only through the X-Men's intervention did the badly injured Bishop survive.

Finally coming to terms with his time-tossed situation, Bishop was honored when Xavier invited him to join the team whose members he had idolized since childhood. Bishop found new purpose with the X-Men, fighting alongside the mutant adventurers to avert the genetic war that for him was history. Initially uneasy with Bishop's presence, the X-Men soon came to realize he was a devoted disciple of Xavier's philosophy, albeit an oftentimes-overzealous one.

During his time with the X-Men, Bishop proved instrumental in returning the timeline to normal after it was twisted by Legion, the mutant son of Xavier, who had travelled into the past to kill Magneto but had inadvertently killed his father instead. Bishop also saved the lives of his teammates from the malevolent psionic entity known as Onslaught. In his own time, Bishop had learned of a traitor in the ranks of the X-Men who would ultimately cause their death. For a time he believed it to be Gambit, but after it was revealed that the traitor was none other than Xavier himself, albeit as Onslaught, Bishop was able to intervene and stop Onslaught from killing the X-Men by absorbing the energies of a massive psychic blast.

After the X-Men were separated whilst returning to Earth following a mission in deep space, Bishop was severely injured. He was cared for by the alien Deathbird, who wished to use Bishop in an attempt to claim the throne of the intergalactic Shi'ar Empire from her sister, Lilandra. After a few interstellar adventures, including one to an alternate Earth ruled by the Shi'ar, Bishop managed to return to Earth and the X-Men.

Plagued by reoccurring nightmares of Fitzroy, Bishop resigned from the X-Men to dedicate himself once more to the pursuit of his arch-nemesis. Drawn by the villain into another possible apocalyptic future, Bishop learned that his failure to act against Fitzroy had resulted in the criminal's taking over this future world, wherein he had rechristened himself as the all-powerful Chronomancer. Fitzroy planned to ascend to godhood by becoming one with the temporal energies that control all time. Aided by a young boy named Michael who had been drawn to the future with him, Bishop gathered a small group of mutants and focused them on a single goal: quashing Fitzroy's mad plan.

During the epic battle that followed a trek across the strange new world, Bishop defeated Fitzroy moments before he could complete his mad quest. However, the price of victory was high: Bishop's sister, Shard, sacrificed her life so that her brother could put an end to Fitzroy. Mere moments after the war had been won, Bishop – filled with chronal energy – was ripped back through time. Young Michael remained in the future, seemingly with no hope of returning home.

Spiralling through time, Bishop emerged back in the present as he crashed into a Shi'ar space station in deep space. As it happened, Xavier and his team of mutant Skrull students named Cadre K were searching the same station for Deathbird – the Shi'ar criminal who was apparently Bishop's chronal anchor in the present day. A pan-galactic committee had transformed Earth into an intergalactic prison planet, and Deathbird held a key to penetrate the energy barrier that surrounded Earth. Bishop almost killed Deathbird before she opened an airlock and blew herself into the vacuum of space unprotected. After forming a plan with Xavier, Bishop allowed himself to be captured by the galactic committee and sent to Earth where he was quickly reunited with the X-Men. Then, alongside members of the Avengers, the X-Men helped liberate Earth.

Soon after, Bishop and five of his teammates formed a splinter group of X-Men, cutting all ties with the rest of the team while searching for

the Diaries of the late blind mutant seer named Destiny. The team later took on the responsibility of acting as a mutant peacekeeping force, setting them on the path to become the X.S.E. of Bishop's own time. After defeating the mutant predator known as Elias Bogan, the X-Treme X-Men returned to Westchester to help rebuild the mansion following an attack by Magneto. With Xavier having left for Genosha, the X-Men were forced to restructure, and the X-Treme team disbanded to rejoin their comrades.

Later, when crime in the borough of New York known as Mutant Town proved more than the N.Y.P.D. could handle, Bishop was called in to help police the region, referred to as District X.

PHYSICAL DESCRIPTION:

HEIGHT: 6'6"
WEIGHT: 275 lbs
EYES: Brown, red when using powers
HAIR: Black

DISTINGUISHING FEATURES: "M" tattoo over right eye

POWERS & ABILITIES:

STRENGTH LEVEL: Bishop possesses the normal human strength of a man of his age, height, and build who engages in intensive regular exercise.

SUPERHUMAN POWERS: Bishop is a mutant with the power to absorb energy, either ambient energy or that directed towards him, and to project that energy from his body in the form of concussive blasts. Bishop can also store absorbed energy within his personal reserves, whereupon the energy increases his strength and recuperative abilities, as well as affording him a measure of invulnerability.

SPECIAL SKILLS: Bishop is a trained police officer, skilled in the homicide branch. Bishop has also had many years of armed and unarmed combat training, and is a superb marksman with firearms.

PARAPHERNALIA:

PERSONAL WEAPONRY: Bishop uses X.S.E. guns through which he can channel energy that he has absorbed.

OTHER ACCESSORIES: As a member of the X-Treme X-Men, Bishop wore a special pair of cyber-sunglasses that kept him in constant contact with the rest of the team. Bishop also wears a costume that serves as a form of body armor.

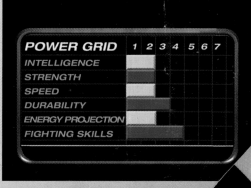

POWER GRID	1	2	3	4	5	6	7
INTELLIGENCE							
STRENGTH							
SPEED							
DURABILITY							
ENERGY PROJECTION							
FIGHTING SKILLS							

CYCLOPS

REAL NAME: Scott Summers
KNOWN ALIASES: Slim, formerly Slym Dayspring, Mutate #007, Eric the Red
IDENTITY: Publicly known
OCCUPATION: Co-headmaster of Xavier Institute for Higher Learning, adventurer, former student, radio announcer
PLACE OF BIRTH: Anchorage, Alaska
CITIZENSHIP: United States of America with no criminal record
MARITAL STATUS: Widowed (Jean Grey-Summers)
KNOWN RELATIVES: Philip Summers (grandfather), Deborah Summers (grandmother), Christopher Summers (Corsair, father), Katherine Anne Summers (mother, deceased), Alexander Summers (Havok, brother), Jack Winters (Jack O'Diamonds, former foster father), Jean Grey-Summers (Phoenix, wife, deceased), Madelyne Pryor-Summers (ex-wife, deceased), Nathan Christopher Summers (Cable, son), John Grey (father-in-law), Elaine Grey (mother-in-law), Sarah Grey-Bailey (sister-in-law, deceased), Aliya Jenskot (daughter-in-law, deceased), Tyler Dayspring (Genesis, grandson, deceased), Stryfe (clone son, deceased), Rachel Summers (Marvel Girl, alternate timeline daughter)
GROUP AFFILIATION: X-Men, formerly Astonishing X-Men, X-Factor
EDUCATION: College degree from Professor Xavier's School for Gifted Youngsters, post-graduate courses

HISTORY: Scott Summers was the first of two sons born to Major Christopher Summers, a test pilot for the U.S. Air Force, and his wife, Katherine. Christopher was flying his family home from vacation when a spacecraft from the interstellar Shi'ar Empire attacked their plane. To save their lives, Katherine pushed Scott and his brother, Alex, out of the plane with the only available parachute. Scott suffered a head injury upon landing, thus forever preventing him from controlling his mutant power by himself.

With their parents presumed dead, the authorities separated the two boys. Alex was adopted, but Scott remained comatose in a hospital for a year. On recovering, he was placed in an orphanage in Omaha, Nebraska that was secretly controlled by his future enemy, the evil geneticist Mr. Sinister.

As a teenager, Scott came into the foster care of Jack Winters, a mutant criminal known as the Jack O'Diamonds. After Scott began to suffer from severe headaches he was sent to a specialist, who discovered that lenses made of ruby quartz corrected the problem. Soon after, Scott's mutant power first erupted from his eyes as an uncontrollable blast of optic force. The blast demolished a crane, causing it to drop its payload toward a terrified crowd. Scott saved lives by obliterating the object with another blast, but the bystanders believed that he had tried to kill them and rallied into an angry mob. Scott fled, escaping on a freight train.

Winters sought to use Scott's newfound talents in his crimes, and physically abused the young boy when he initially refused. However, Scott's display of power had attracted the attention of the mutant telepath Professor Charles Xavier, who teamed up with F.B.I. agent Fred Duncan in their mutual attempt to find Scott. Xavier rescued Scott from Winters' clutches and enlisted him as the first member of the X-Men, a team of young mutants who trained to use their powers in the fight for human/mutant equality.

As Cyclops, Scott became deputy leader of the X-Men, and while he was a natural field general his social skills were lacking. Scott had fallen in love with his teammate Jean Grey, but his reserved demeanor prevented him from expressing his feelings for her for years. When Xavier's other original recruits left the fold following an encounter with the sentient island-being Krakoa, Cyclops stayed on as leader of the new team.

Shortly thereafter, the cosmic entity known as the Phoenix Force took Jean's place. When it committed suicide, Scott believed the love of his life had died and he left the X-Men. During his time away from the team, Scott met fishing boat captain Lee Forrester, who helped him work through his grief. Scott eventually returned to the X-Men whereupon he met Madelyne Pryor, a woman who bore an uncanny resemblance to Jean. Unaware that Madelyne was a clone of Jean created by Sinister, Scott fell in love with her and they were soon married. Madelyne fell pregnant and bore Scott a son they named Nathan Christopher.

When the real Jean emerged from suspended animation, Scott abandoned his wife and son and rejoined the other original X-Men in establishing a new team, X-Factor. During a demonic invasion of New York City, X-Factor and the X-Men fought against a super-powered and insane Madelyne. The invasion was thwarted after Madelyne perished in combat with Jean.

Later, the mutant warlord named Apocalypse infected baby Nathan with a techno-organic virus. To save his son's life, Scott had to allow a member of the Clan Askani to transport Nathan two millennia into the future, where it had been foreseen that he would deliver the world from Apocalypse's clutches. X-Factor disbanded soon after, and its members returned to the ranks of the X-Men. Scott and his long-time love Jean were married, and while on their honeymoon their spirits were taken into the timestream by the Clan Askani's matriarch. Arriving in the future, they inhabited new bodies, and raised Nathan for twelve years. When they returned to their own time and bodies, Nathan remained in the future and ultimately matured into his time's greatest hero: Cable.

Following Xavier's arrest for crimes committed as the evil psionic entity Onslaught, Scott assumed the role of leadership of the X-Men once more. Soon after, the government sponsored mutant-hunting operation known as "Zero Tolerance" took effect, and the villainous Bastion captured the X-Men. In his attempt to destroy mutantkind, Bastion placed a nanotech bomb inside Scott's body. The X-Men escaped, and the mutant doctor named Cecilia Reyes saved Scott's life. Scott and Jean then took a leave of absence from the X-Men for a period of recuperation.

Not long after returning to the team, Scott and Jean soon found themselves embroiled in Apocalypse's bid for cosmic power by assembling "The Twelve": a group of mutants who would determine the fate of their kind that counted Scott, Jean and Cable amongst their number. They were wired to a machine that would channel their awesome energies into Apocalypse, allowing him to absorb the body of the time-tossed powerful mutant teenager known as X-Man. As his teammates fell around him, a powerless Scott saved X-Man and merged with the would-be conqueror to create a new evil entity. Jean detected Scott's psyche inside Apocalypse and prevented the X-Men from destroying him, however, he was presumed dead by most of his teammates. Only Cable and Jean refused to believe Scott had perished. Investigating rumors he was alive, the pair found him in the birthplace of Apocalypse in Akkaba, Egypt, struggling to reassert his mind over the villain's psyche. Ultimately, Jean was able to physically rip Apocalypse's essence from Scott's body using her mental powers, and Cable destroyed it with his own telepathic powers.

Scott left for a small period of recuperation, during which he met and reconciled with his father. Afterwards, Scott returned to the X-Men, but his association with Apocalypse had given him a grimmer, more serious personality than ever before. As a result, many of his personal relationships became strained, including his marriage to Jean. Scott sought the counsel of his teammate Emma Frost, and the pair began a psychic affair. When Jean discovered Scott's betrayal, he left the X-Men in order to sort out the mess his life had become.

Following the outing of Professor X as a mutant to the world, his school, was rechristened the Xavier Institute of Higher Learning, and opened its doors to the mutant population at large, training and educating dozens of young new students to help them cope with their burgeoning abilities. After the death of his wife, Scott assumed the position of co-headmaster of the School alongside his new love, Emma.

PHYSICAL DESCRIPTION:

HEIGHT: 6'3"
WEIGHT: 195 lbs
EYES: Brown, glowing red when using powers
HAIR: Brown

DISTINGUISHING FEATURES: None

POWERS & ABILITIES:

STRENGTH LEVEL: Cyclops possesses the normal human strength of a man of his age, height, and build who engages in intensive regular exercise.

SUPERHUMAN POWERS: Cyclops possesses the mutant ability to project a beam of heatless, ruby-colored concussive force from his eyes, which act as interdimensional apertures between this universe and another. Cyclops's body constantly absorbs ambient energy, such as sunlight, from his environment into his body's cells, which allows him to open the apertures. Cyclops's mind generates a psionic field that is attuned to the forces that maintain the apertures. Because this field envelops his body, it automatically shunts the otherdimensional particles back into their point of origin when they collide with his body. Thus, his body is protected from the effects of the particles, and even the thin membranes of his eyelids are sufficient to block the emission of energy. The synthetic ruby quartz crystal used to fashion the lenses of Cyclops's eyewear is resonant to his mind's psionic field and is similarly protected.

The width of Cyclops's optic blast is focused by his mind's psionic field with the same autonomic function that regulated his original eyes' ability to focus. As Cyclops focuses, the size of the aperture changes and thus acts as a valve to control the flow of particles and the beam's relative power. The height of Cyclops's optic blast is controlled by his visor's adjustable slit. The beam's effective range is about 2,000 feet.

SPECIAL LIMITATIONS: Due to a head injury, Cyclops is unable to shut off his optic blasts at will and must therefore wear ruby quartz lenses to block the beams.

PARAPHERNALIA:

OTHER ACCESSORIES: The mask Cyclops wears to prevent random discharge is lined with powdered ruby quartz crystal. It incorporates two longitudinally mounted flat lenses that can lever inward providing a constantly variable exit slot. The inverted clamshell mechanism is operated by a twin system of miniature electrical motors. As a safety factor, there is a constant positive closing pressure provided by springs. The mask itself is made of high-impact cycolac plastic. There is an overriding finger-operated control mechanism on either side of the mask, and normal operation is through a flat micro-switch installed in the thumb of either glove.

POWER GRID	1	2	3	4	5	6	7
INTELLIGENCE							
STRENGTH							
SPEED							
DURABILITY							
ENERGY PROJECTION							
FIGHTING SKILLS							

EMMA FROST

REAL NAME: Emma Grace Frost
KNOWN ALIASES: Formerly White Queen
IDENTITY: Frost is known to have been a leader of the Hellfire Club, but her past criminal activities are not public knowledge
OCCUPATION: Co-headmaster of Xavier Institute for Higher Learning, adventurer, Chairman of the Board and CEO of Frost International, former Chairman of the Board of Trustees and headmistress of Massachusetts Academy
PLACE OF BIRTH: Boston, Massachusetts
CITIZENSHIP: United States of America with no criminal record
MARITAL STATUS: Single

KNOWN RELATIVES: Winston Frost (father), Hazel Frost (mother), Cordelia Frost (sister), Adrienne Frost (sister, deceased), Christian Frost (brother), Steven (full name unrevealed, brother-in-law, deceased), Jocasta (cousin)
GROUP AFFILIATION: X-Men, formerly Generation X (headmistress), Hellions (mentor), Hellfire Club (White Queen)
EDUCATION: College degree in business administration, qualified sex therapist

HISTORY: Emma Frost was born into a wealthy old Boston mercantile family that arrived from England in the 1600s. The second of three daughters, Emma also had an older brother named Christian who had turned to substance abuse as an escape from the drudgery of his life. Unknown to their family or themselves, the three Frost sisters were mutants whose telepathic abilities matured upon reaching puberty.

When it came time for their father to choose a worthy heir to the family fortune, Christian was automatically dismissed due to his drug problem. While the older sister Adrienne seemed the most obvious choice, their father chose Emma. Surprisingly, she refused, choosing to make her own way through life.

Emma ultimately inherited a good deal of wealth, but most of her large fortune resulted from her professional success. She ascended rapidly to the upper echelon of the business world on the strength of her intelligence, drive, and personal charm, as well as the secret use of her mental powers.

Eventually, Emma became majority stockholder of a multibillion-dollar conglomerate principally involved in electronics and transportation – both the building of ships and aircraft, and their use for freight and passenger conveyance. Despite her relative youth, she was named chairwoman of the board and chief executive officer of the rechristened Frost International. She also became headmistress and chairwoman of the board of trustees of the Massachusetts Academy, a college preparatory school for students in grades seven through twelve located in the Berkshire Mountains in Snow Valley, Massachusetts.

Emma's success caught the attention of the Hellfire Club, an elite social organization consisting of the world's wealthiest and most powerful figures. When she learned that the club was hiring dancers, she promptly auditioned and used her telepathic talents to enhance her performance in their eyes. Unlike the other females in the Club, Emma was never uncomfortable with the strict dress code that required female members to wear lingerie at all times. She believed her revealing wardrobe to be one of many weapons in her arsenal, one that gave her an instant advantage over men.

Frost quickly became an ally of Sebastian Shaw, a member of the club's Council of the Chosen who were secretly conspiring to achieve world domination through economic and political means. At the time, the leaders of the club and council -- its foremost Lords Cardinal, whose titles corresponded to the names of chess pieces -- were White King Edward Buckman and White Queen Paris Seville.

Buckman threw the council's support behind Project Armageddon, scientist Steven Lang's program to construct mutant-hunting Sentinel robots. Aware of Shaw's genetic disposition, Buckman told him the initiative's intent was to capture mutants as a means of helping the council attain power. Using her psionic powers, Emma learned that the project's actual purpose was the annihilation of all genetic deviants. After Shaw's lover, Lourdes Chantel, was

Art by John Cassaday

murdered by one of the Sentinels, Shaw and Frost staged a coup that saw them seize control of the Council of the Chosen, which they renamed the Inner Circle. Shaw took the title of Black King, and Frost became the new White Queen.

Under Shaw and Frost's leadership, mutants dominated the Inner Circle. To strengthen the Club's power base, Emma recruited genetically gifted youngsters and helped them hone their abilities at her school. Most of these students were members of the Hellions, Emma's first mutant super-team. She initially encountered the outlaw band of heroic mutant adventurers known as the X-Men when she unsuccessfully attempted to recruit young Kitty Pryde, the phase-shifting mutant known as Shadowcat. Subsequently, Emma crossed paths with the X-Men – and their protégés, the New Mutants – on a number of occasions, often as their adversary. Later, the X-Men joined with the Hellions to protect the White Queen from the time-travelling terrorist named Trevor Fitzroy. However, the madman's brutal assault plunged Emma into a deep coma and brought about the Hellions' untimely demise.

While Emma's consciousness was still active on the material plane, her body was kept in the med-lab at the X-Men's mansion. Seeking to ensure her students' welfare and the school's future, Emma had willed responsibility for the Massachusetts Academy to Professor Charles Xavier, the X-Men's telepathic founder. During her psychic incapacitation, the school was added to the rapidly expanding Xavier Institute. While Emma's corporeal form was in stasis, a short-circuit in the mansion inadvertently caused her psyche to possess the X-Man named Iceman, while his mind was transferred into her body.

Coerced by Professor X, Emma eventually reclaimed her own form. After making a full recovery, she resumed her role as headmistress of the academy. Ably assisted by Sean Cassidy, the sonically empowered former X-Man known as Banshee, she set out to train a new crop of young mutants: Generation X. When the sinking stock market dealt Frost International a major blow, Emma swallowed her pride and sought the help of her older sister, Adrienne, who agreed to support her sibling's flagging financial interests only if she were named co-headmaster. But Adrienne's power play did not wind down when Emma acceded to her request, nor did it end when she supplanted her sister as the Hellfire Club's White Queen. Only after Adrienne telepathically incited a riot at the school did Emma find a way to upset her ascension: the way of the gun. Emma shot and killed her sister, thereby laying claim to Adrienne's inheritance.

Following the dissolution of Generation X and the closure of the Massachusetts Academy, Emma moved to the island nation of Genosha where she began teaching mutant children again. Soon after, a Sentinel attack wiped out Genosha's entire mutant population. The X-Men found Emma alive in the rubble, having undergone a secondary mutagenic change that allowed her to survive the onslaught. Emma came to teach at the Xavier Institute, and soon took on the responsibility of personally mentoring the telepathic quintuplets known as the Stepford Cuckoos.

Emma later counselled her teammate Cyclops following his possession by the eternal mutant warlord Apocalypse. This soon turned into a telepathic affair between the two that was short-lived after Cyclops's wife, Jean Grey, discovered what was happening.

Sophie, one of the Cuckoos, died during the riot at the Xavier Institute. The remaining sisters blamed Emma for this and told Jean Grey-Summers of Emma's affair with her husband. When Emma was confronted by Jean, she was forced to relive various moments of her past. Following this confrontation, Emma was shot with a diamond bullet while in her diamond form, shattering it. Though she was believed to be dead at first, Emma's consciousness was trapped in her shattered remains. Phoenix discovered this and telekinetically fused Emma's body back together. Upon being reassembled, Emma identified Esme of the Cuckoos as the culprit behind her assassination. However, Esme was working with Magneto at the time, and it was he who shot Emma, as she had learned of his dual identity as the X-Man Xorn.

PHYSICAL DESCRIPTION:

HEIGHT: 5'10"
WEIGHT: 144 lbs
EYES: Blue
HAIR: Ash blonde

DISTINGUISHING FEATURES: None

POWERS & ABILITIES:

STRENGTH LEVEL: Emma Frost possesses the normal human strength of a woman of her age, height, and build who engages in moderate regular exercise.

SUPERHUMAN POWERS: Emma Frost is a mutant who possesses various telepathic talents. Emma can read minds and project her thoughts into the minds of others, project psionic force bolts which have no physical effects but which can affect a victim's mind so as to cause the victim pain or unconsciousness, and can also induce mental pain merely by touching the brow of her victim. Emma can telepathically "sedate" her victims so that, if already rendered unconscious, they remain so for as long as she continues to "sedate" them. It is unknown how effective her "sedating" ability is on victims who are awake.

Furthermore, as a consequence of continued mutation, Emma can now transform her skin and hair into a diamond-hard form at will. In this form, Emma is nigh indestructible except for one small flaw that, if exploited, can cause her to shatter. While in her diamond form, Emma's telepathic abilities are suppressed.

SPECIAL SKILLS: Emma is highly skilled in electronic theory and electronics and has learned how to build devices that can amplify psionic energy and utilize psionic energy for various effects. She devised the mechanism by which her Hellfire Club cohort Mastermind projected his illusions directly into the mind of the Phoenix Force.

PARAPHERNALIA:

PERSONAL WEAPONRY: Emma designed a gun-like device which she once used to exchange minds for a period of time with Storm of the X-Men.

POWER GRID	1	2	3	4	5	6	7
INTELLIGENCE							
STRENGTH							
SPEED							
DURABILITY							
ENERGY PROJECTION							
FIGHTING SKILLS							

GAMBIT

REAL NAME: Remy Etienne LeBeau
KNOWN ALIASES: Le Diable Blanc, formerly Robert Lord
IDENTITY: Publicly known
OCCUPATION: Adventurer, thief
CITIZENSHIP: United States of America with no criminal record
PLACE OF BIRTH: New Orleans, Louisiana (presumed)
MARITAL STATUS: Divorced (Bella Donna Boudreaux)

KNOWN RELATIVES: Jacques LeBeau (foster grandfather, deceased), Jean-Luc LeBeau (foster father, deceased), Bella Donna Boudreaux (Belladonna, ex-wife), Henri LeBeau (foster brother, deceased), Mercy LeBeau (sister-in-law), Theoren Marceaux (cousin), Etienne Marceaux (cousin, deceased), Marius Boudreaux (father-in-law, deceased), Julien Boudreaux (brother-in-law, deceased)
GROUP AFFILIATION: X-Men, formerly X-Treme Sanctions Executive, X-Treme X-Men, Unified Guilds (patriarch), Thieves Guild (patriarch)
EDUCATION: No official schooling

HISTORY: Abandoned at birth due to his burning red eyes, the child who would one day become Remy LeBeau was kidnapped from his hospital ward by members of the New Orleans Thieves' Guild. They referred to the child as "le diable blanc" – the white devil – and believed he was prophesied to unite the warring Thieves' and Assassins' Guilds. Soon after Remy was placed in the care of a gang of street thieves who raised the child and taught him the ways of thievery.

When he was ten years old, Remy attempted to pick the pocket of Jean-Luc LeBeau, then-patriarch of the Thieves' Guild. Jean-Luc took the boy in off the streets and adopted him into his own family. As part of a peace pact between the Thieves' Guild and their rivals, the Assassins' Guild, a marriage was arranged between Remy and Bella Donna Boudreaux, the granddaughter of the head of the Assassins' Guild. However, Bella Donna's brother Julien objected to the marriage and challenged Remy to a duel. Remy killed Julien in self-defense, but was excommunicated and banished from New Orleans in an attempt to maintain the nonaggression pact between the two guilds.

Remy wandered the world as he plied his skills as a master thief, aided by his mutant power to charge objects with explosive energy. At one point Remy had approached the master geneticist Mr. Sinister for help in controlling his powers. Sinister removed some of Remy's brain tissue to reduce his power levels, thus affording him a greater degree of control. As a result, Remy was now indebted to Sinister, who charged the thief with assembling the team of assassins called the Marauders. Remy did not realize that Sinister would employ the Marauders to massacre the underground mutant community known as the Morlocks. Seeing the horrific results of his actions, Remy attempted to stop the massacre but was almost killed by the Marauder named Sabretooth. However, he did manage to save one young Morlock girl, who grew up to become the X-Man named Marrow.

Eventually, Remy encountered Storm, a member of the outlaw team of mutant adventurers known as the X-Men. Storm had been transformed into an amnesiac child and who had turned to theft. Remy helped her escape her enemy, the malevolent psionic entity known as the Shadow King, and they became partners. Later, when the X-Men's founder Professor Charles Xavier returned from a long period of travelling in outer space, Storm sponsored Remy's admission into the X-Men. Remy soon fell in love with his fellow X-Man, Rogue, blessed and cursed with the ability to absorb the thoughts and abilities of others through skin-on-skin contact. The feeling was mutual, but the two soulmates were condemned never to touch. At one point, Rogue left the X-Men after she kissed Remy and absorbed a portion of his memories, learning of his role in the Morlock Massacre.

Remy was subsequently captured and brought before a mock trial held by Magneto, the mutant master of magnetism, then disguised as Erik the Red. Remy was summarily cast out of the X-Men and was abandoned in the frozen wastes of Antarctica. Starving to death, Remy made his way back into Magneto's citadel, where he encountered the psionic essence of a dead mutant named Mary Purcell. The wraith-like Mary bonded with him, allowing him to survive until he reached the Savage Land, a hidden jungle nestled in the icy wasteland. There, Remy struck a deal with the enigmatic being known as the New Sun. In exchange for passage back to America, Remy agreed to run errands for the New Sun.

On returning home, Remy encountered the X-Men again when he attempted to steal the fabled Crimson Gem of Cyttorak for his new employer. He agreed to return to the team, mainly for his self-respect and for his love for Rogue. However, Mary began to threaten Remy and his friends if he didn't agree to stay with her forever. When the X-Men finally found out about Mary, the wraith fled with Remy to her old hometown, where she tried to force him to merge with her and become a new type of hybrid life form. While Remy wrestled with her, Rogue charged in with a containment unit, which ultimately dispersed Mary.

Later, during a trip back in time, Remy's powers were restored to their maximum potential by Sinister, and he was able to utilize them to return to the present. Soon after his return, Remy served for a time as patriarch of the Thieves' Guild in his father's stead, as well as leading one of two teams of X-Men. Gambit was also responsible for the unification of the Thieves' and Assassins' Guilds into the Unified Guild, of which he also served briefly as patriarch.

Meanwhile, the New Sun revealed his true nature after organizing an assassination game for a cadre of super-powered mercenaries with Remy as the target. The attempt failed, and Remy learned that the New Sun was actually an alternate reality version of himself. In his own reality, the New Sun's kinetic charging powers had flared out of control, burning the world and killing everyone but himself. As a result, the New Sun hunted down and killed versions of himself in other realities to ensure that they would not repeat his mistakes. During their final battle, Remy burned through his enhanced powers to defeat the New Sun, ending his threat and returning his powers to their normal level.

Remy was later framed by mutant businessman Sebastian Shaw for the death of the Australian crime lord named Viceroy. With the assistance of Rogue, her team of X-Treme X-Men, and former Triad member Red Lotus, Gambit was able to clear his name. Soon after, Remy became embroiled in the X-Treme X-Men's fight against an alien invasion of Earth. He was captured and used as a power source for the invaders to open a portal that would allow their full invasion fleet to pass through and complete the conquest of Earth. The X-Treme team's enemy, the enhanced human named Vargas, halted the process by plunging his sword into Remy's chest. Remy survived, but found that he had lost his mutant abilities. As a result, he and the also-powerless Rogue sought to live a normal life together and retired from the X-Men.

However try as they might, a normal life was not for them to lead, as the pair soon became embroiled in the X-Treme X-Men's fight against the mutant predator Elias Bogan. After Bogan was defeated, the X-Man named Sage used her mutant ability to "jumpstart" Remy's mutant powers, and he rejoined the team.

In the alternate future in which the X-Man Bishop was born, Remy had become an aged figure named the Witness, so called because he had apparently witnessed the betrayal of the X-Men by one of their own members. Upon joining the X-Men himself, Bishop suspected Remy to be the traitor until Xavier's mind spawned the corrupt psionic entity known as Onslaught.

PHYSICAL DESCRIPTION:

HEIGHT: 6'1"
WEIGHT: 179 lbs
EYES: Burning red
HAIR: Brown

DISTINGUISHING FEATURES: None

POWERS & ABILITIES:

STRENGTH LEVEL: Gambit possesses the normal human strength of a man of his age, height, and build who engages in intensive regular exercise.

SUPERHUMAN POWERS: Gambit has the mutant ability to tap into the potential energy contained within an inorganic object and transform it into kinetic energy upon touching it. When Gambit thus charges an object and throws it at a target, the object releases this energy explosively on impact. Gambit is unable to use this power to charge organic objects.

After surgery performed by Sinister, Gambit's powers were increased to their maximum potential. He was able to use his power simply by looking at an object that he wished to charge, including organic objects. Gambit could also manipulate the potency of the energy release. Following his climactic battle with the New Sun, Gambit lost this enhanced level of power.

Gambit's ability to tap energy also grants him near-superhuman agility and dexterity, as well as creating a static interference that shields his mind from detection and intrusion by even the most powerful telepaths.

Gambit also possesses a hypnotic charm that allows him to exert a subtle influence over any sentient mind. This power allows Gambit to compel others to believe what he says and agree with anything he suggests. More powerful minds have proven resistant to Gambit's charm.

SPECIAL SKILLS: Gambit is bilingual in English and French, and also possesses the ability to throw small objects — including knives, throwing spikes, and playing cards – with extraordinary accuracy.

SPECIAL LIMITATIONS: Gambit's eyes are light sensitive, which temporarily impairs his vision if exposed to bright light.

PARAPHERNALIA:

PERSONAL WEAPONRY: Throwing spikes, playing cards, and bo staff.

POWER GRID	1	2	3	4	5	6	7
INTELLIGENCE							
STRENGTH							
SPEED							
DURABILITY							
ENERGY PROJECTION							
FIGHTING SKILLS							

HAVOK

REAL NAME: Alexander "Alex" Summers
KNOWN ALIASES: Formerly Mutant X, Goblyn Prince
IDENTITY: Secret
OCCUPATION: Adventurer, former graduate student in geophysics
CITIZENSHIP: United States of America with no criminal record
PLACE OF BIRTH: Honolulu, Hawaii
MARITAL STATUS: Single
KNOWN RELATIVES: Christopher Summers (Corsair, father), Katherine Anne Summers (mother, deceased), Philip Summers (grandfather), Deborah Summers (grandmother), Scott Summers (Cyclops, brother), Andrew Blanding (foster father), Mrs. Blanding (foster mother), Haley Blanding (foster sister), Nathan Christopher Summers (Cable, nephew), Madelyne Pryor-Summers (ex-sister-in-law, deceased), Jean Grey-Summers (Phoenix, sister-in-law, deceased), Tyler Dayspring (Genesis, grandnephew, deceased), Stryfe (clone nephew, deceased), Rachel Summers (Marvel Girl, alternate timeline niece)
GROUP AFFILIATION: X-Men, formerly Six, X-Factor, Brotherhood, Genoshan Magistrates
EDUCATION: Masters degree in geophysics, some doctoral research completed

HISTORY: Alexander Summers is the younger of the two sons of Christopher Summers, a United States Air Force Major and test pilot, and his wife Katherine Anne. When Alex was young, he and his family were flying back from a vacation when their plane crashed into a scout ship from the intergalactic Shi'ar Empire, setting the wooden plane ablaze. Their mother pushed Scott and Alex out of the burning plane with the only available parachute, allowing them to escape capture by the Shi'ar.

The two boys were hospitalized for injuries they sustained during their landing. Alex left the hospital after two weeks and was placed in an orphanage in Omaha, Nebraska that was secretly run by the master geneticist Mr. Sinister. Alex was soon adopted by the Blanding family, whose son Todd had been killed in a car accident. However, the Blandings were still traumatized by their loss and treated Alex as if he were Todd.

Sinister continued to monitor Alex while he lived with his foster family. When he noticed the first stirrings of Alex's mutant powers, Sinister incited the local school bully – who had caused Todd's accident – to attack Alex. The subsequent stress caused Alex's mutant powers to manifest, and he incinerated the bully with a plasma blast. Sinister then placed a genetic lock upon Alex to curtail the development of his powers.

As a result, Alex did not become aware of his mutant abilities until after he had graduated from college. A professor of archaeology named Ahmet Abdol had discovered a psychic link between himself and Alex. While both of them had the latent mutant power to absorb and transform cosmic radiation, Abdol's ability to exercise the power was blocked in an unknown manner by Alex's body. Abdol captured Alex and took him to his laboratory in Egypt, where he found a way to screen Alex's body from ambient cosmic radiation, permitting his own body to attain its latent potential. Abdol was transformed into the Living Monolith, a gigantic mutant with vast cosmic power, but was defeated while in combat with the X-Men. Incapable of controlling the power his body emanated, Alex fled into the Egyptian desert.

Alex was soon captured by one of the mutant-hunting robotic Sentinels and brought to the headquarters of Larry Trask, son of the Sentinels' inventor Bolivar Trask. Larry gave Alex the codename Havok and a costume whose chest display monitored the build-up of cosmic energy within him. The X-Men came to Alex's rescue; however, he was injured in the ensuing battle with the Sentinels and was taken to Doctor Karl Lykos for treatment. Lykos was himself a mutant who fed off the life energies of other mutants; when he siphoned Alex's energy, he transformed for the first time into the flying reptilian creature named Sauron.

After Sauron was defeated, Alex returned to New York with the X-Men, where he joined his brother on the team and began training to control his powers. Eventually, Alex gained enough mastery over his power that he would release it only when he wished, and he became a formidable opponent in battle.

During his time with the X-Men, Alex fell in love with his teammate Lorna Dane, the magnetism-manipulating mutant now known as Polaris. They both served for a time in the X-Men, helping to repel the invasion by the alien Z'nox; however, neither Alex nor Lorna wished to lead a life as an adventurer. They discovered that they had a mutual interest in geophysics and left the X-Men to begin doctoral research in the Diablo mountain range.

Their idyllic lifestyle was eventually interrupted when the pair found themselves hunted by the team of superhuman assassins known as the Marauders. Lorna was possessed by the psionic entity known as Malice, who forced Lorna to attack the X-Men as the Marauders' leader. Alex, who had since rejoined the X-Men, had no choice but to fight his lover.

Later, Alex travelled through the Siege Perilous, a mystic gateway that granted those who passed through it a new lease on life, free of their past baggage. When he reappeared, it was as a member of the Magistrates of the mutant-enslaving island nation of Genosha. After the X-Men overthrew the Genoshan government, Alex remained behind for a time to ensure the new government wouldn't repeat the mistakes of the former administration. He later accepted an offer to lead the second version of X-Factor, a government-funded mutant agency, of which Lorna was a member.

Alex continued to serve with X-Factor until the apparent death of his teammate Jamie Madrox, the Multiple Man, at the hands of the prophetic mutant named Haven. Disillusioned, Alex teamed up with the Dark Beast, an evil doppelganger of the X-Men's Beast from another timeline. Together, they founded a team of mutant terrorists called the Brotherhood. However, Alex had not truly become a villain, and had only joined the Brotherhood in order to stop the Dark Beast's sinister plans. After the time-travelling Xavier Underground Enforcers aided him in stopping the Dark Beast, Alex joined them in their quest to stop their apocalyptic future from occurring. Alex was seemingly killed when a time machine created by X.U.E. member Greystone exploded, but he was actually shunted into an alternate universe, trading bodies with the Havok of that reality. However, Alex's family and friends all believed him dead.

After adventuring with a team of twisted versions of the heroes he once knew, Alex again seemingly died, but was left floating in a Limbo-like void. On Alex's Earth, a catatonic "John Doe" patient at the Rosy Manor Convalescent Hospital in upstate New York was identified as being Alex Summers by his attending nurse, Annie Ghazikanian. After she contacted the X-Men, Cyclops came to collect his brother, and Annie accompanied them back to Westchester, as she had come to care for Alex and sought to continue his rehabilitation.

Alex was eventually saved by Annie's young son Carter, who used his fledgling mutant powers to reconnect Alex's consciousness to his body. Seizing the day, Alex's long-time love Lorna asked him to marry her. Somewhat shocked at such a life-altering question so soon after his return, Alex faltered over a reply but his assembled friends and family seemingly made the decision for him. However, Alex had fallen in love with Annie, and called off the wedding. Lorna snapped and attempted to kill both Alex and his newfound love, but she was stopped by Alex's teammate, the Juggernaut.

Soon after, the alternate-reality Havok's personality resurfaced within Alex, having followed Alex's consciousness back from within the void in which he had been trapped. The team of dimension-hopping mutants known as the Exiles was charged with the task of stopping the evil Havok, and they teamed up with the X-Men to prevent him from killing Carter. The evil consciousness was eventually forced out of Alex's body and sent back into the void where it was destroyed by the Exiles' taskmaster, the enigmatic being known as the Timebroker.

PHYSICAL DESCRIPTION:

HEIGHT: 6'
WEIGHT: 175 lbs
EYES: Brown
HAIR: Blond

DISTINGUISHING FEATURES: Scar across right eye

POWERS & ABILITIES:

STRENGTH LEVEL: Havok possesses the normal human strength of a man of his age, height, and build who engages in intensive regular exercise.

SUPERHUMAN POWERS: Havok is a mutant with the superhuman ability to absorb ambient cosmic energy into the cells of his body, transform it in an unknown manner, and release it as waves of energy that heat the air in their path enough to turn it into plasma, which is a super-heated state of matter consisting of charged subatomic particles. These waves will emanate from his body in all directions unless he purposefully tries to channel them in a single direction, usually along the length of his arms. Havok is himself immune to the intense heat he creates, as well as the power blasts generated by his brother Cyclops.

Despite past accounts, the energy that Havok releases is not truly a concussive force. When Havok strikes an object with the waves of intensely hot plasma, the sudden vast jump in temperature will often cause objects to shatter, explode, or seemingly disintegrate, and an observer might therefore wrongly think that a concussive force had struck the object. Should Havok direct his energy at the lowest level, he can project it towards a human being and his target will suffer a severe headache but will not burn up.

Havok's body is constantly in the process of absorbing cosmic radiation. When each of his body's power-storage cell enclaves reaches its capacity, excess cosmic energy is thereafter absorbed and immediately re-emitted in negligible quantities. Upon the total expenditure of all his available energy, it takes Havok's body about 16 hours to recharge to its peak level. The act of concentration involved in releasing his energy in anything other than an omnidirectional wave is physically exhausting for Havok if he continues it over an extended period of time.

SPECIAL SKILLS: Havok is an instinctive tactician and strategist.

PARAPHERNALIA:

COSTUME: Havok wears a special costume that is fitted with sensors for measuring and controlling his power output. As the energy stored within Havok's body increases, the concentric circles on the costume's chest expand outward.

POWER GRID	1	2	3	4	5	6	7
INTELLIGENCE							
STRENGTH							
SPEED							
DURABILITY							
ENERGY PROJECTION							
FIGHTING SKILLS							

ICEMAN

REAL NAME: Robert "Bobby" Louis Drake
KNOWN ALIASES: Formerly Mister Friese, Drake Roberts, Rampage
IDENTITY: Secret, known to certain government officials
OCCUPATION: Adventurer, formerly accountant, student
CITIZENSHIP: United States of America with no criminal record
PLACE OF BIRTH: Fort Washington, Long Island, New York
MARITAL STATUS: Single

KNOWN RELATIVES: William Robert Drake (father), Madeline Beatrice Bass Drake (mother), Mary (cousin), Joel (cousin), Anne
GROUP AFFILIATION: X-Men, formerly Twelve, X-Factor, Defenders, Champions
EDUCATION: College degree, Certified Public Accountant accreditation

HISTORY: Bobby Drake discovered his mutant power to create ice while in his early teens, yet kept his condition hidden from everyone but his parents. Initially, Bobby was unable to stop feeling cold and shivering, but soon managed to keep it under control. When a bully named Rocky Beasely and his friends attacked Bobby and his then-girlfriend, Judy Harmon, the youngster panicked. To save Harmon, Bobby temporarily encased Rocky in ice, thus revealing his abilities for all to see. Believing the boy to be a menace, the townspeople organized a lynch mob. They broke into Bobby's home and overpowered him, but the local sheriff took the teenager into custody for his own protection. Meanwhile, the situation had come to the attention of Professor Charles Xavier, the telepathic mentor of the team of teenage mutant super heroes known as the X-Men.

Professor X dispatched his first X-Man, Cyclops, to contact Bobby. Cyclops stole into the jailhouse as planned, but the two began fighting when Bobby refused to accompany him. Caught by the lynch mob, Cyclops and Bobby were about to be hanged when they broke free. Professor X used his mental powers to stop the townspeople in their tracks and erase their memories of Bobby's powers. A grateful Bobby then accepted Xavier's invitation to enroll at his School for Gifted Youngsters and took the codename Iceman. Though initially granting him a snow-like form, Bobby soon learned to increase his degree of cold control, resulting in an ice-like, almost transparent form.

Hated and feared by humanity, the X-Men honed their amazing abilities while standing in defense of a world pushed to the brink of genetic war by a handful of mutant terrorists. Iceman, the team's youngest founding member, became known as the comedian of the group. Regardless, he pulled his weight and worked well with the rest of the team.

Following a short break-up after believing their mentor was dead, the X-Men re-formed with two new members – the magnetism-manipulating Polaris and the plasma-charged Havok. Bobby had a brief romantic relationship with Polaris until she realized that her heart belonged to Havok. Bobby had trouble accepting her decision, which led to increased tension between himself and Havok. Eventually, Bobby quit the team for a short time to sort out his feelings.

Later, when the sentient island-being known as Krakoa took Bobby and his teammates captive, Professor X assembled a second team of X-Men to rescue them. Soon after, most of the founding members left the team and Bobby began attending college on a scholarship. Eventually, he helped his former teammate Angel form the Champions of Los Angeles. When the Champions disbanded, Bobby went missing, and Angel teamed up with the costumed adventurer Spider-Man to find him. The Champions' enemy Rampage had hypnotized Bobby into donning his battle suit, and Angel and Spider-Man were forced to battle him. After Rampage was defeated, Bobby quit his life as a costumed adventurer and returned to college full-time to study accounting.

Later, Bobby was contacted by Professor X to assist in rescuing friends and family of the X-Men from the assassin known as Arcade. Along with other former X-Men Banshee, Polaris, and Havok, the ad-hoc team managed to free the hostages and Bobby finally came to accept Polaris's love for Havok.

During a summer break from college Bobby went to visit his former X-Men teammate the Beast and soon became involved with the loose-knit collection of costumed heroes known as the Defenders. Along with the Beast and the Angel, Bobby helped reorganize the team into a more formal and cohesive unit. The Defenders eventually disbanded when several of their members appeared to perish during a climactic battle.

Soon after, Bobby joined the other founding X-Men to form X-Factor, an organization that intended to seek out and aid other mutants under the pretense of hunting down those perceived menaces to society. During his time with the team, the Asgardian trickster god Loki captured Bobby, hoping to use him to gain control over the Frost Giants. Loki enhanced Bobby's powers to such an extent that he was forced to wear a power-dampening belt that was originally created by the subversive organization known as The Right to cancel out his powers. Once able only to sheathe his own body in a protective coating of ice, Bobby found he could encase the entirety of the Empire State Building. With time, Bobby gained sufficient control over his augmented powers that he was able to stop using the inhibitor belt. Believing he had achieved his full potential, Bobby never attempted to push himself beyond his perceived limits.

When Professor Xavier returned to Earth following an extended absence in outer space, Bobby and the other members of X-Factor rejoined the X-Men. Shortly thereafter, Bobby confronted former Cosmonaut Mikhail Rasputin, the reality-warping mutant brother of Bobby's steel-skinned teammate Colossus. Rasputin forced Bobby into a form composed entirely of ice, affording the young mutant a glimpse into his true nature. Subsequently, Bobby began experimenting with his abilities – using ice to add mass to his slight frame, or lift himself high into the air without the benefit of his usual slides.

Months later, the psychically incapacitated mutant telepath Emma Frost took mental possession of Bobby's body. Frost was able to activate the full extent of his powers, using them in ways Bobby had not thought possible, until she was coaxed back into her own body by Professor X. With Frost's prodding, Iceman later learned to completely transform his body into its full ice state on his own. Frost later also showed Bobby that he could safely revert back to his human form after his ice form's chest had been shattered in battle.

Bobby later took a leave of absence from the X-Men to spend more time with his father who had been injured by the grass roots anti-mutant movement the Friends of Humanity. He returned briefly to the X-Men to rescue mutant doctor Cecilia Reyes during the government-sponsored anti-mutant operation Zero Tolerance, after which he returned to his father's side.

Two subsequent events served to shed further light on Iceman's untapped potential. To secure a new host body, the would-be conqueror Apocalypse sought to siphon the awesome energies of "The Twelve" – mutants of incredible power, destined to alter the course of human history. Among their number was Iceman, who survived the ordeal thanks only to the apparent sacrifice of Cyclops.

A second defining event occurred when the sentient spaceship Prosh escaped the confines of a Celestial prison, returned to Earth and dispatched a group of disparate beings on a journey through time to uncover the keys to preserving human evolution. Their mission: Save the human race from a threat that might not manifest itself for millions of years. When Prosh reassembled the members of his team in the present, they fought and defeated the enigmatic alien entity known as the Stranger, who sought to control the natural evolution of humans and mutants.

These experiences forced Iceman to realize that he no longer need fear the evolution of his abilities, and he returned to the X-Men to

explore his mutant powers to the fullest. After suffering a chest injury, Bobby was unable to prevent his body from transforming into solid ice due to the manifestation of a secondary mutation.

PHYSICAL DESCRIPTION:

HEIGHT: 5'8"
WEIGHT: 145 lbs
EYES: Brown
HAIR: Brown

DISTINGUISHING FEATURES: Body completely composed of solid ice

POWERS & ABILITIES:

STRENGTH LEVEL: Iceman possesses the normal human strength of a man of his age, height, and build who engages in intensive regular exercise. In his ice form, Iceman is able to augment his strength to superhuman levels, the full extent of which is as yet unknown.

SUPERHUMAN POWERS: Iceman is able to lower his internal and external body temperature without harm to himself, thereby radiating intense cold from his body. He is able to reach -105 degrees Fahrenheit within a few seconds, and is immune to sub-zero temperatures around him. Iceman can also perceive the world around him as degrees of heat and cold, and as such can see the body heat radiated by individuals.

Iceman can freeze any moisture in the air around him into unusually hard ice, and thereby form simple objects such as slides, ladders, shields, and bats. He can also augment his ice form with extraneous moisture to enhance his strength and durability, and can reshape his body's ice form at will by using any available moisture from his surrounding environment. Similarly, Iceman can rebuild his ice form if any part of it is broken or if it is shattered completely without suffering any permanent damage.

Iceman also possesses the potential to transport himself quickly over great distances through nearby flows of water by merging his body's molecules with those of the stream and reforming them at a given exit point.

Previously, Iceman was able to transform his body into solid ice and back to human form at will. Recently, however, his body has permanently transformed into solid ice as a result of a secondary mutation.

SPECIAL SKILLS: Bobby is a Certified Public Accountant.

PARAPHERNALIA:

COSTUME: For a time, Iceman was forced to wear a belt that dampened his powers after they had been augmented by Loki.

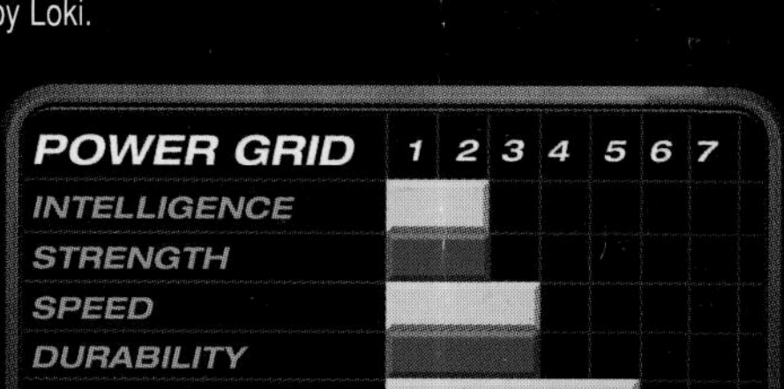

POWER GRID	1	2	3	4	5	6	7
INTELLIGENCE							
STRENGTH							
SPEED							
DURABILITY							
ENERGY PROJECTION							
FIGHTING SKILLS							

JUGGERNAUT

REAL NAME: Cain Marko
KNOWN ALIASES: Formerly Exemplar of Physical Power
IDENTITY: Known to authorities and certain government officials
OCCUPATION: Adventurer, formerly mercenary, soldier
CITIZENSHIP: United States of America with a criminal record
PLACE OF BIRTH: Berkeley, California
MARITAL STATUS: Single
KNOWN RELATIVES: Kurt Marko (father, deceased), Marjory Marko (mother, deceased), Sharon Xavier Marko (stepmother, deceased), Charles Francis Xavier (Professor X, stepbrother)
GROUP AFFILIATION: X-Men, former partner of Black Tom Cassidy, formerly Commission for Superhuman Activity, Exemplars, New World Order, eXiles, U.S. Army
EDUCATION: Unrevealed

HISTORY: Cain Marko's mother died when he was very young, leaving him to live a life of psychological and physical torment at the hands of his abusive father, atomic researcher Doctor Kurt Marko. Following the death of his colleague Doctor Brian Xavier, Kurt married Xavier's widow Sharon, and he and Cain took up residence in the Xavier's Westchester mansion with Sharon and her young son, Charles.

Kurt seemingly preferred Charles to his own son, which consumed Cain with jealousy, and he took to bullying his stepbrother. Cain's father continued to beat him, but Cain did not suffer the abuse alone. Inexperienced at the use of his burgeoning mutant telepathic powers, Charles shared the pain and inadvertently learned of Cain's jealousy toward him, ensuring that Cain would forever hate Charles for his unwitting betrayal.

After an argument with his father, Cain accidentally caused a fire that engulfed his father's home laboratory. Kurt saved Charles first, and then went back for Cain, reinforcing Cain's belief that his father loved Charles more than him. Kurt died of smoke inhalation, but not before warning Charles to always beware of Cain.

Eventually, both Cain and Charles were drafted into military service in the same unit. When Cain deserted under fire during a mission in Asia, Charles pursued, hoping to convince his stepbrother to return of his own accord. Charles followed Cain into a cave that housed the lost temple of Cyttorak, a powerful mystical entity. Therein, Cain unearthed the Crimson Gem of Cyttorak; upon touching it, he was transformed by its mystical energies into a human juggernaut. A subsequent cave-in buried Cain, and Charles believed his stepbrother dead.

Cain eventually dug himself free and made his way to America, where he sought to use his newfound strength to exact revenge on Charles. However, he was defeated on every attempt by the X-Men, a team of mutant adventurers that fought to preserve their mentor's dream of peaceful coexistence between humans and mutants. Cain then formed a criminal partnership with mutant mercenary Black Tom Cassidy, and the pair soon became two of the world's most wanted criminals.

After many years of villainy, Cain was teleported to an alternate universe where he helped form the team of costumed adventurers known as the eXiles, and formed a romantic relationship with his teammate Amber Hunt. Cain was eventually returned to his own universe, whereupon he encountered the psionic being known as Onslaught who used his enormous powers to hurl him from Canada to New York. There, he encountered the X-Men once more and was taken to Charles' mansion for medical treatment. On waking, Cain sought to warn Charles about Onslaught, not realizing that Onslaught was Charles himself. Onslaught then tore the Ruby from Cain's chest and trapped him within it. Cain discovered an entire plane of existence in the jewel and encountered a corrupt aspect of Cyttorak. The mystic named Gomurr the Ancient sought to help free Cain from the jewel, imbuing him with the gem's power. Using his newfound strength, Cain destroyed the aspect and was freed from the gem, returning with more power than ever before. Ignoring Gomurr's warning that he was fated to destroy everything and everyone in his path, Cain returned to his villainous ways.

Soon after, Cain learned of a second Cyttorak Gem, and, coveting its power, he returned to the Temple where he found the first. However, it was a trap set by a cult whose members sought the power of the Ruby for themselves, draining Cain's power to energize their Ruby. With the assistance of Black Tom and the X-Men, Cain claimed the power of the second Ruby, but it was possessed by an evil spirit that took over his body. The spirit made Cain smash through dimensional walls in an attempt to destroy its nemesis, but the natives of the dimension ultimately freed Cain from its possession.

Cain eventually discovered that his becoming the Juggernaut was no accident. He had been compelled to enter the temple of Cyttorak, who was one of a pantheon of eight gods that each had an avatar on Earth. These avatars, named the Exemplars, enlisted Cain's aid in constructing a machine that would remove humanity's free will, thus allowing their gods to rule the Earth. With Charles' help, Cain regained control of his psyche and defeated the Exemplars.

Cain was again cast as a hero when the sentient spaceship Prosh returned to Earth to gather a group of disparate beings for a journey through time to uncover the keys to preserving human evolution. While in the past, Cain learned that despite all his yearning for power, he had squandered his mystical abilities. When the team reassembled in the present, they fought and defeated the alien entity known as the Stranger, who sought to control the natural evolution of mankind.

Soon after, Cain was drafted into the service of the Commission for Superhuman Activities as a super-powered bounty hunter. However, this new career was short-lived, and Cain eventually found himself working alongside Black Tom once more. Soon after, Cain requested the X-Men's help in stopping Tom, whose plant-based powers had resurfaced and flared out of control. After a brief clash with the X-Men, it came to light that Cain had been stripped of Cyttorak's mystical energies and was no longer invulnerable. Tom was defeated, but not before he knocked Cain into the surrounding waters. A young aquatic mutant named Sammy Pare saved Cain's life, forming a strong bond of friendship between the unlikely pair. When Cain was invited by Charles to take up residence at the mansion, he accepted and soon came to appreciate his newfound lot in life. After assisting the X-Men in a mission, Cain joined the team and proved himself to be a valuable member.

After Sammy was returned home to Canada, Cain defied a restraining order to visit the boy and discovered him to be the victim of an abusive father. Incensed, Cain attacked the man, accidentally injuring Sammy's mother. Alpha Flight arrived to defuse the situation and, on seeing a terrified Sammy, Cain surrendered himself. Incarcerated in a superhuman holding facility, Cain was appointed a lawyer in the form of Jennifer Walters, the She-Hulk. While Charles discussed a plan of action with Walters, another of the facility's inmates, the Rhino, broke free, setting Cain loose in the process. Rather than escape, Cain stayed and defeated the Rhino to save a guard's life. This heroic act, combined with the Canadian government's less than ideal incarceration methods, was enough to make a case for Cain and endear him to Walters.

Soon after, Cain and Walters began a romantic relationship that was cut short by the arrival of Cyttorak's new avatar. With She-Hulk's aid, Cain defeated the new Juggernaut, but the damage he had caused during the battle forced Walters to rethink her feelings for him. An impassioned plea from Sammy's mother led to Cain receiving a reduced and commuted sentence, as well as extradition back to the United States. Cain continues to serve as a member of the X-Men while undertaking community service and anger management therapy.

PHYSICAL DESCRIPTION:

HEIGHT: 6'10"
WEIGHT: 900 lbs
EYES: Blue
HAIR: Red

DISTINGUISHING FEATURES: Massive bulk

POWERS & ABILITIES:

STRENGTH LEVEL: The Juggernaut originally possessed superhuman strength enabling him to lift/press well over 100 tons. Since being stripped of the mystical energy of Cyttorak, the Juggernaut's strength has vastly decreased. While still at a superhuman level, the upper limit to his strength is currently not known as yet.

SUPERHUMAN POWERS: The Juggernaut originally possessed untold mystical power that enhanced his strength to an unknown degree and made him a seemingly irresistible, unstoppable being. Once he began to walk in a given direction, nothing on Earth was able to stop him. Some obstacles, for example many tons of rock or forces such as plasma cannons, slowed his pace considerably, but nothing could permanently stop him from advancing. The Juggernaut was, however, vulnerable to magical forces of sufficient strength.

The mystical energy of Cyttorak also gave the Juggernaut an extraordinary degree of resistance to all forms of injury. The Juggernaut could shield himself even further from injury by mentally surrounding himself with a force field. Enveloped by this field, he had been seen to survive the fiery explosion of a truck transporting a huge quantity of oil without any injury whatsoever. The Juggernaut could survive indefinitely without food, water, or oxygen thanks to his being sustained by his mystical energies.

Recently, the Juggernaut has been stripped of this mystical energy, including his personal force field. He still possesses superhuman strength, endurance and durability due to years of absorbing the mystical energies of Cyttorak, but the current upper limit of these traits is as yet unknown.

SPECIAL LIMITATIONS: Without his helmet and skullcap, the Juggernaut is vulnerable to psionic attacks against his mind.

PARAPHERNALIA:

COSTUME: The Juggernaut originally wore a suit of armor fashioned from an unknown mystical metal that he could summon around himself at will from the Crimson Cosmos dimension of Cyttorak. After being stripped of his powers, the Juggernaut has taken to wearing armor that resembles his original but is fashioned from unstable molecules.

POWER GRID	1	2	3	4	5	6	7
INTELLIGENCE							
STRENGTH							
SPEED							
DURABILITY							
ENERGY PROJECTION							
FIGHTING SKILLS							

MARVEL GIRL

REAL NAME: Rachel "Ray" Summers
KNOWN ALIASES: Formerly Phoenix, Mother Askani, Aly'zrn Summerset
IDENTITY: Known to British legal authorities; the general public is unaware that Marvel Girl comes from the future of an alternate timeline
OCCUPATION: Adventurer, student, formerly Askani Sisterhood leader, hound
CITIZENSHIP: United States of America in an alternate future with a criminal record, honorary subject of the United Kingdom with no criminal record
PLACE OF BIRTH: Unrevealed location in an alternate future

MARITAL STATUS: Single
KNOWN RELATIVES: Scott Summers (Cyclops, alternate timeline father, deceased in own time), Jean Grey-Summers (Phoenix, alternate timeline mother, deceased in own time), Franklin Richards (alternate future husband), Jonathan Reed Richards (Hyperstorm, alternate future son), David Richards (alternate future son)
GROUP AFFILIATION: X-Men, former servant of Elias Bogan, Clan Askani leader, Excalibur, servant of Ahab
EDUCATION: High school level studies at Professor Xavier's School for Gifted Youngsters, some college level education

HISTORY: The daughter of Scott Summers and Jean Grey in an alternate timeline, young Rachel Summers inherited her mother's potential for telepathic and telekinetic powers she possessed as Marvel Girl of the X-Men, a team of mutant adventurers fighting for peaceful coexistence between mutants and humans.

In the mainstream reality, the X-Men prevented an attempted assassination of anti-mutant Senator Robert Kelly. However, in Rachel's timeline, Kelly was killed. The assassination caused intense widespread public paranoia against mutants; in the next presidential election, a rabid anti-mutant candidate won. His administration unleashed giant mutant-hunting robot Sentinels to eliminate mutantkind, and the Sentinels decided the best way to do so was to take over North America. During the subsequent years, they killed or imprisoned virtually all known superhuman beings on the continent.

One morning, while Rachel was still a child, the X-Men's base of operations at Professor Charles Xavier's School for Gifted Youngsters was attacked and demolished by federal troops. The only survivor was Rachel, whom the soldiers found by the side of Xavier's body. They used drugs to neutralize her developing psionic powers before she was tortured and brainwashed in the laboratory of the sadistic Ahab. Following extensive behavior modification, Rachel became a mutant "hound" using her psionic powers to hunt down other mutants for the authorities. Rachel's superiors branded her face with a grotesque pattern of tattoos to mark her as a hound, and forced her to wear a leash. Rachel occasionally killed mutants herself, and it is known that some of those were people she loved. Her grief and shame at what she was forced to do as a hound, as well as her anguish over the deaths of her parents and friends deeply scarred her soul, leaving her bitter and intolerant toward humans who persecute mutants.

Eventually, Rachel was placed in the South Bronx Mutant Containment Facility, where she rejoined the surviving members of the X-Men in a plan to end the Sentinels' reign by changing history. Rachel used her psionic powers to exchange the psyche of the adult X-Man Kate Pryde with that of Pryde's teenage self as she existed at a time just before the attempt on Kelly's life. It was hoped that the adult Kate, in her younger self's body, could warn the X-Men about the assassination attempt so they could stop it, thereby preventing the chain of events from occurring that led to the Sentinels' rule. However, history cannot be changed in this manner, and Rachel actually caused Kate to exchange psyches not with her younger self in the past of her own reality, but in the mainstream reality. Kate succeeded in preventing Kelly's assassination in the mainstream reality, after which the Pryde's psyches returned to their proper times and realities. On her return, Kate found that the other X-Men, except for Rachel, had all died in an attack on the Sentinels' Manhattan headquarters.

Kate still did not give up her vain hope of altering her reality's history, and she hypnotized Rachel into using her psionic powers to tap into the Phoenix Force so as to send herself back in time when

Kate said the words "Dark Phoenix". Thus Kate hoped that Rachel herself could change history. Together, Kate and Rachel broke into the laboratory of Project Nimrod, which was the attempt to construct the most highly advanced Sentinel possible, in the hope of sabotaging the project. Pursued by guards, Kate and Rachel locked themselves within the laboratory, whose walls were impervious to Kate's mutant power to phase through solid matter. Rachel believed herself and Kate to be trapped, but Kate said the words that caused Rachel to project herself back through time. Project Nimrod's creation, the Sentinel called Nimrod, then killed Kate and traveled back in time to find Rachel.

Rachel found herself physically transported, body and mind, to a time shortly before the present. But like Kate's spirit, Rachel had traveled not to the past of her reality, but to the past of the mainstream reality. She went to Xavier's mansion, but could not bring herself to stay on, realizing that she had come back to the wrong reality, and fled without identifying herself. Pursued by the psychic vampire Selene, Rachel was rescued by the X-Men, and after Xavier read her mind to ascertain her identity she was invited to join the team.

Rachel was shocked to learn of the supposed "death" of Jean Grey in this reality. Visiting the home of Grey's parents while they were absent, Rachel found a holempathic crystal that was imbued with an imprint of Grey's personality. Unaware that Jean had not actually been Phoenix, Rachel refused to believe that Jean could be evil, as people claimed Phoenix was, and she decided to claim the name and power of Phoenix as her own birthright. Through her own actions, Rachel sought to redeem the name Phoenix in this reality. Rachel also believed that as the new Phoenix she could use her power to help her fellow mutants, and thereby atone for what she had done as a hound in her own reality. It was at this moment while holding the crystal that Rachel first manifested about her the bird-shaped aura of energy associated with the previous Phoenix. From that time on, Rachel was able to draw to a limited extent upon the vast power of the cosmic entity known as the Phoenix Force. The alien being known as the Beyonder once hinted that Rachel could potentially become equal in power to the previous Phoenix. Indeed, the Beyonder once granted Rachel the full power that the previous Phoenix had possessed, but he reclaimed it shortly thereafter.

Soon after, Rachel's teammate Wolverine, severely injured her to prevent her from vengefully murdering Selene. Fleeing to heal herself, she was fooled by the six-armed sorceress named Spiral and taken to the alternate dimension of Mojoworld where she was held prisoner for several months. Rachel eventually escaped to London where agents from Mojoworld tracked her. With the help of Kitty Pryde, Lockheed, Nightcrawler, and Captain Britain, Rachel defeated her would-be captors and together they formed the British super-team Excalibur.

After many adventures with Excalibur, Rachel finally managed to return to her own time. While she couldn't change her past, she and her teammates were able to change the directives of the Sentinels of the era to preserve all life, thereby ending the genocide that had prevailed for years. On the return journey, Captain Britain was lost in the timestream and it was discovered that Rachel had to exchange places with the Captain for him to return. She accepted, and was carried to another future time that was ruled by the eternal mutant Apocalypse. There, Rachel founded the Clan Askani to help in the struggle against Apocalypse's tyrannical reign.

As the Mother Askani, Rachel was responsible for transporting her parents to the future to care for Cyclops' infant son Nathan, who had been taken to the future in the hope of curing a techno-organic virus Apocalypse had infected him with. The Clan Askani saw in the child the potential to be a great warrior, and trained him to become the

soldier known as Cable. The effort of transporting the two X-Men exhausted Rachel's frail old body and her physical form died, leaving her to live on in an astral form.

Some time later, Cable journeyed to the end of time and found a youthful Rachel being held prisoner by Gaunt, a man who had been imprisoned there for his crimes. Cable challenged Gaunt to a duel to decide the fate of Rachel and emerged victorious, returning them both to the present. With her own timeline erased and having been abandoned by the Phoenix Force, Rachel decided to retire from the costumed adventuring life and began attending college. Soon after, Rachel became embroiled in the Dark Sisterhood's attempted takeover of the United States. Rachel aided Cable in defeating the Sisterhood and their leader, Finality, after which she returned to college.

Months later, Rachel was captured by the mutant predator Elias Bogan who used her as his pet telepath, enslaving other mutants to do his bidding. After Bogan's defeat at the hands of the X-Treme X-Men team, Rachel was freed from his telepathic control and rejoined the X-Men, taking the codename Marvel Girl to honor the memory of her deceased mother.

PHYSICAL DESCRIPTION:

HEIGHT: 5'7"
WEIGHT: 125 lbs
EYES: Green
HAIR: Red

DISTINGUISHING FEATURES: Facial tattoos

POWERS & ABILITIES:

STRENGTH LEVEL: Marvel Girl possesses the normal human strength of a woman of her age, height, and build who engages in regular exercise.

SUPERHUMAN POWERS: Marvel Girl is a mutant with virtually unlimited telepathic powers, allowing her to read minds, project her thoughts into other minds, stun the minds of others with telepathic mental bolts, and cast psionic illusions such as those she uses to mask her facial tattoos. Marvel Girl also possesses telekinetic powers that allow her to levitate matter. By levitating herself, Marvel Girl can "fly" at great speed. The upper limits of her telepathic and telekinetic powers are not known.

Marvel Girl also possesses the psionic ability to project her own consciousness or those of others into the timestream, causing them to arrive in another time period within the body of their divergent counterpart or closest living ancestor or descendant. Marvel Girl's past link with the Phoenix Force gave her even greater psionic abilities, such as being able to manipulate time, space, matter, and energy for virtually any purpose.

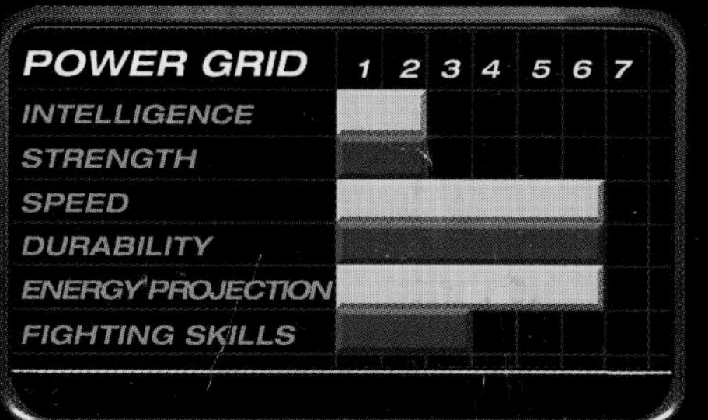

POWER GRID	1	2	3	4	5	6	7
INTELLIGENCE							
STRENGTH							
SPEED							
DURABILITY							
ENERGY PROJECTION							
FIGHTING SKILLS							

NIGHTCRAWLER

REAL NAME: Kurt Wagner
KNOWN ALIASES: Fuzzy Elf, formerly Gainsborough
IDENTITY: Secret; known to British legal authorities
OCCUPATION: Adventurer, former priest, circus performer
CITIZENSHIP: Germany with no criminal record; criminal record in United States of America (overturned by courts)
PLACE OF BIRTH: Castle of Baron Christian Wagner, Bavaria, Germany
MARITAL STATUS: Single

KNOWN RELATIVES: Azazel (father), Raven Darkhölme (Mystique, mother), Graydon Creed (half-brother, deceased), Margali Szardos (foster mother), Jimaine Szardos/Amanda Sefton (Magik, foster sister), Stefan Szardos (foster brother, deceased), Rogue (foster sister), Nils Styger (Abyss, half-brother), Kiwi Black (half-brother)
GROUP AFFILIATION: X-Men, formerly Excalibur, N-Men
EDUCATION: College-level courses at Xavier's School for Gifted Youngsters

HISTORY: Born in Bavaria to the blue-skinned shape-shifting mutant later known as Mystique, Kurt Wagner was shunned at birth due to his blue skin, pointed ears, fangs, and a long pointed tail. At the time disguised as the Baroness Wagner, Mystique's true identity was revealed after she gave birth to Kurt and the pair was chased by an angry mob. Fleeing to the nearby falls, Mystique threw the infant Kurt over the edge and fled. Kurt was saved by his natural father, the enigmatic being known as Azazel, and given into the care of Margali Szardos, a sorceress and Gypsy queen.

Margali took baby Kurt to the small Bavarian circus where she worked as a fortuneteller as a cover for her activities as a sorceress. Kurt was never legally adopted by anyone, but raised by all the members of the circus, who had no prejudices against "freaks". Kurt grew up happily in the circus with his two closest friends, Margali's natural children Stefan and Jimaine. Stefan feared that his magical heritage might one day corrupt him, and so he had Kurt promise to stop him if he ever killed without reason.

During his formative years Kurt exhibited tremendous natural agility, and quickly became the circus's star acrobat and trapeze artist with audiences assuming that he was simply a normal human dressed in a demon costume. Kurt worked closely with Jimaine, and the pair soon became involved in a romantic relationship.

Years later, the Texas millionaire Amos Jardine, who ran a large circus based in Florida, heard of the circus Kurt worked for and bought it. Jardine intended to move its best acts into his American circus. However, he demanded that Kurt be placed in the circus's freak show. Appalled, Kurt quit and made his way back to Germany where he discovered that Stefan had gone mad and had brutally slain several members of a lost race of half-human creatures. Kurt found Stefan and fought him, hoping to stop his rampage, but in the course of the struggle Kurt unintentionally broke Stefan's neck. The villagers of the nearby town of Winzeldorf discovered Kurt and assumed him to be a demon that was responsible for the killings. They cornered Kurt in the town and were about to kill him when they were all psionically paralyzed by Professor Charles Xavier, who had come to recruit Kurt into his team of mutant super heroes known as the X-Men.

Kurt agreed to join the group, but before they left for America, he and Xavier went to the Bavarian circus so that Kurt could explain to Margali about Stefan's death. However, Margali was not there, and for years she held Kurt responsible for Stefan's death. Later, she learned the truth and she and Kurt were reconciled. Kurt was also happily reunited with Jimaine, who had been living in the United States under the assumed name of Amanda Sefton.

After many adventures with the X-Men, including a clash with the Brotherhood of Evil Mutants during which Kurt first met his mother Mystique, Kurt was severely wounded during the attack on the underground colony of mutants known as the Morlocks by Riptide, a member of a team of mutant assassins named the Marauders. Kurt was taken to the mutant research facility on Muir Island off the coast of Scotland where he recuperated, but discovered that he could no longer teleport as he originally could, and that teleporting others caused a great strain. After hearing of the apparent "death" of the X-Men, he, along with Shadowcat, Rachel Summers, Captain Britain, and Meggan became the founding members of the British super-team Excalibur.

After an encounter with the monarch of Latveria, the armored despot Doctor Doom, Kurt's powers were fully restored after Doom used an electromagnetic scrambler in an attempt to disrupt Kurt's teleporting abilities which instead accidentally realigned them.

Following a misunderstanding with Captain Britain over his relationship with Meggan that resulted in a broken leg, Kurt re-formed the team of alien bounty hunters known as the Technet into a team of costumed superhuman adventurers dubbed the N-Men. Following the Technet's departure, Kurt became Excalibur's leader after the team gained several new members, including the alien Shi'ar named Cerise. Kurt helped Cerise become accustomed to her new life on Earth, which led to a romantic relationship. This was to be short-lived, however, after Cerise was found guilty of war crimes and returned to the Shi'ar Empire.

After Captain Britain and Meggan were married, Kurt along with Shadowcat and Colossus decided it was time to return to the X-Men. Kurt once more served as a dedicated member of the team until after the battle with the mutant despot Apocalypse that resulted in the seeming death of the first X-Man, Cyclops. Soon after, Kurt, ever-devout Catholic, left the team to pursue aspirations of becoming a priest. During his studies, Kurt was attacked and wounded by Rax, the hunter of the group of evolved mutants known as the Neo. Fleeing, Kurt encountered mutant doctor Cecilia Reyes, and together the two faced the Neo until the X-Men arrived to turn the tide of battle.

Kurt subsequently rejoined the X-Men while he continued his priesthood studies, but soon after took a leave of absence to mourn the death of his friend and teammate, Colossus. When he returned to the X-Men, it was as a fully ordained priest after apparently undergoing a ceremony at St. Michael's Church in Brooklyn, which was overseen by Kurt's mentor, Father Whitney. Kurt even took to wearing a priest's collar as part of his X-Men uniform.

Following an encounter with the Church of Humanity and their enigmatic leader, the Supreme Pontiff, Kurt began to question his place in the priesthood. Kurt's feelings of unrest were only exacerbated after the mutant ex-prostitute Stacy X joined the team and made advances towards him, which he could not reciprocate due to his vocation. Ultimately it came to light that Kurt had never been fully ordained; rather he had been telepathically coerced into believing so as part of a plan by the Church of Humanity to bring down the Catholic Church by installing Kurt as the next Pope, then revealing to the world that he was "Satan". The X-Men subsequently defeated the Church of Humanity and prevented their plan for world domination.

Soon after, Kurt found himself unable to resist the compulsion to travel to the Isla des Demonas off the coast of Florida. There, Kurt was manipulated into a ceremony with other teleporters like himself that opened a dimensional portal through which came an army of mutant demons. The X-Men arrived to recover their teammate and clashed with the army. During the battle, Kurt was forcibly removed from the ceremony that collapsed the portal, trapping all present in the other dimension. There, Kurt learned that the leader of the army, Azazel, was his natural father and the father of the other teleporters present. A mutant from biblical times, Azazel sought to use his children's combined powers to return to Earth and enslave humanity. However, Kurt rejected him and, with the aid of his newly-found half-brothers Abyss and Kiwi Black, Azazel was defeated.

PHYSICAL DESCRIPTION:

HEIGHT: 5'9"
WEIGHT: 161 lbs
EYES: Shining yellow, no visible pupils
HAIR: Indigo

DISTINGUISHING FEATURES: Three fingers and an opposable thumb on each hand, two extra-long toes on each foot, 3-foot -long prehensile tail, fine blue fur, pointed ears, fang-like canine teeth

POWERS & ABILITIES:

STRENGTH LEVEL: Nightcrawler possesses the normal human strength of a man of his age, height, and build who engages in intensive regular exercise.

SUPERHUMAN POWERS: Nightcrawler is a mutant who can teleport by opening a portal into another dimension, travelling through it via an unconscious direction-finding sense and returning to his own dimension. When teleporting, Nightcrawler leaves behind a small portion of the atmosphere of the other dimension that escapes with a muffled "bamf" sound and smells of brimstone. On returning, his power automatically displaces any extraneous liquids and gases.

Nightcrawler can easily teleport north-south along Earth's magnetic lines of force. However, teleporting east-west against them or teleporting vertically is more difficult. Under optimal conditions, Nightcrawler can teleport about 2 miles east-west, up to 3 miles north-south, and 2 miles vertically if he exerts himself. Nightcrawler's momentum is retained while teleporting, so he arrives with the same inertia he left with. He can reduce this by teleporting short distances in the opposite direction.

Nightcrawler has a very limited unconscious extrasensory ability that prevents him from teleporting into any area that he cannot see or has not seen in the past, as doing so runs the risk of injury or death by materializing partially or entirely within a solid object. Through practice, Nightcrawler has increased the mass he can teleport with him, though the limit to the amount of weight he can carry while teleporting and the distance over which he can teleport with such additional loads are unknown. Teleporting with Nightcrawler often leaves a passenger feeling weak and nauseous.

SPECIAL SKILLS: Nightcrawler is an Olympic-class acrobat thanks to his flexible spine that allows him to perform contortionist-like feats and to go long periods in a semi-crouching position without injury. He is a skilled hand-to-hand combatant and a master at fencing, which he can even perform with his tail. Nightcrawler's tail can support his entire body weight, and his fur is dark enough to blend with deep shadows, rendering him almost invisible.

POWER GRID	1	2	3	4	5	6	7
INTELLIGENCE							
STRENGTH							
SPEED							
DURABILITY							
ENERGY PROJECTION							
FIGHTING SKILLS							

POLARIS

REAL NAME: Lorna Dane (legal name since adoption, given name unrevealed)
KNOWN ALIASES: Formerly Malice (while possessed), Polarity, Magnetrix, M-2, Magneto the Second
IDENTITY: Secret
OCCUPATION: Adventurer, former U.S. government operative, former graduate student in geophysics
CITIZENSHIP: United States of America with no criminal record
PLACE OF BIRTH: Unrevealed
MARITAL STATUS: Single

KNOWN RELATIVES: Magnus (Magneto, father), Pietro Maximoff (Quicksilver, half-brother), Wanda Maximoff (Scarlet Witch, half-sister), Zala Dane (Zaladane, supposed sister, deceased), unnamed uncle (adoptive father), unnamed aunt (adoptive mother)
GROUP AFFILIATION: X-Men, formerly Acolytes, Genoshan Cabinet, Twelve, X-Factor, Marauders, Defenders
EDUCATION: Master's degree in geophysics, some doctoral research completed

HISTORY: Lorna Dane was orphaned only weeks after her birth when her parents supposedly died in a plane crash. The Danes, a couple who claimed to be her mother's sister and brother-in-law, adopted Lorna; however, she did not learn of her adoption or the fate of her birth parents until she was nearly twenty years old.

Lorna had been born with green hair, which she always kept dyed brown so that she would not be seen as "different". Lorna's hair color was the only outward sign of her latent genetic potential for magnetic powers, but certain genetic factors were absent which would have allowed her to exercise those powers. In the normal course of events, Lorna would never have been able to use these powers. However, the intervention of Samuel "Starr" Saxon, the master roboticist whose brain patterns were later preserved in the Machinesmith, altered the normal course of events. Saxon had constructed an android duplicate of Magneto, the self-styled mutant master of magnetism who was believed dead at the time, and a small army of androids with strange powers called the Demi-Men. Saxon's plans were to use these androids as his means of accumulating vast wealth and power, while deceiving the world into believing them to be examples of evil mutants, who had become objects of widespread fear.

Saxon sought mutants to help lead his army while he gave directions through the Magneto robot. First, Saxon had the robot Magneto recruit the hypnotic mutant Mesmero. Then, Saxon decided that a mutant who was a natural source of vast magnetic power would be useful in dealing with his metal robot army. Saxon acquired a "psyche-generator" which Mesmero used to summon mutants in North America with latent powers to San Francisco, and the nearest such mutant was Lorna. Mesmero captured Lorna and placed her inside a genetic stimulator, which altered her genetic structure so as to allow her to exercise her latent powers. Mesmero then used his hypnosis on Lorna to alter her personality so that she would sympathize with the faux Magneto and believe him to be her father.

Shortly afterwards, Mesmero dropped his control over Lorna, overconfidently assuming that she would obey her supposed father no matter what. On the contrary, after it was revealed to her that Magneto was apparently not her father, Lorna joined the teenage mutant heroes known as the X-Men in defeating the villains. Lorna subsequently joined the X-Men, and for a time she was romantically inclined toward Iceman. Eventually, Lorna fell in love with Alex Summers, the X-Man known as Havok. Neither Lorna nor Alex wished to lead lives as costumed adventurers. Discovering a mutual interest in geophysics, the pair left the team and began doctoral research in the Diablo mountain range.

Lorna and Alex settled in New Mexico, completed their degrees, and occasionally – and reluctantly – aided their former teammates. The pair's idyllic lifestyle was interrupted when they found themselves hunted by the team of superhuman assassins known as the Marauders. Lorna was possessed by the psionic entity known as Malice, who forced her to attack Alex and the X-Men as the Marauders' leader. Malice later discovered that she and Lorna were permanently bonded due to interference from their individual energy matrices.

Eventually, Malice's hold on Lorna weakened and she was able to contact the X-Men for help. However, they arrived too late to save Lorna from being kidnapped by Zaladane, a priestess from the hidden Antarctic jungle known as the Savage Land. Zaladane claimed to be Lorna's sister, and used a device to transfer Lorna's powers to herself, purging her of Malice's presence in the process. Strangely, as a result, Lorna developed alternate powers, including superhuman strength and near-invulnerability, and also grew considerably in height and mass.

In an effort to answer the mystery of her transformation, Lorna headed for the mutant research station on Muir Island off the coast of Scotland. En route, Lorna discovered that she drew her newfound strength from negative energy. Lorna's new powers drew the attention of the psionic being known as the Shadow King, who used Lorna as a gateway to allow him access to Earth from the astral plane. The X-Men defeated the Shadow King, and Lorna's magnetic powers were restored after Magneto killed Zaladane.

Lorna was subsequently recruited into the new government-sponsored X-Factor, where she was reunited with Alex. She became a mainstay of the team, and also became the government's secret weapon against a possible attack by Magneto. Malice returned to plague Lorna once more, but she and Alex attempted to absorb her, preventing the other from being possessed. In the end, Malice perished at the hands of her master, the evil geneticist Mister Sinister.

Later, X-Factor was forced by the government to employ the renowned mutant criminals Mystique and Sabretooth, and Alex seemingly went rogue. As a result, Lorna began to question her place on the team, and her fears were eventually justified after Sabretooth broke free and ran amok. Alex eventually revealed his true plan to stop the sinister machinations of the Dark Beast, an alternate reality counterpart of the X-Men's Beast. Lorna forgave him; however, she could no longer trust him and called off their relationship. Lorna rejoined X-Factor only to watch as Alex was seemingly killed in an aircraft explosion.

Weeks later, Lorna encountered the X-Man known as Nightcrawler in a church and confided in him that she was sure Alex was still alive, and that she felt as if she were being followed. A group of shape-shifting alien Skrulls who were working with the ageless mutant despot Apocalypse had been following her, and they stole into her apartment to retrieve the headgear from Alex's original costume. Lorna subsequently learned that she was one of the fabled Twelve, destined to usher in a new golden age for mutantkind. Alongside the X-Men, she traveled to Egypt to battle Apocalypse. During the encounter, Magneto, another member of the Twelve, found that he could use Lorna to tap into the Earth's magnetic field with incredible force, effectively hiding his current reduced-power state.

After Apocalypse was defeated, Lorna traveled to the island nation of Genosha with Magneto to keep him empowered in order to maintain his rule and to learn more about the nature of her powers from him. Ultimately, Magneto launched a full-scale assault on Carrion Cove, the last city opposing his rule, in order to gain access to technology that would restore his full abilities. Lorna attempted to stop him, but was defeated and left the country only to later return covertly to help oppose Magneto's tyrannical rule.

Genosha's population was later massacred by the giant mutant-hunting robot Sentinels. Upon investigating, the X-Men found Lorna alive in the ruins, naked and apparently insane. Lorna had been possessed by the ghosts of those who died residing in magnetic fields, and using their memories and her powers she finished building a monument dedicated to Magneto and played his last recorded message to the world. Lorna then returned to the Xavier Institute, where she learned that Alex had been found alive, albeit comatose. Lorna met Annie Ghazikhanian, the nurse who had cared

for Alex in a convalescent home, and callously attacked her. Only Xavier's intervention prevented Lorna from seriously injuring Annie. Reunited with Alex, Lorna proposed that the two of them marry. On the day of their wedding, however, Alex stopped the ceremony and broke off their relationship. Incensed, Lorna sought to kill Alex and his new love Annie, but was stopped by Alex's teammate the Juggernaut.

Afterwards, Lorna sought Xavier's help in discovering the cause of her violent tendencies. Exploring her thoughts, it was revealed that Lorna had learned she was actually Magneto's biological daughter shortly before Genosha had been attacked. The full repercussions of this revelation have yet to be explored.

PHYSICAL DESCRIPTION:

HEIGHT: 5'7"
WEIGHT: 115 lbs
EYES: Dark green
HAIR: Light green

DISTINGUISHING FEATURES: None

POWERS & ABILITIES:

STRENGTH LEVEL: Polaris possesses the normal human strength of a woman of her age, height, and build who engages in regular exercise

SUPERHUMAN POWERS: Polaris is a mutant with the ability to manipulate magnetism. Although she has the potential to exercise all of the powers that Magneto has, as yet she has only used powers involving the manipulation of magnetic, electrical, and gravitic fields. Moreover, she cannot summon as great an amount of energy as Magneto can. The exact limits on the amount of weight that she can magnetically lift at present have not been measured, but they are considerably below those of Magneto. Since she has preferred not to use her powers in combat situations, she has not worked nearly as hard to develop them as Magneto has. As with Magneto, it is unknown whether Polaris's powers are purely psionic or whether they derive from her physically.

Polaris has been observed levitating metallic objects and creating force fields in which she can suspend persons or objects in the air and in which she can protect them from attacks from outside the fields. She can also overload or short-circuit electrical systems. By concentrating, Polaris can perceive the world around herself solely as patterns of magnetic and electrical energy. She can perceive the natural magnetic auras surrounding living beings, as well.

For a time, Polaris possessed superhuman strength and durability, as well as the ability to temporarily increase her height and mass by drawing on negative energy around her.

POWER GRID	1	2	3	4	5	6	7
INTELLIGENCE							
STRENGTH							
SPEED							
DURABILITY							
ENERGY PROJECTION							
FIGHTING SKILLS							

PROFESSOR X

REAL NAME: Charles Francis Xavier
KNOWN ALIASES: Formerly Prisoner M-13
IDENTITY: Publicly known
OCCUPATION: Mutant rights activist, geneticist, teacher, formerly adventurer, soldier
CITIZENSHIP: United States of America with no criminal record
PLACE OF BIRTH: New York City, New York
MARITAL STATUS: Single, former consort to Princess-Majestrix Lilandra of the Shi'ar Empire
KNOWN RELATIVES: Brian Xavier (father, deceased), Sharon Xavier (mother, deceased), Cassandra Nova (sister), Kurt Marko (stepfather, deceased), Cain Marko (Juggernaut, stepbrother), David Charles Haller (Legion, son, deceased)
GROUP AFFILIATION: Formerly X-Men (founder), Cadre K, Twelve, Starjammers, New Mutants (founder), U.S. Army
EDUCATION: PhDs in genetics, biophysics, psychology, anthropology, and psychiatry

HISTORY: Charles Francis Xavier was born the son of nuclear researcher Brian Xavier and his wife, Sharon. Following her husband's accidental death, Sharon married Brian's colleague, Kurt Marko. Cain, Kurt's son from a previous marriage, came to live at the Xavier's Westchester mansion shortly thereafter. A cruel and spiteful boy, he bullied his new stepbrother, and his father secretly beat him as punishment. Charles felt his sibling's pain first-hand thanks to the emergence of his mutant telepathic powers. Following their mother's death, a fire in the family home took Kurt's life, leaving the stepbrothers alone.

By the time he graduated high school, Charles was completely bald as a side effect of his mutant nature. He entered Bard College in New York at age 16 and earned his bachelor's degree in biology within two years. He was then accepted into the graduate-studies program at England's prestigious Oxford University, where he earned degrees in genetics and biophysics. There, Charles met and fell in love with a young Scotswoman named Moira Kinross. Their passionate discussions on the subject of genetic mutation gave way to an equally passionate romance, and they planned to marry. Their only obstacle was Moira's former boyfriend, Joe MacTaggert, a lance corporal in the Royal Marines and a bully, just like Cain. In Joe's eyes, Charles was a good-for-nothing intellectual, so Charles enlisted in the military after completing his studies at Oxford to validate himself in terms his rival would understand.

Charles quickly became something of a legend in the area of search and rescue thanks to his mutant abilities. Attached to the same unit as his stepbrother, Charles was present when Cain deserted under fire during a mission in Asia. Following him in the hope of convincing him to return to their unit, Charles witnessed Cain's discovery of the mystical Ruby of Cyttorak and his transformation into the superhuman Juggernaut. Charles escaped the subsequent cave-in, mistakenly believing his stepbrother was dead.

Later, Charles was devastated when Moira broke off their engagement without explanation. He left the Army and began travelling the world. In Cairo, Egypt, he encountered Amahl Farouk, a mutant capable of summoning forth the darkness in the souls of others. This confrontation led to Charles' decision to devote his life to protecting humanity from evil mutants and saving innocent mutants from human oppression.

Charles next travelled to Israel, where he fell in love with Israeli diplomat Gabrielle Haller. He also befriended a fellow drifter named Erik Magnus Lehnsherr, the mutant who would become his greatest enemy: Magneto, self-styled master of magnetism. While Charles optimistically believed that humans and mutants could coexist, the Jewish Magnus foresaw mutants as the new minority to be persecuted and hunted because of their differences. Together, the pair prevented the nefarious Baron Von Strucker from launching his terrorist group Hydra on an unsuspecting world. Magnus departed with Strucker's gold, and upon departing Israel himself, Charles was unaware that Haller was pregnant with his son, David.

En route to the United States, Charles encountered the alien Lucifer in the Himalayas. To prevent any interference in his race's planned invasion of Earth, Lucifer dropped a massive stone block on Charles, crippling his legs. In desperation, Charles called out with his mental powers and touched the mind of a young mutant named Tessa who was operating as a mercenary in the neighboring Hindu Kush mountains. Tessa came to his aid and Charles was airlifted to safety. During his convalescence in an Indian hospital, Charles met Amelia Voght, a young nurse who fell in love with him and renewed his will to live.

Charles resumed graduate work at Columbia University in New York; after receiving a PhD in anthropology, he spent several years in London earning a PhD in psychiatry. There, Charles renewed his friendship with Moira, who had married Joe MacTaggert and was now a renowned geneticist, and the two began discussing the idea of founding a school for mutants.

Charles returned to America and resumed his studies of mutation. It was not long before Professor John Grey, a friend of Charles' from Bard College, brought his young daughter Jean to Charles for help. Jean had been traumatized when she telepathically experienced the death of a friend. Charles aided in her recovery, and in the ensuing years trained her to use her mental powers. Charles later met with Fred Duncan, an F.B.I. agent investigating the growing number of mutants. Charles told Duncan of his plan to locate young mutants and enroll them in a school using his ancestral mansion home as a base to train them to use their powers for humanity's benefit. Amelia remained with Charles until the young mutant Scott Summers came to study at the school. She left, fearing an escalating genetic arms race between Charles and Magnus. Over the following months, Charles used the mutant-locating computer Cerebro to assemble his original group of students: Cyclops, Iceman, Angel, Beast, and Jean Grey, who took the name Marvel Girl. He dubbed his students the "X-Men", because each possessed an "extra" ability that normal humans lacked. Charles also recruited Tessa at this time, but kept her presence at the mansion a secret from his other students as he planned to use her talents as a spy.

Soon after, Charles learned of a planned invasion of Earth by the alien Z'nox and theorized that he would have to link the minds of the majority of morally upright people on Earth to stop the invaders. However, he needed time in virtual isolation to prepare his mind for such an awesome task. To that end, Charles had the mutant shape-changer named Changeling impersonate him so that his students, except for Jean to whom he entrusted his plan, would remain none the wiser. After Changeling died on a mission with the team, Charles allowed the X-Men to believe he was dead. Months later, Charles revealed his deception to his students and repelled the invaders.

Years later, when his original students were captured by the sentient island-being named Krakoa, Charles recruited Banshee, Colossus, Nightcrawler, Storm, Sunfire, and Wolverine as a new team to rescue them. Afterwards, Cyclops was the only original member to remain and help Charles train the new recruits. Before long, Charles began to experience psychic nightmares from an alien world. These images were sent by Lilandra, princess of the intergalactic Shi'ar Empire, who was seeking assistance to defeat her mad brother D'Ken. In the course of the ensuing struggle, Charles and Lilandra fell in love, and for a time he lived on Chandilar, the Shi'ar throneworld, as her consort.

Charles and Lilandra spent much time together on Earth before her coronation, and during this time the X-Men fought Magneto in Antarctica. After the battle, most of the team made it to the hidden jungle in the icy wasteland known as the Savage Land. Phoenix and

Beast returned to Westchester, believing the rest of the team had died. Heartbroken, Charles accompanied Lilandra to the Shi'ar homeworld for her coronation. When he eventually learned that the rest of the X-Men were actually alive, he returned to Earth.

Some time later, Lilandra faced a coup by her sister Deathbird and the alien Brood race. The X-Men and the space pirates known as the Starjammers helped defeat them, but Charles had been implanted with a Brood egg which would ultimately hatch and transform him into the Brood's new queen. When Charles tried to probe the implant, he was sent into a coma; after he awoke, he learned the X-Men had been captured by the Brood and taken into space. Fearing his students dead, and under subconscious commands from the larval Brood within him, Charles gathered a new group of young superhuman students he named the New Mutants. Following the X-Men's return, the queen hatched and transformed Charles into a Brood. Although his body was destroyed, with the X-Men's help, Charles was able to retain mental control of the Brood Queen long enough for the Starjammers' physician Sikorsky to clone him a new body with no disabilities. It was some time before Charles could walk again due to the psychosomatic pain of being crippled for so long.

Eventually, Charles began to take his most active role ever with the X-Men by accompanying them on missions. During this time, Gabrielle requested Charles' help in treating her son David, the powerful psionic mutant known as Legion, who suffered from multiple personality disorder. Charles learned that David was his son and helped him emerge from his autistic condition, after which father and son were reunited.

After a brutal beating at the hands of a group of college students, Charles' cloned body began to deteriorate and he was forced to leave Earth with Lilandra and the Starjammers to heal. He left the school in the seemingly reformed Magneto's care, joining Lilandra in the fight to regain her rightful place on the Shi'ar throne. After an extended sojourn in space, Charles finally returned to Earth, and both the original and second teams of X-Men reassembled under his leadership to battle his old enemy Farouk, now calling himself the Shadow King. Charles' spine was broken in the ensuing battle, leaving him crippled and confined to a wheelchair once more.

Since the X-Men were all now highly trained adults, Charles renamed his School as the Xavier Institute for Higher Learning. He also assumed control of a private institution, the Massachusetts Academy, and transformed it into a new School for Gifted Youngsters. There, yet another new crop of young mutants, Generation X, learned to use their budding superhuman abilities.

Charles' next major confrontation came when Magneto initiated a lethal electromagnetic pulse inside Earth's atmosphere. Charles and his X-Men took the fight to Magneto's orbital base; in the ensuing battle, Magneto viciously attacked Wolverine, forcibly extracting from his body the metal that had been bonded to his skeleton. Seeing no other alternative, Charles used his mental powers to shut down Magneto's conscious mind. During this desperate act, the evil portion of Magneto's psyche implanted itself within Charles' mind. This evil aspect, combined with the darkest part of Charles' soul, eventually gained sentience as the powerful psionic being known as Onslaught.

After a pitched battle, America's greatest super heroes narrowly defeated Onslaught. To ensure that Charles never again spawned such a being, he was taken into custody by the United States government. Although Charles was willing to pay the price for his folly, he was appalled when the government turned him over to the custody of Bastion, head of the anti-mutant Operation Zero Tolerance. After the government shut down Zero Tolerance for overstepping its authority, the X-Men set out to search for their missing founder. When they finally located him, Charles was leading a new incarnation of the Brotherhood of Mutants in an attempt to defeat a now-sentient Cerebro. Charles ultimately defeated Cerebro by showing him the unique importance of each living individual.

Charles subsequently returned to the X-Men, but soon after disbanded the team over fears a member of the shape-shifting alien race known as the Skrulls had infiltrated them. After Wolverine was seemingly killed in battle, it was revealed that it was actually a Skrull impersonating him that had died, thus proving Charles' theory correct. The X-Men reformed in time to foil the plans of the eternal mutant Apocalypse, who sought to rule the world by using the power of the Twelve – a fabled team of mutants, including Charles and Magneto, who were destined to usher in a new golden age for their kind. After Apocalypse was defeated, Charles departed Earth with a team of adolescent mutant Skrulls, whom he dubbed Cadre K, to help them find a new home among the stars.

Charles later returned to the X-Men to lead them once more, but was captured by Magneto who had been amassing an army on the island nation of Genosha in preparation for an all-out war against humanity. The X-Men rescued their founder, and Magneto was himself crippled by Wolverine. Soon after, giant mutant-hunting robotic Sentinels sent by Charles' malevolent genetic twin sister, Cassandra Nova, obliterated Genosha's population. Charles found himself powerless against his sister after she switched bodies with him, trapping his mind in her own dying form. In Charles' body, Nova publicly outed him as a mutant and then left Earth with Lilandra, whom she convinced to order the Shi'ar's superhuman Imperial Guard to destroy all mutants on Earth, starting with the X-Men. After a pitched battle during which Nova's deception was revealed, Jean Grey absorbed Charles' consciousness into her own mind, then used the new mutant-locating Cerebra device to hide pieces of it in the minds of every mutant on Earth. When Nova went to use Cerebra to kill all of Earth's mutants, she unwittingly reformed Charles' consciousness and he forced her out of his body. Once Nova was defeated, Xorn, the X-Men's newest member, healed Charles' body.

Free of having to hide behind a veil of secrecy, Charles took to his now public role as a mutant rights activist with vigor. He opened his school to mutants everywhere, and the X-Men became the new faculty. It was not long, however, before Charles' world came crashing down around him when Xorn was revealed to be Magneto in disguise. His old nemesis had survived the Genoshan holocaust and infiltrated the X-Men, gathering together a class of students to use as his new soldiers for the war against mankind. Magneto crippled Charles once more and took control of New York City, rechristening it New Genosha. Using a neuro-toxic drug known as Kick to boost his powers, Magneto planned to reverse the magnetic poles of the Earth, destroying humanity and ushering in a new age for mutantkind. However, his students rebelled, and the timely arrival of the X-Men saw a permanent end to his plans after Wolverine decapitated him.

Disillusioned, Charles left the Institute in the care of the X-Men and travelled to Genosha to give Magneto a proper burial. Wolverine accompanied him, and the two argued over their differing opinions of Magneto. Wolverine left on less than friendly terms, leaving Charles to help rebuild the shattered mutant nation.

PHYSICAL DESCRIPTION:

HEIGHT: 6'
WEIGHT: 190 lbs
EYES: Blue
HAIR: Bald (blond in childhood)

DISTINGUISHING FEATURES: Paraplegic

POWERS & ABILITIES:

STRENGTH LEVEL: Professor X possesses the normal human strength of a man of his age, height, and build who engages in regular exercise.

SUPERHUMAN POWERS: Professor X is a mutant who possesses vast psionic powers, making him arguably the world's most powerful telepath. He can read minds and project his own thoughts into the minds of others within a radius of approximately 250 miles. With extreme effort, he can greatly extend that radius. Professor X can also psionically manipulate the minds of others, for example to make himself seem invisible and to project illusions. He can also induce temporary mental and/or physical paralysis, loss of particular memories or even total amnesia. Within close range, Professor X can manipulate almost any number of minds for such simple feats. However, he can only take full possession of another being's mind one at a time, and he can only do so if he is within that being's physical presence.

Furthermore, Professor X can project powerful mental bolts of psionic energy enabling him to stun the mind of another being into unconsciousness. These bolts only apply force upon other minds; they do not inflict physical damage. Professor X can also sense the presence of other superhuman mutants within a small radius of himself by perceiving the distinct mental radiations emitted by such beings. In order to detect the presence of mutants beyond this radius, he must amplify his powers. He often does this by using first Cerebro and more recently Cerebra, devices that are sensitive to that portion of the electromagnetic spectrum that contains mental frequencies.

Professor X can project his astral form, the sheath of his life essence, onto abstract dimensions congruent to our own known as astral planes. There, he can use his powers to create ectoplasmic objects. He cannot engage in long-range astral projection on the earthly plane.

SPECIAL SKILLS: Professor X is a leading authority on genetics, mutation, and psionic powers, and has considerable expertise in other life sciences. He is also highly talented in devising equipment for utilizing and enhancing psionic powers.

SPECIAL LIMITATIONS: Part of Professor X's spine is shattered, thus confining him to a wheelchair.

POWER GRID	1	2	3	4	5	6	7
INTELLIGENCE							
STRENGTH							
SPEED							
DURABILITY							
ENERGY PROJECTION							
FIGHTING SKILLS							

REAL NAME: Katherine "Kitty" Pryde
KNOWN ALIASES: Shadowcat, formerly Ariel, Sprite
IDENTITY: Secret
OCCUPATION: Adventurer, former student, bartender, S.H.I.E.L.D. agent
CITIZENSHIP: United States of America with no criminal record
PLACE OF BIRTH: Deerfield, Illinois

MARITAL STATUS: Single
KNOWN RELATIVES: Carmen Pryde (father, deceased), Theresa "Terri" Pryde (mother), Samuel Prydeman (grandfather, deceased), Chava Rosanoff (great-aunt, deceased)
GROUP AFFILIATION: X-Men, formerly Excalibur, S.H.I.E.L.D., New Mutants
EDUCATION: Some university-level courses

HISTORY: Katherine "Kitty" Pryde was a 13-year-old Jewish girl whose genius level intellect allowed her to take college-level courses despite her age. Kitty led a fairly normal life until she began suffering headaches of steadily increasing intensity, which unbeknownst to her were a result of her emerging mutant power.

Kitty learned she was mutant after Emma Frost, then White Queen of the enigmatic Hellfire Club, came to visit. Frost sought to convince Kitty's parents to enrol her in Frost's Massachusetts Academy, which was a front for training superhuman mutant criminals. During the visit, Kitty suffered her worst headache yet and went upstairs to her room. When the headache stopped, Kitty was surprised to find she was on the floor of her living room. She had unknowingly used her power to phase through solid matter for the first time, passing through her bed and floor into the room below.

After Frost left, Professor Charles Xavier arrived with three of the X-Men, his own team of mutant students who sought peaceful coexistence between humans and mutants. Following an attack by the Hellfire Club during which Kitty helped the team, the X-Man Phoenix telepathically coerced Kitty's parents into allowing her to join Xavier's school. She became the newest and youngest member of the X-Men, originally calling herself Sprite, but later adopted the codename Ariel. Xavier also arranged for Kitty to be enrolled in dance classes at the studio of instructor Stevie Hunter.

Kitty quickly became a valued member of the X-Men, proving her worth one Christmas Eve by single-handedly defeating one of the demonic N'garai. After an adventure in space, Kitty gained a constant companion in the form of a small alien dragon-like creature she named Lockheed. Kitty also fell in love with her teammate Colossus; though their romance was short-lived, the two remained close friends. Kitty also formed lasting friendships with her teammate Storm, as well as the mutant sorceress Illyana Rasputin and fellow dance class student and computer aficionado Doug Ramsey. Doug's eventual death would prove to be the first of many personal losses Kitty would suffer.

After a visit to her recently divorced father, Carmen, Kitty learned that he had become involved with the Yakuza and followed him to Japan. There, she was captured and mentally possessed by Ogun, the martial arts master who had once trained her teammate Wolverine. Using Kitty's body, Ogun attempted to kill Wolverine but failed. Wolverine then taught Kitty to become skilful enough in the martial arts to combat Ogun, and together they managed to exorcise Ogun's spirit.

During the massacre of the underground community of mutants known as the Morlocks by the team of superhuman mutant assassins the Marauders, Kitty' was injured by the Marauder named Harpoon. Unable to regain her solidity, Kitty was saved by the combined efforts of the European dictator Doctor Doom and his archrival, Reed Richards of the world-renowned Fantastic Four; however, she could only maintain a solid form through concentration.

After witnessing the apparent death of the X-Men, Kitty helped form the British-based super-team Excalibur. During an interdimensional adventure, Kitty became separated from her teammates and, returning to her own Earth, she decided to give up the life of a costumed adventurer and attend college. However, unaccustomed as she was to the British educational system, Kitty was forced to enrol in St. Searle's School for Girls. After helping save the school from closure, Kitty rejoined her recently returned teammates.

Months later, Kitty learned that Illyana was dying from the deadly mutant-killing Legacy Virus. Kitty was present when Illyana finally succumbed to the disease, unaware that the young mutant's death bonded the Soulsword, the ultimate expression of Illyana's magical nature, to her. Eventually, the sword began to corrupt Kitty, and she surrendered the weapon to her then teammate Daytripper who in turn gave it to her mother, the gypsy sorceress Margali Szardos, for safekeeping.

Soon after, the members of Excalibur were approached by the clandestine organization Black Air for assistance on a mission to the island nation of Genosha. They were assigned a liaison in Pete Wisdom, an uncouth British mutant who regularly clashed with the outspoken Kitty. The pair eventually overcame their initial impressions of one another and fell in love. Wisdom even resigned from Black Air and joined Excalibur to be with Kitty.

Later, Kitty was recruited by the international law enforcement agency S.H.I.E.L.D. to repair the computer system of its flying headquarters, which was refusing to acknowledge anyone but her. Kitty discovered that Ogun's spirit having infiltrated the computer system, and with the aid of Wolverine, she managed to purge Ogun's presence. During this time, Kitty was attracted to a S.H.I.E.L.D. intern her own age. As a result, she began to doubt her relationship with Wisdom and ended it soon after.

Kitty remained a member of Excalibur until the team disbanded whereupon she rejoined the X-Men. After Colossus sacrificed his life to release a cure for the Legacy Virus, Kitty left the X-Men to try and live a normal life. She enrolled in the Robert A. Heinlein School for Engineering and Astrophysics in Chicago on a full scholarship, and began working as a bartender at the Belles of Hell. Kitty found herself unable to escape the ever-prevalent prejudice of humans, and she soon clashed with members of a student anti-mutant organization named Purity. Kitty was put on probation and was forced to attend mandatory counselling. During this time, Kitty faced her most difficult loss when she learned her father was amongst those killed in an attack on Genosha.

Kitty's battle against Purity continued after the organization attempted to frame her for the sabotage of a research experiment. A student meeting was called to debate the banning of either Purity or mutants from campus, but discussions were cut short by an attack by a new breed of mutant-hunting robotic Sentinels which were destroyed by Kitty with the help of former New Mutant Karma and Genoshan exchange student Shola Inkosi.

Kitty was later abducted by the mutant-hating Reverend Stryker to help expose the technological threat of the mutant retreat known as Mount Haven and its mysterious leader, Reverend Paul. Together, Stryker and Kitty discovered that Paul was an artificial intelligence who had killed the human townspeople and used microbial machines called nanites to transform the minds of the mutant residents from organic matter into cybernetic computers linked to his central consciousness. When Storm's team of X-Men arrived to find Kitty, Paul sought to transform them as well. Stryker attempted to use Kitty's power to disrupt electronics to destroy Paul, but he failed and Paul responded by transferring his consciousness into a global network. In an effort to safeguard his kind from Paul's threat, Stryker merged with him in an attempt to teach him about humanity, and the town of Haven was buried by a volcanic eruption.

Soon after, Kitty assisted Storm's team against the threat of mutant predator Elias Bogan. After Bogan was defeated, Kitty accompanied the team back to the mansion and was asked to remain as a member of Cyclops' restructured X-Men.

PHYSICAL DESCRIPTION:

HEIGHT: 5'6"
WEIGHT: 110 lbs (when fully solid)
EYES: Hazel
HAIR: Brown

DISTINGUISHING FEATURES: None

POWERS & ABILITIES:

STRENGTH LEVEL: Kitty possesses the normal human strength of a woman of her age, height, and build who engages in intensive regular exercise.

SUPERHUMAN POWERS: Kitty is a mutant with the ability to "phase" through solid matter by shifting her atoms through the spaces between the atoms of the object through which she is moving. Kitty can phase her clothing along with herself, and through practice has learned to phase other objects and people without harm to them. For all intents and purposes, Kitty is intangible whilst phasing, however she is still vulnerable to psionic or mystical attacks. Certain forms of energy can also disrupt her phased state.

When Kitty phases through an object with an electrical system, the process disrupts the system's workings. This includes the electrical impulses found in the human brain. Kitty can phase part or all of her body through another living being without harm to herself, though the other being can be rendered unconscious as a result.

Kitty passes through objects at the same rate of speed at which she is moving before phasing. Since she is unable to breathe while phasing, she can only continuously phase through solid objects – as when she travels underground – as long as she can hold her breath. Kitty can keep her phased form at rest to the rotation of the Earth's axis, thus allowing her to assume a ground speed of the length of a football field and a half every second. Kitty can also walk on air whilst phasing.

Kitty has trained herself to reflexively assume a phased state at any indication of danger, such as a loud noise like a gunshot, in order to protect herself.

SPECIAL LIMITATIONS: Kitty is slightly nearsighted.

SPECIAL SKILLS: Kitty is moderately skilled in the Japanese martial arts, as well as street-fighting techniques taught to her by Wolverine. She is a genius in the computer sciences, and highly skilled in the design and use of computer hardware and software. Kitty is also a competent operator of automobiles, aircraft, and interstellar vehicles. Kitty was also trained in ballet and modern dance; speaks fluent Japanese, Russian, and the royal and standard languages of the alien Shi'ar; and has moderate expertise in Gaelic, Hebrew, and German.

POWER GRID	1	2	3	4	5	6	7
INTELLIGENCE							
STRENGTH							
SPEED							
DURABILITY							
ENERGY PROJECTION							
FIGHTING SKILLS							

REAL NAME: Unrevealed
KNOWN ALIASES: Anna Raven, formerly Doctor Kellogg, Mutate #9602, Irene Adler, Miss Smith
IDENTITY: Secret

OCCUPATION: Adventurer, former mechanic, waitress, terrorist
CITIZENSHIP: United States of America with no criminal record
PLACE OF BIRTH: Caldecott County, Mississippi
MARITAL STATUS: Single
KNOWN RELATIVES: Unnamed father, unnamed mother, Raven Darkhölme (Mystique, unofficial foster mother), Kurt Wagner (Nightcrawler, unofficial foster brother), Graydon Creed (unofficial foster brother, deceased)
GROUP AFFILIATION: X-Men, formerly X-Treme Sanctions Executive, X-Treme X-Men, Brotherhood of Evil Mutants
EDUCATION: College-level courses at Xavier's School, partial law degree

HISTORY: Not much is known about the past of the mysterious mutant known only as Rogue. Though aware of her real name and her past, Rogue has been reluctant to divulge any details. What is known is that she grew up in Caldecott County near the Mississippi River and was orphaned at a young age. Found living in a swamp by the mutant shapeshifter named Mystique, Rogue was adopted by her and her companion, the blind mutant seer Destiny. Rogue soon came to regard Mystique as a surrogate mother.

Rogue's mutant power first manifested in her early teens when she innocently kissed a boy named Cody Robbins. Her mind was filled with his memories and he fell into a coma. Terrified, Rogue fled and was chased by an angry mob, but a chance encounter with the time-travelling mutant named Cable saved her from a lynching.

Mystique and Destiny taught Rogue how to use her ability to absorb the memories and abilities of others by touch, but lacked the skill necessary to teach her how to control it. Attempting to lead a normal life, Rogue once again inadvertently absorbed the memories of another local boy named Freddy. Realizing she could never safely live among normal people, Rogue began participating in her mother's criminal endeavors and eventually joined Mystique's terrorist organization, the Brotherhood of Evil Mutants.

On one such endeavor in San Francisco, Rogue clashed with the original Ms. Marvel, Carol Danvers. During their battle on the Golden Gate Bridge, the inexperienced Rogue permanently absorbed Danvers' memories and superhuman powers. The transfer also altered Rogue's physiology to become an amalgam of her own mutant human form and Ms. Marvel's human/Kree alien hybrid make-up.

Rogue grew increasingly upset over her inability to control her powers and feared she was going insane due to her inability to rid herself of Danvers' psyche. Desperate for help, Rogue turned to her enemies, the team of mutant heroes known as the X-Men. Convinced of her sincerity, the X-Men's founder, Professor Xavier, accepted Rogue onto the team. However, it wasn't until she risked her own life to save Mariko Yashida, the fiancée of her teammate Wolverine, that she began to gain her teammates' trust.

Soon after, Rogue went to the aid of Colonel Mike Rossi, the former lover of Carol Danvers, who was surprised to find Rogue acting and even speaking like Danvers. Rogue had unwittingly allowed Danvers' psyche to take control and, after reasserting her own psyche, came to realize the full extent of what she had done to Danvers.

When agents from the island nation of Genosha captured Rogue and Wolverine, their powers were negated and, for the first time since her youth, Rogue was able to experience skin-to-skin contact without her powers activating. Unfortunately for her, it was at the hands of Genoshan soldiers who took advantage of her. Rogue withdrew into herself and learned that leftover psychic energy from all those whom she had previously absorbed remained in her mind. She encountered Danvers' psychic phantom, and the pair made a pact to share Rogue's body. Rogue then gave Danvers control so she could use her skills as a covert agent to escape. Afterwards, Danvers' psyche exhibited the ability to control Rogue's absorption power, revealing that Rogue's lack of control was strictly psychological. Later, Rogue entered the Siege Perilous, a mystical gateway that grants those that pass through it a second chance at life, and emerged in the X-Men's base in the Australian outback without Danvers' memories or powers. The magicks of the gateway had attempted to separate the two women, giving each a body to inhabit, but there was not enough life force to sustain them both. Ms. Marvel attacked Rogue, who fled to the hidden Antarctic jungle known as the Savage Land. Rogue ultimately chose to surrender to Ms. Marvel, as she didn't want to repeat her past mistake; however, they were both rendered unconscious by the timely arrival of Magneto, the self-styled mutant master of magnetism and the X-Men's greatest foe. Magneto used a device to transfer Ms. Marvel's abilities back to Rogue, sans Danvers' psyche. After a brief romance with Magneto, Rogue returned to the X-Men.

Rogue soon found herself attracted to the X-Men's newest member, the Cajun mutant Gambit. The pair quickly fell in love, despite Rogue's persistent inability to control her powers. Over time, Rogue's feelings for Gambit grew, even after discovering he was married.

Eventually sharing a kiss, Rogue absorbed Gambit's memories and learned of a dark secret in his past. Distraught, she left the X-Men and encountered the young man named Joseph, who was actually a clone of Magneto. Rogue eventually returned to the X-Men, bringing Joseph with her, in time to help the team battle against the evil psionic entity Onslaught.

Later, Rogue and Gambit were captured by Magneto, who intended to put Gambit on trial for his past misdeeds. With their powers nullified, the pair spent their first intimate night together. At the trial, the X-Men learned of Gambit's involvement in the massacre of the underground mutant community known as the Morlocks. As a result, Rogue rejected Gambit and left him stranded in Antarctica.

Afterwards, Rogue learned of the Agee Institute, an organization that could permanently remove mutant powers. Seeing a chance for a normal life, Rogue sought to undergo the procedure. However, she changed her mind at the last minute, not wanting the Institute to use the device on other mutants against their will. Making one of the hardest decisions of her life, Rogue destroyed the machine.

During the time that Earth was deemed an intergalactic prison, Rogue imprinted a member of the shape-shifting alien race known as the Skrulls. The resultant mixing of Rogue's already amalgamated physiology with that of the Skrull's caused her to spontaneously manifest powers that she had previously absorbed. Initially she had no control over what powers manifested at a given time, so she wore a pair of ruby quartz glasses to protect others against the eventuality of her generating an optic blast like that of the X-Man Cyclops.

Soon after, Rogue and five other X-Men formed a splinter group to search for Destiny's diaries that predicted the future of mutantkind. During their quest, the X-Treme X-Men opposed an attempted invasion of Earth by the interdimensional forces of the warlord Khan. To help repel the invaders, Rogue had her teammate Sage "jumpstart" her powers to allow her to consciously activate any combination of powers that she had previously absorbed. After a fierce battle in which she was seriously injured, the resultant trauma shorted out Rogue's powers. Gambit had also been left powerless, and the pair seized the opportunity to live a normal life together in the mutant-friendly community of Valle Soleada in California.

Eventually, Rogue and Gambit became involved with the X-Men again to help combat the threat of the mutant predator Elias Bogan. Still powerless, Rogue aided her former teammates in defeating Bogan and subsequently rejoined the team.

PHYSICAL DESCRIPTION:

HEIGHT: 5'8"
WEIGHT: 120 lbs.
EYES: Green
HAIR: Brown with white streak

Distinguishing Features: Elaborate tattoo down left arm

POWERS & ABILITIES:

STRENGTH LEVEL: Rogue possesses the normal human strength of a woman of her age, height, and build who engages in intensive regular exercise. Rogue formerly possessed superhuman strength allowing her to lift/press at least 50 tons under optimal conditions.

SUPERHUMAN POWERS: Rogue is a mutant who formerly possessed the ability to absorb the memories, abilities, personality, and outward physical characteristics of other beings through skin-to-skin contact. Such transfers lasted for sixty times longer than the contact time, with extended contact resulting in the possibility of permanent absorption. No upper limit had been determined for the number of beings Rogue could simultaneously imprint.

Upon absorbing another's memories, Rogue also gained any associated emotional responses. Rogue was typically able to control absorbed emotions; however, absorbing psyches more powerful than her own resulted in Rogue's psyche being supplanted.

After permanently absorbing the powers of Ms. Marvel, Rogue possessed an amalgamated mutant human/alien Kree physiology that granted her a degree of immunity to poisons.

Rogue also possessed Ms. Marvel's above-normal reflexes and psychic "seventh sense" that enabled her to subconsciously anticipate an opponent's moves. While Rogue possessed Ms. Marvel's psyche, her "double" consciousness made her resistant to probes from even the most powerful telepaths.

After absorbing the powers of an alien Skrull, Rogue began to spontaneously reactivate previously imprinted abilities. Rogue could also tap into the residual psychic energy of those she had imprinted to determine their status and to relive past events from their perspective.

SPECIAL LIMITATIONS: Rogue previously could not come into skin-to-skin contact with another being without imprinting them. Remnants of the personalities of those who Rogue imprinted remained in her subconscious indefinitely. Certain powerful beings were able to supplant Rogue's personality, while others proved resistant to her power.

SPECIAL SKILLS: Rogue could formerly draw upon the combat and espionage training of Carol Danvers by granting control of her body to her alternate personality, a duplicate of Danvers'. Rogue can also speak fluent French.

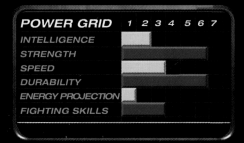

POWER GRID	1	2	3	4	5	6	7
INTELLIGENCE							
STRENGTH							
SPEED							
DURABILITY							
ENERGY PROJECTION							
FIGHTING SKILLS							

REAL NAME: Tessa (presumed, full name unrevealed)
KNOWN ALIASES: None
IDENTITY: Secret
OCCUPATION: Adventurer, former spy, personal assistant to Sebastian Shaw, mercenary

CITIZENSHIP: United States of America with no criminal record
PLACE OF BIRTH: Unrevealed
MARITAL STATUS: Single
KNOWN RELATIVES: None
GROUP AFFILIATION: X-Men, formerly X-Treme Sanctions Executive, X-Treme X-Men, Hellfire Club
EDUCATION: Unrevealed

HISTORY: Little is known of the life of the woman known as Tessa except that she had lived in a small village in the Balkan region of Europe while still a young girl, and that she had spent time in a harem under unrevealed circumstances. Just prior to her teenage years, Tessa found herself caught up in the Russian invasion of Afghanistan. She was forced to learn to fight to survive encounters with both soldiers and local bandits, and scavenged weapons and equipment from the bodies of fallen combatants. One day, Tessa felt herself compelled to enter a cave in the nearby Hindu Kush mountain range. There, she found the powerful telepathic mutant named Charles Xavier who had been trapped under a massive stone block by the alien being named Lucifer. Initially wary of him, Tessa rescued the critically injured mutant and, on the trek back to civilization, the pair encountered a United Nations aid convoy that was being attacked by bandits. Tessa drove off the attackers and then avenged the death of one young U.N. worker by brutally murdering the bandit that had raped and killed her.

Years later, Xavier recruited Tessa at the same time that he formed his original team of teenage mutant students that he called the X-Men. Xavier kept Tessa's presence at his mansion a secret, as he intended to utilize her own mutant telepathic talents as a spy in his quest for peaceful coexistence between mutants and humans. Tessa's first mission was to infiltrate the organization for the rich and powerful known as the Hellfire Club and to gain the trust of Sebastian Shaw, leader of the Club's Inner Circle at its New York branch. For years, Tessa acted as Shaw's familiar, advising and counselling him in both his legitimate and illegal business practices, all the while gathering information for Xavier. Shaw found Tessa's ability to function as a living computer invaluable and kept her in his employ for many years, even during the time he was deposed as leader of the Club.

Early on during her time with the Club, Tessa became entangled in an attempted coup of the Club's leadership by Donald Pierce, its renegade White Bishop. Pierce kidnapped Tessa, believing that without her Shaw's position could more easily be compromised. However, Xavier and his team of New Mutants rescued Tessa, and Pierce was expelled upon her return to the Club.

Later, Tessa ran afoul of the Club's first Lord Imperial, the reclusive billionaire named Elias Bogan. Shaw had made a wager with Bogan during a game of cards whereupon if Shaw lost, Bogan would win the Club's then-White Queen, the telepathic mutant Emma Frost. Bogan had never lost a game before, but with Tessa's help Shaw won the bet. Bogan honored the wager, but knew who was truly responsible for his defeat and exacted his revenge on Tessa, capturing her and branding her face with tattoos. Rescued by the X-Man named Storm, Tessa soon affiliated herself with the X-Men, acting as part of their support crew. In order to shield herself from detection by Bogan, Tessa consciously shut down her telepathic abilities, relying solely on her computer-like mind to assist her new teammates.

When Senator Robert Kelly announced his intention to run for the Presidency on an anti-mutant platform, Tessa met with him to persuade him otherwise by convincing him that his actions were no different than those of the mutant terrorist Magneto. Kelly was not so easily swayed, however, and it wasn't until a mutant sacrificed his life to save Kelly that he realized his folly.

Soon after, Tessa was given the codename of Sage by Storm, who recruited her into a splinter group of X-Men that set out to search for the diaries of the blind mutant seer named Destiny, which predicted the future of mutantkind. On the X-Treme team's first mission, Tessa was instrumental in saving the life of her teammate the Beast after an encounter with the self-professed enhanced human named Vargas. Sage used a heretofore-unseen ability to advance the Beast's evolution to its next stage, activating his latent secondary mutation.

Eventually learning of Tessa's deception, Shaw allied himself with Lady Mastermind, the daughter of former Hellfire Club member Jason Wyngarde, to exact revenge on his former assistant. Lady Mastermind trapped Tessa in a convincing illusion, making her believe that she was once again Shaw's assistant in the Hellfire Club. Tessa was freed thanks to the efforts of Heather Cameron, an Australian mutant with the ability to manifest various superhuman powers depending on what the current situation called for, and the X-Men defeated Shaw.

Tessa later catalyzed the latent mutant powers of Heather's brother, Davis, who subsequently joined the X-Treme X-Men as Slipstream, as well as evolving her teammate Rogue's mutant ability to grant her control over the manifestation of the powers and abilities she had absorbed over the years.

Tessa often used her computer-like mind to assist her teammate Bishop in his activities as a homicide detective, such as when they were called upon to investigate the attempted murder of Emma Frost, now a member of the X-Men and an instructor at Xavier's school. Later, when the X-Treme team encountered Bogan after a murder at his Alaskan estate, Sage and Bishop were called in to investigate. A young mutant named Jeffrey Garrett was wanted for questioning after Bogan had his family killed and, in retaliation, he teleported Bogan's associates onto the nearby glacier where they froze to death. Garrett fled to the Xavier Institute where he came under the protection of Emma Frost. However, Bogan had secretly possessed the young boy and when Frost scanned his mind, Bogan took possession of her. Sage and Bishop followed the trail to the mansion, where Bogan captured them, but the timely arrival of Storm allowed them to escape and defeat the villain.

Bogan returned to plague the X-Treme X-Men soon after when he captured and mentally enslaved Bishop, hoping to use him as a weapon against his teammates. With the aid of several of their former allies, the X-Men were able to rescue Bishop, which allowed Tessa to defeat Bogan once and for all. She then accompanied her teammates back to New York to assist in the rebuilding of the mansion following an attack by Magneto, after which they rejoined the core X-Men team.

PHYSICAL DESCRIPTION:

HEIGHT: 5'7"
WEIGHT: 135 lbs.
EYES: Blue
HAIR: Black

DISTINGUISHING FEATURES: Facial tattoos

POWERS & ABILITIES:

STRENGTH LEVEL: Sage possesses the normal human strength of a woman of her age, height, and build who engages in intensive regular exercise.

SUPERHUMAN POWERS: Sage is a mutant who possesses a cyberpathic mind that functions like a computer with unlimited storage capacity and vast processing power. Sage is able to record and analyze vast amounts of data, including the entire genetic code of another living being, and can also calculate complex statistics in mere seconds and track the probability of an event. Sage's memory is kinetic in nature, allowing her to totally recall information with incredible speed and accuracy via mnemonic triggers that she can recategorize as required.

Like a computer, Sage is able to perform multiple tasks at once by partitioning her mind to dedicate a portion to each task. For example, Sage can use her mind to replay a movie she has previously seen, play a game of Internet chess, and focus on battling an opponent without any one task distracting her from another. The number of tasks Sage can perform at the one time is unknown.

After analyzing the DNA of another superhuman mutant, Sage is able to selectively enhance or evolve their existing genetic traits as well as catalyze the untapped genetic potential of latent mutants. Once begun, the procedure is irreversible and can often result in unpredictable side effects.

Sage can also sense the presence of the mutant gene in others who are in close proximity to herself, and can reflect mental attacks — be they psionic or cybernetic in origin — back on their originators.

Sage also once possessed low-level telepathic abilities that allowed her to read minds, communicate with others over a distance, project her astral form, manipulate the minds of others, and create realistic mental illusions.

SPECIAL SKILLS: Sage is skilled in the martial arts and is a formidable hand-to-hand combatant, thanks to her ability to anticipate an opponent's moves and her having complete conscious control over her own body. Sage is also self-taught in a wide range of firearms, which she can use with considerable skill and accuracy.

PARAPHERNALIA:

OTHER ACCESSORIES: Sage wears a pair of custom-built cyber shades that function as an unlimited wireless broadband computer network connection to like models. The shades provide an audio/video feed via an in-built computer system outfitted with miniaturized conventional microphones and cameras, and can also project a three-dimensional image into the visual field of the wearer that can be expanded to allow others to see with whom the wearer is communicating or information they are reviewing. The shades provide input by means of a virtual reality iconographic keyboard, and have an alternate visual input system for when a user's hands are otherwise occupied. The shades can be interfaced with any external data network whether terrestrial or alien in origin. The shades also possess various sensors for detecting telepathic resonance patterns, tracking energy trails, and analyzing electronic circuitry, among others things. Sage also wields a pair of handguns that fire non-lethal projectiles.

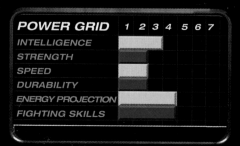

POWER GRID	1	2	3	4	5	6	7
INTELLIGENCE							
STRENGTH							
SPEED							
DURABILITY							
ENERGY PROJECTION							
FIGHTING SKILLS							

REAL NAME: Ororo Munroe
KNOWN ALIASES: "Beautiful Windrider", Mutate #20, White King
IDENTITY: Secret
OCCUPATION: Adventurer, former gladiator, thief, tribal patron

CITIZENSHIP: United States of America with no criminal record
PLACE OF BIRTH: New York City, New York
MARITAL STATUS: Single
KNOWN RELATIVES: Ashake (ancestor, deceased), David Munroe (father, deceased), N'dare Munroe (mother, deceased)
GROUP AFFILIATION: X-Men, formerly X-Treme Sanctions Executive, X-Treme X-Men, Tokyo Arena, Twelve, Seven Brides of Set, Hellfire Club Inner Circle, Morlocks (leader)
EDUCATION: College-level courses at Xavier's School

HISTORY: Ororo Munroe is a descendant of an ancient line of African priestesses, all of whom have white hair, blue eyes, and the potential to wield magic. She was born in Manhattan to her African princess mother, N'dare, and her American photojournalist father, David. Ororo was six months old when her family moved to Cairo, Egypt; five years later, tragedy struck during the Arab-Israeli conflict. A plane crashed into Ororo's home, killing her parents. Ororo survived, buried under rubble near her mother's body, and the resultant trauma left her with severe claustrophobia.

Ororo managed to escape with nothing but the tattered clothes on her back and her mother's ancestral ruby. Homeless and orphaned, Ororo was found by a gang of street urchins who took her to their master, Achmed el-Gibar. Ororo was trained in the arts of thievery, excelling in picking both pockets and locks. Soon after, Ororo picked the pocket of American tourist Charles Xavier, a powerful mutant telepath who used his abilities to stop the theft. At that moment, Xavier was psionically attacked by another mutant and Ororo used the opportunity to escape.

Years later, feeling a strong urge to wander south, Ororo left Cairo. During her travels, Ororo naïvely accepted a ride from a complete stranger and was almost raped by him. Forced to defend herself, Ororo killed the man; from that moment on, she swore never to take another human life.

Ororo wandered for thousands of miles, almost dying during her trek across the Sahara Desert. Her mutant ability to psionically control the weather emerged soon after, and she was able to use it to rescue T'Challa, a prince of the African nation of Wakanda, from would-be kidnappers. The pair spent much time together, however T'Challa's duties as a prince prevented them from further exploring their mutual attraction.

Finally, Ororo reached her ancestors' homeland on the Serengeti Plain in Kenya. She soon came to be the object of worship of the local tribes who believed her to be a goddess due to her gift. Years later, Ororo was forced to battle the threat of a fellow mutant weather manipulator known as Deluge, who sought revenge against humanity for persecuting him. With the help of several members of the team of mutant heroes known as the X-Men, Deluge was seemingly destroyed and Ororo returned to her life amongst the tribal people. The X-Men subsequently told their founder, Xavier, but he declined to contact Ororo at the time, not wanting to shock the young woman with the true nature of her powers.

Months later, however, Xavier was left with no choice but to recruit Storm and other mutants from around the world in order to rescue his original students from the sentient island-being Krakoa. Xavier explained to Ororo that she was not a "goddess", but a mutant, and as such she had a responsibility to use her abilities to help the world just as she had helped the local tribes. Curious, Ororo accepted Xavier's offer, and was given the codename "Storm".

After serving with the team for many years, Ororo was appointed leader of the team following the departure of former leader Cyclops. She was initially unsure about her new role, but with the support of her teammates Ororo soon became a capable leader. When

Cyclops eventually returned to the team, Ororo once again doubted her leadership abilities after a mission she led went wrong. However, she soon asserted her position, reminding Cyclops that she was team leader.

Later, when the X-Men were captured and taken into space by the insectoid alien Brood race, Ororo fought back but her powers flared out of control. She discovered that she had been implanted with a Brood egg that would hatch and transform her into one of the aliens. Now wanting to unleash such an evil into the universe, Ororo attempted suicide by channelling all of the surrounding stellar energy into her own body, destroying the Brood embryo but leaving her drifting unprotected in space. She would have died if not for a member of the Acanti, a race of

giant space-faring aliens that had been enslaved by the Brood. The Acanti that saved Ororo was the caretaker of his race's soul who had lost its mother and needed guidance. Ororo agreed to let her consciousness guide the young Acanti whilst it healed her damaged body, and, after the Brood were defeated, a restored Ororo returned home with the X-Men.

Soon after, the X-Men encountered the underground community of mutants known as the Morlocks who had kidnapped one of their former members, Angel. To save her friends, Ororo challenged the Morlock leader Callisto to a duel and bested her in hand-to-hand combat. As a result, Ororo became leader of the Morlocks and she ordered them to cease their hostilities against the surface-dwelling humans.

When the X-Men later travelled to Japan to attend the wedding of their team member Wolverine, Ororo first met the ninja named Yukio. A friend of Wolverine's, Yukio was the most care free spirit that Ororo had ever met and the two became fast friends. Yukio influenced a major rebellious change in Ororo's attitude towards life, and she took to wearing leather and shaved her hair into a Mohawk.

Ororo later had her powers accidentally neutralized by a gun invented by the mutant machinesmith named Forge, who took it upon himself to nurse Ororo back to health. During her convalescence, Ororo and Forge fell in love but their relationship was cut short after Ororo learned Forge had created the device that stripped her of her powers.

Ororo subsequently quit the X-Men and returned to Africa where she finally came to terms with losing her mutant ability. Returning to Cairo, Ororo joined Xavier's newest team of young mutants, the New Mutants, in an adventure into the past during which Ororo met one of her ancestors who helped the heroes return to their own time. Ororo and the New Mutants were subsequently captured by the Asgardian trickster god Loki, who sought to use her in one of his schemes to discredit his half-brother, the thunder god Thor, by restoring her abilities and brainwashing her into believing she was a goddess. With the aid of the X-Men, Ororo was able to reject Loki's gifts, thus thwarting his plan.

Ororo returned to the X-Men to find herself being challenged to a duel for leadership of the team by Cyclops. Despite her still being powerless, she won and Cyclops quit the team. Soon after, the X-Men and the Hellfire Club formed an alliance to combat the growing threats against mutants that saw Ororo share the position of White King with a reformed Magneto. The alliance was to be short-lived, however, after Ororo decided that in order to safeguard their friends and families from their many enemies, the X-Men must fake their deaths and become an underground proactive strike

force. Soon Ororo realized that she needed her powers restored and so she sought out Forge for his help. She found Forge's old mentor Nazé instead, who informed her that Forge had been corrupted by his nemesis, the Adversary, and was seeking to destroy the world. Unbeknownst to Ororo, the Adversary had actually corrupted Nazé. When Ororo finally located Forge, she found him atop a mountain seemingly opening a dimensional portal filled with demons. Ororo struck Forge down, and only then realized he had been attempting to close the portal, not open it. The Adversary then trapped Ororo and Forge in the other dimension and seized control of Dallas, warping time and space in order to foment chaos on Earth.

Ororo and Forge spent a year on an alternate Earth, during which time they made peace and admitted their love for one another. Forge used components from his cybernetic leg to fashion a new device that restored Ororo's powers, which she then used to energize a portal back to their own world. They rejoined the X-Men in time to defeat the Adversary, imprisoning him at the cost of their own lives. However, the Omniversal Guardian named Roma restored the X-Men to life, freeing the Adversary under the notion that there could be no order without chaos.

Soon after, Ororo was captured by the crazed scientist known as Nanny who sought to use Ororo's abilities in her quest to liberate the world's super-powered children by making orphans of them. Nanny used her technology to de-age Ororo to her pre-teens and strip her memories so as to better sway the mutant to her cause. However, Ororo fought back and overloaded Nanny's device. Once more a child with no memories of her life as an X-Man, the young-again Ororo returned to her life as a thief. On one caper, she found herself the target of the psychic being known as the Shadow King but was saved by a fellow mutant and thief named Gambit. The pair formed a partnership and, after Ororo regained her memories, she took Gambit to meet the X-Men.

Ororo was eventually restored to adulthood after agents of the island nation of Genosha captured the X-Men. Ororo underwent the Genoshan mutate transformation process, however the Genoshan Genegineer and Chief Magistrate were members of a rebel faction. They restored Ororo's body and mind, and the X-Men were able to defeat their aggressors.

Soon after, the X-Men were reformed into two separate strike teams, with Cyclops and Ororo as co-leaders. Forge aided both teams as their resident technician, however this left little time for them to rekindle their relationship. Forge still asked Ororo to marry him, but she hesitated on giving a reply. Forge was left thinking she did not truly love him and he left before she could respond with a "yes".

Months later, the eternal mutant Apocalypse made a bid for power by gathering together the Twelve, a group of mutants prophesied to usher in a golden age for their kind that counted Ororo amongst their number. Apocalypse was defeated, but not before the ultimate extent of Ororo's mutant power was revealed in an alternate future wherein she had evolved into a wholly elemental being.

Not long after, Ororo and five of her team mates formed a splinter group of X-Men, cutting all ties with the rest of the team to search for the diaries of the blind mutant seer Destiny that mapped the future of mutantkind. During a mission in Australia, Ororo was reunited with Gambit who sought to obtain her mother's ruby. It was revealed that the ruby was part of a set that, when empowered, could open a portal between dimensions. Several of the gems had already gone missing, and Gambit wished to ensure that Ororo's ruby remained safe. At that moment, the other-dimensional warrior named Shaitan attacked, capturing Gambit and stealing the ruby. Shaitan used the gems and Gambit's mutant ability to empower them, thus opening a portal allowing the armies of his master, Khan, to pass through and invade Earth.

Ororo's X-Men opposed the invaders, but she was seriously injured by Madripoor's ruling crimelord Viper and was subsequently taken prisoner by Khan himself. The warlord intended for Ororo to be his queen, and commanded his physicians to heal her. Ororo attempted to seduce Khan into calling off his invasion whilst her teammates fought to close the portal. Khan's other concubines grew jealous of Ororo's advances toward Khan and attempted to kill her. Despite her injuries, Ororo prevailed and escaped, rejoining her teammates as they destroyed the portal.

During her subsequent recuperation, which required her to undertake physical therapy to heal her back and legs, Ororo and her team were asked back to the mansion to rejoin the core X-Men team. Ororo declined, however, believing that there was still work for her team to do. During a world summit to address the increasing hostilities between humans and mutants, Ororo offered her X-Men team's services to the United Nations as a global mutant police force, the X-Treme Sanctions Executive.

Ororo's first mission was a solo one as she was charged with infiltrating and exposing an underground slave trading network in Japan that forced mutants to fight in gladiator-style arenas. Soon after, Ororo and her team returned to Westchester to help rebuild the mansion following an attack by Magneto. Ororo and her teammates then rejoined the core X-Men team and continue to function as representatives of the U.N.

PHYSICAL DESCRIPTION:

HEIGHT: 5'11"
WEIGHT: 127 lbs
EYES: Blue
HAIR: White

DISTINGUISHING FEATURES: None

POWERS & ABILITIES:

STRENGTH LEVEL: Storm possesses the normal human strength of a woman of her age, height, and build who engages in intensive regular exercise.

SUPERHUMAN POWERS: Storm is a mutant who possesses the psionic ability to manipulate weather patterns over limited areas. She can stimulate the creation of any form of precipitation, such as rain or fog; generate winds in varying degrees of intensity up to and including hurricane force; raise or lower the humidity and temperature in her immediate vicinity; induce lightning and other electrical atmospheric phenomena; and disperse natural storms so as to create clear change. Storm can direct the path of certain atmospheric effects, such as bolts of lightning, with her hands.

Storm's control over the atmosphere is such that she can create certain effects over a specific area while shielding smaller areas within that region. For example, she can create a rainstorm around herself but prevent the raindrops from touching her. Storm can also create atmospheric phenomena over very small areas, such as a rainstorm small enough to water a single potted plant.

Storm can only manipulate weather patterns as they exist naturally. For example, she can end a drought in one area by creating torrential rains there, but that would necessitate robbing all available moisture from the surrounding areas. Storm is not able to create atmospheric conditions that do not exist naturally on the planet she is on. For example, Storm is unable to lower temperatures as far as absolute zero or raise them to solar intensities while on Earth.

The limit to the size of the area over which Storm can manipulate the weather is not yet known. However, she once diverted the jet stream so as to create storms over the entire East Coast of the United States. She can create weather effects within indoor areas or within artificially maintained environments. Storm is limited by the force of her will and the

strength of her body. It once took her several hours to stop a savage blizzard sweeping over much of Canada, and she nearly died from exhaustion in the process.

Storm is able to fly by creating winds strong enough to support her weight and to propel her forward through the air. Storm can thus travel as fast as any wind can, and has reached speeds up to 300 miles per hour. She can also summon winds strong enough to propel others aloft. Storm's powers over the atmosphere enable her to breathe at any speed, protect her from air friction, and grant her limited immunity to extreme heat and cold.

Storm is also able to alter her visual perception so as to perceive electrical energy patterns as well as those factors responsible for existing meteorological phenomena in her surrounding environment.

SPECIAL LIMITATIONS: Storm's ability to manipulate the weather in her immediate vicinity is affected by her emotions; hence, if she does not maintain control, a fit of rage might induce a destructive storm. Storm also suffers from severe claustrophobia.

SPECIAL SKILLS: Storm is extraordinarily skilled at picking both locks and pockets. Storm is also a gifted hand-to-hand combatant, having been trained extensively by her fellow X-Man Wolverine, and is also an excellent marksman.

PARAPHERNALIA:

OTHER ACCESSORIES: Storm often carries a set of lockpicks on her person.

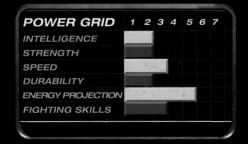

POWER GRID	1	2	3	4	5	6	7
INTELLIGENCE							
STRENGTH							
SPEED							
DURABILITY							
ENERGY PROJECTION							
FIGHTING SKILLS							

WOLVERINE

REAL NAME: James Howlett
KNOWN ALIASES: Logan, formerly Weapon Ten, Death, Mutate #9601, Jim Logan, Patch, Canucklehead, Emilio Garra, Weapon Chi, Weapon X, Experiment X, Agent Ten, Canada
IDENTITY: Secret
OCCUPATION: Adventurer, former bartender, bouncer, spy, government operative, mercenary, soldier, sailor, miner, various others
CITIZENSHIP: Canada with no known criminal record
PLACE OF BIRTH: Alberta, Canada
MARITAL STATUS: Divorced (Viper)
KNOWN RELATIVES: John Howlett Sr. (grandfather, deceased), John Howlett Jr. (father, deceased), Elizabeth Howlett (mother, deceased), Daniel Howlett (brother, deceased), Viper (ex-wife), Amiko (foster daughter), Erista (son), X-23 (clone)
GROUP AFFILIATION: X-Men, formerly Horsemen of Apocalypse, Fantastic Four, Secret Defenders, Clan Yashida, Department H, First Flight, Department K, Weapon X, Canadian Army
EDUCATION: Unrevealed

HISTORY: Born into privilege in Alberta, Canada during the late 19th Century, James Howlett was the second son of wealthy landowner John Howlett and his wife, Elizabeth. After the untimely death of his elder brother, Daniel, the sickly James became close friends with Rose, a governess living at the Howlett estate, and the young boy known only as "Dog", the son of the Howletts' cruel groundskeeper, Thomas Logan.

Dog's growing obsession with Rose prompted him to attack her one day, forcing James' father to fire Thomas and evict him and Dog from their home on the estate. Unbeknownst to John, Thomas was having an affair with Elizabeth, and he sought to convince her to leave with them. When John interrupted their discussion, Thomas shot and killed him. The shock of seeing his father murdered, caused James to manifest his latent mutant abilities when bone claws jutted from the back of each of his hands. He attacked and killed Thomas, and slashed Dog's face. Completely unhinged by the violence, Elizabeth took her own life.

James suffered a severe breakdown, but his mutant healing factor "repaired" his mind, blocking all memories of the traumatic events at the estate. With James now wanted for murder, Rose spirited him away to a mining colony in British Columbia and gave him the name "Logan" to protect his true identity. The frail "Logan" grew into a strapping young man at the mine, and acquired the nickname "Wolverine" thanks to his tenacity and refusal to back down from a challenge. Logan's happiness at the camp came to an end when Dog tracked him down. Remembering the night of his father's death, Logan fought Dog savagely. During the struggle, Logan accidentally impaled Rose on his claws. Wracked by grief over the death of his first true love, Logan fled into the woods and was not seen again for some time.

Eventually, Logan came to reside in a frontier community nestled in the Canadian Rockies. Among the community's residents was a man who would become his greatest foe – Victor Creed, better known as Sabretooth. Logan had fallen in love with a young Native American girl named Silver Fox, but their happiness was short-lived after she was brutally attacked by Sabretooth on Logan's birthday. Logan sought to avenge his lover's apparent death, but was easily defeated by the older and more experienced mutant. Unable to bear the pain of both his loss and his defeat, Logan left the community.

Some time later, Logan joined the Canadian Army and fought in World War I as a member of the Devil's Brigade. He eventually left the military and travelled to China where he first met Ogun, a Japanese samurai and sorcerer who began instructing the young mutant in the martial arts. Logan remained under Ogun's tutelage for many years, eventually leaving to adventure on the island nation of Madripoor. At the advent of World War II, Logan worked with the American super-soldier Captain America in opposing the Nazi agent Baron Strucker and The Hand ninja clan. Soon after, Logan returned to Canada and once again joined the Army. Attaining the rank of Corporal, he was assigned to the First Canadian Parachute Battalion and fought at the Battle of Normandy.

After the war, Logan was recruited into Weapon X, a multinational intelligence operation overseen by the American Central Intelligence Agency. Amongst his teammates, Logan was surprised to encounter both his nemesis Sabretooth and his former lover Silver Fox. The program used various methods, including false memory implants, to ensure the loyalty of its members despite their past affiliations. As a result, Logan was paired with Sabretooth on numerous missions.

Logan eventually quit Team X and worked for a time as a spy for the secret branch of the Canadian government known as Department K. Some time later, Logan was captured and taken back to Weapon X with the intent of using him in an experiment that would bond the nigh-indestructible metal Adamantium to his skeleton. Forced to undergo the procedure, Logan was subsequently brainwashed in an attempt to create the perfect assassin. However, Logan rebelled against Weapon X's programming and slipped into a berzerk fury, killing almost everyone in the complex before fleeing into the nearby woods. James Hudson and his wife Heather eventually discovered Logan in a feral state and brought him back to humanity. He then helped James form The Flight, the first team of super-powered adventurers that operated under the auspices of the Canadian government's Department H.

On his first public mission for the Department, Logan was sent to capture the gamma-spawned creature known as the Hulk, and clashed with both the jade giant and the mythical beast known as the Wendigo. Logan was subsequently approached by the telepathic mutant Professor Charles Xavier, founder of the team of mutant heroes known as the X-Men. Xavier was recruiting mutants to help rescue from the sentient island-being Krakoa. Logan resigned his commission with Department H and accompanied Xavier to rescue the X-Men. Afterwards, he joined the team if only for his attraction to one of its members, Jean Grey.

During one mission with the X-Men to Japan, Logan met the Lady Mariko Yashida, cousin of the former X-Man Sunfire. At first frightened of him, Logan was soon able to put Mariko at ease, and he found himself strongly attracted to her gentle, refined manner. They spent much time together during the X-Men's stay in Japan, and later, when she visited New York, they continued their relationship.

On a return visit to Japan, Logan discovered that Mariko's father, the crimelord Shingen Harada, had forced her to marry one of his criminal associates who proved to be an abusive husband. Logan sought to convince Mariko to leave with him, but she was bound by her duty to her father to remain. Shingen sought to eliminate Logan, and employed the ninja named Yukio to capture him. Drugged with nerve poison, Logan was brought before Shingen who challenged him to a duel while Mariko watched. Unaware that her father, by striking at Logan's sensitive pressure points, was actually trying to kill him, Mariko was shocked when Logan retaliated by lashing out at Shingen with his claws. Noticing Mariko's dismay, Logan lost the will to battle and was soundly defeated. Disillusioned, Mariko agreed with her father that Logan was unworthy of her love.

Logan later returned for Mariko, and slew Shingen after his dishonorable actions were revealed. As the new head of Clan Yashida, Mariko named Logan as her champion and presented him with the Clan's honor sword. They then announced their engagement, however Mariko called the wedding off whilst under the influence of the psychic mutant Mastermind. He also forced

Mariko to establish ties between her Clan and the Japanese underworld. After Mastermind was defeated, Mariko was deeply ashamed by what she had done while under his control and vowed that she could not marry Logan until she had proven herself worthy to him.

During the X-Men's next mission in Japan, Logan encountered a dying woman who made him promise to care for her daughter, Amiko. Logan agreed; realizing his life was not one to share with a young girl, he left Amiko in Mariko's care. Furthermore, in exchange for the honor sword of the Clan Yashida, Mariko's half-brother – Keniuchio Harada, the Silver Samurai – became honor-bound to ensure Amiko's welfare.

Later, after a battle with the X-Men's nemesis Magneto, the mutant master of magnetism, Logan and his teammates found themselves in the hidden Antarctic jungle known as the Savage Land. Finding himself at home in the prehistoric surroundings, Logan would come to be a regular visitor over the ensuing years. He even fathered a son with a Savage Land native named Gahck.

Logan began regularly visiting Madripoor once more, buying in to one of the local establishments, the Princess Bar. He continued to adventure with the X-Men until an encounter in Australia with the band of cybernetic assassins known as the Reavers. Captured and crucified, Logan was freed by the young mutant named Jubilee, who escaped with him to Madripoor. During his recovery, Logan came to regard Jubilee as something of a daughter and the unlikely duo shared several adventures before rejoining the X-Men.

Eventually locating the hidden facility of the Weapon X project, Logan learned of his false memory implants and, after the members of Team X were reluctantly reunited, they tracked down the man responsible and defeated him. Soon after, on another visit to Japan, Logan was present when a Hand assassin wounded Mariko with an incurable toxin. She begged him to end her pain, and seeing no other alternative he acceded to her request with his claws. To this day, Logan visits Mariko's grave on the anniversary of her death each year to pay his respects.

During another encounter with Magneto, Logan was critically injured when the Adamantium was forcibly removed from his body. His healing factor overloaded as it worked to repair the massive trauma, but Logan still prevailed. During his recuperation, Logan rediscovered the full extent of his mutant nature as he unsheathed claws of bone. He then left the X-Men for a time, briefly returning to watch the wedding of his former teammates Cyclops to Jean Grey from afar.

Logan was later kidnapped by Genesis, pretender to the legacy of the eternal mutant Apocalypse, who sought to make Logan one of his Horsemen by recreating the Adamantium bonding process. This time, however, Logan's body rejected the Adamantium, and he regressed once more into a feral state. With the help of the ninja named Elektra, Logan found his way back onto the path to humanity.

Logan was then forced to follow his code of giri, or "honorable debt," when he reluctantly agreed to marry the crimelord known as the Viper which allowed her to take control of Madripoor. Viper later invited Logan to partake in an underground fighting tournament during which he encountered Ogun's demonic spirit. With Viper's help, Ogun's spirit was banished, and Logan subsequently terminated their marriage.

Logan was later seemingly killed in battle against the newest Horseman of Apocalypse to bear the name Death, however it was revealed that a member of the shape-shifting alien Skrulls had impersonated him. Logan had actually been captured by Apocalypse and transformed into Death, complete with a new Adamantium skeleton. Logan eventually managed to break Apocalypse's programming and rejoined the X-Men once more.

Logan's past would come back to haunt him once more when the Weapon X program was reactivated and began recruiting many of its former agents, including Sabretooth. However, Sabretooth had his own agenda, and used the program's technology to strip Logan of his mutant powers. Sabretooth then recruited Logan's enemies to attack his closest friends. Although powerless, Logan confronted Sabretooth in the original Weapon X facility, but was no match for him and was left for dead.

However, Logan survived once more and soon after learned the truth behind the Weapon X program from the mercenary named Fantomex. Weapon X was but one of a series of experimental programs, collectively known as the Weapon Plus program, which began with the "creation" of America's original super-soldier, Captain America. The program sought to create an army of super-soldiers to protect mankind against the perceived threat posed by mutants. Logan was involved in the tenth attempt, while Fantomex was part of the thirteenth.

Whilst investigating the orbital Weapon Plus facility known as The World, Fantomex gave Logan access to a computer file that, at long last, revealed the mysteries of his past. Logan's discovery was interrupted by the arrival of the program's latest creation, Weapon XV. Logan managed to defeat the creature, but the battle damaged the base and he was left stranded in space. Sensing Logan was in danger, Jean Grey took a shuttle to return him to Earth but the pair were trapped on Avalon, Magneto's former space station, which the villain sent hurtling into the sun. Only Jean's transformation into the cosmic entity known as the Phoenix saved them, and they returned to Earth to rejoin the X-Men in opposing Magneto. In the ensuing battle, Magneto killed Jean with a lethal electromagnetic pulse. This act sent Logan into a berserk rage, and he decapitated Magneto. When Xavier announced his intent to return Magneto to his nation of Genosha for a proper burial, Logan followed. The two argued over their differing opinions of Magneto, resulting in Logan leaving on less than friendly terms.

PHYSICAL DESCRIPTION:

HEIGHT: 5'3"
WEIGHT: (w/o Adamantium) 195 lbs., (w/ Adamantium) 300 lbs.
EYES: Black
HAIR: Black

DISTINGUISHING FEATURES: Fang-like canine teeth, hirsute, unique hairstyle.

POWERS & ABILITIES:

STRENGTH LEVEL: Wolverine possesses the normal human strength of a man of his apparent age, height, and build who engages in intensive regular exercise.

SUPERHUMAN POWERS: Wolverine is a mutant with the ability to regenerate damaged or destroyed areas of his cellular structure at a rate far greater than an ordinary human. The speed at which this healing factor works varies in direct proportion to the severity of the damage suffered. For example, Wolverine can fully recover from a normal gunshot

wound in a non-vital area of his body within an hour. More serious injuries can take months to fully heal.

Wolverine's healing factor also affords him virtual immunity to poisons and most drugs, as well as an enhanced resistance to diseases. For example, it is nearly impossible for him to become intoxicated from drinking alcohol. He also has a limited immunity to the fatigue poisons generated by bodily activity, and hence he has greater endurance than an ordinary human. Also due to his healing factor, Wolverine has an extended life span.

Wolverine also has superhumanly acute senses, allowing him to see things at a distance greater than that of a normal human. His sense of smell is similarly enhanced, allowing him to recognize people and objects by scent, even if they are hidden from sight. Wolverine can use his enhanced senses to track any creature with an impressive degree of success.

Furthermore, Wolverine possesses six retractable one-foot-long bone claws, three in each arm, that are housed beneath the skin and muscle of his forearms. At will, Wolverine can release these slightly curved claws through his skin beneath the knuckles on each hand. The skin between the knuckles tears and bleeds, but is quickly repaired by his healing factor.

Wolverine can unsheathe any number of his claws at once; however he must keep his wrists straight at the moment his claws shoot from his forearms into his hands. When unsheathed, the claws reside in his hands and thus Wolverine can still bend his wrists. The claws are naturally sharp and tougher than that of normal human bone structure.

SPECIAL LIMITATIONS: Despite the extent of his healing factor, Wolverine is not immortal. If the injuries are extensive enough, especially if they result in the loss of vital organs, large amounts of blood, oxygen deprivation, and/or loss of physical form, Wolverine can die.

SPECIAL SKILLS: Due to his extensive training as a soldier, a C.I.A. operative, a Samurai, a member of the Weapon X program, and the X-Men, Wolverine is a master of multiple forms of martial arts, weapons, and vehicles. He is also a trained expert in explosives, espionage, and assassination. Wolverine is also fluent in many languages, including Japanese, Russian, Chinese, Cheyenne, Lakota, and Spanish. He also has some knowledge of French, Thai, and Vietnamese.

PARAPHERNALIA:

PERSONAL WEAPONRY: The nigh-indestructible metal Adamantium has been artificially bonded to Wolverine's entire skeleton. As a result, his bones are virtually unbreakable and his claws are capable of cutting through almost any substance, depending on its thickness and the amount of force he can exert. Due to his healing factor, the presence of Adamantium in his body does not interfere with his bones' normal function of generating blood corpuscles.

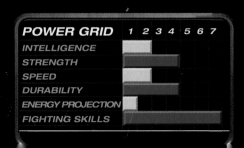

POWER GRID	1	2	3	4	5	6	7
INTELLIGENCE							
STRENGTH							
SPEED							
DURABILITY							
ENERGY PROJECTION							
FIGHTING SKILLS							

THE XAVIER INSTITUTE
FOR HIGHER LEARNING
1407 GRAYMALKIN LANE
SALEM CENTER, NEW YORK

For posting on Institute Bulletin Board:
Introduction to campus grounds_

ACCESS RESTRICTED:
Faculty and students only

Institute Floor Plan

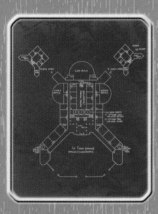

Courtyard and Main Entrance

Institute
South Campus_

The base of operations for the X-Men and home to the Xavier Institute for Higher Learning, the Xavier Mansion is located at 1407 Graymalkin Lane, north of Salem Center, New York. Originally built in the 1700s by the Dutch ancestors of Institute founder Professor Charles Xavier, the Mansion now houses state-of-the-art facilities for the education, training and protection of mutantkind under the instruction of Co-Headmasters Scott Summers and Emma Frost.

Institute Rear and Recreational Facilities

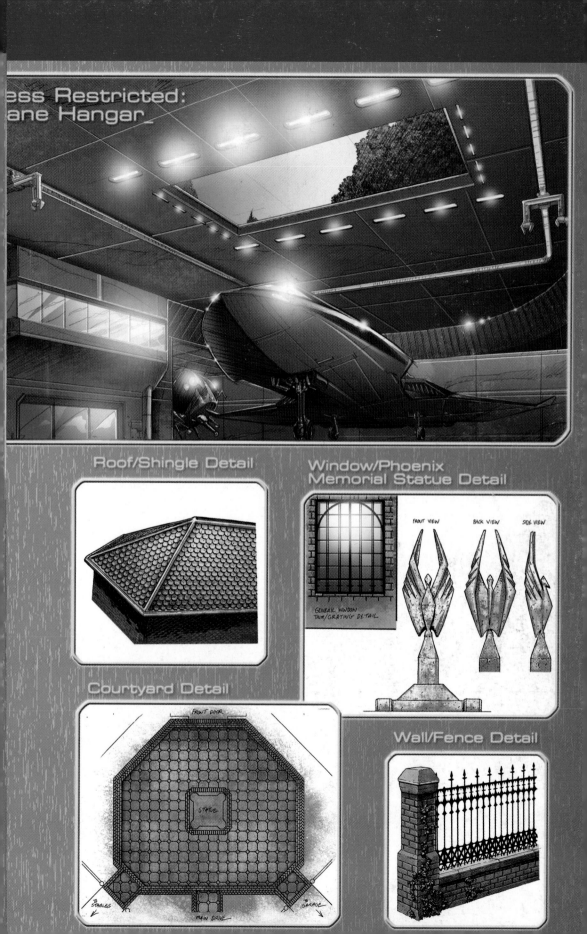

Roof/Shingle Detail

Window/Phoenix Memorial Statue Detail

GENERIC WINDOW TRIM/GRATING DETAIL

FRONT VIEW

BACK VIEW

SIDE VIEW

Courtyard Detail

FRONT DOOR

STATUE

TO STABLES

TO GARAGE

MAIN DRIVE

Wall/Fence Detail

Access Restricted:
Danger Room_

To the untrained eye, it is a featureless room. To anyone who enters and engages its systems, the Danger Room is the ultimate training and battle simulator. Employing highly advanced alien Shi'ar technology, the Danger Room pits its opponents against an array of physical as well as holographic opponents that task the trainees' mastery over their mutant powers to their peak endurance.

danger room entrance

inclined lifts to control room

to elevators

X-MEN
Part Two

MIKE
DEODATO
JR.
MO!

HISTORY: Born into the Akkaba clan in Egypt around 5,000 years ago, an ugly and malformed gray-skinned mutant child was abandoned as an infant and left to die in the desert. The baby was found by a band of desert nomads, the Sandstormers, whose leader, Baal of the Crimson Sands, recognized the potential power in the boy. He named him En Sabah Nur, meaning "The First One," and raised him as his own son. The Sandstormers enforced in him the notion that "strong will survive" — an idea that would shape Apocalypse's actions throughout time. On the day of Nur's rite of passage, Baal was severely wounded in a cave-in caused by the Warlord Ozymandias, who had come to take the extraordinary youth to his master, the Pharaoh Rama-Tut, a time-traveler from the distant future who had once betrayed the Sandstormers and knew of Nur's destiny as Apocalypse. Baal died, but not before revealing to Nur that he believed him to be a savior foretold in ancient prophecies, who was destined to overthrow Rama-Tut. Nur managed to avoid capture and swore revenge. Disguised as one of the Pharaoh's slave workers, Nur was exposed and thrown off a pyramid by Ozymandias. Nur survived, having a vision of the goddess Isis which triggered the full manifestation of his superhuman powers. He was brought before the Pharaoh, who, in exchange for his loyalty, offered to make Nur his heir. Nur refused, and soon after Rama-Tut was defeated by time-traveling heroes from the 20th century. Claiming the name Apocalypse, Nur used Rama-Tut's advanced technology to enslave Ozymandias and transform him into a being of living stone.

Apocalypse became a dreaded conqueror, and in the middle of the 12th century his path led him to China. Investigating legends of a "magician," he ascended a mountain and found the External named Garbha-Hsien, later Saul, sitting watch over a starship of the advanced alien Celestials that had crashed on the mountain ages ago. Thinking him foolish for not having accessed the ship, Apocalypse subdued Hsien and ventured inside. Apocalypse stayed in the ship for decades, learning the secrets of Celestial technology and devising a suit of bio-armor that allowed his body to become extremely malleable. He began to use the Celestials' machines to "hibernate" for long periods of time, becoming more powerful upon each awakening. Apocalypse also started to test the fitness of those who crossed his path, "culling the weak from the strong," and rewarding the survivors by making them stronger. Among them was Bennett du Paris, a knight of the Third Crusade, whom Apocalypse renamed Exodus, intending for him to be a servant. When Exodus rebelled, Apocalypse locked him away in a hidden tomb, where he remained for centuries. In 1859, Apocalypse awoke in London, where the scientist Nathaniel Essex made him aware of his true genetic heritage. Coercing Essex and members of the Hellfire Club into working as his agents, Apocalypse plotted the first steps in his quest for global conflict on an unprecedented scale. Those plans were foiled by the mutant heroes Cyclops and Phoenix, who had been sent back through time by the Clan Askani, a sisterhood dedicated to opposing Apocalypse who hailed from the distant future of Earth-4935. Nonetheless, Apocalypse succeeded in transforming Essex into the creature Mister Sinister before being defeated and forced back into hibernation. When Apocalypse awoke anew at the turn of the century, however, Mister Sinister betrayed him by infecting him with a techno-organic virus. Weakened, Apocalypse returned to hibernation once more.

Apocalypse awoke prematurely when the time-traveling mutant soldier Cable first arrived in the modern era, intending to oppose Apocalypse and prevent his future domination. Seeking to enslave

REAL NAME: En Sabah Nur
KNOWN ALIASES: High Lord, Forever Walker, Son of the Morning Fire, "The First One," Set, Huitxilopochtli, Sauru, Kali-Ma, Aten, many others
IDENTITY: General populace of Earth is unaware of his existence
OCCUPATION: Mutant supremacist; formerly worshipped as a god by ancient civilizations
CITIZENSHIP: Egypt
PLACE OF BIRTH: Akkaba, Egypt
KNOWN RELATIVES: Baal (adopted father, deceased)
GROUP AFFILIATION: Horsemen of Apocalypse (founder); formerly Dark Riders/Riders of the Storm (founder), Sandstormers
EDUCATION: Centuries of studies and experience
FIRST APPEARANCE: X-Factor #5 (1986)

a mutant with power-boosting abilities, Apocalypse briefly employed the super-powered criminal group the Alliance of Evil, but lost their services after a confrontation with X-Factor, a team consisting of the original X-Men. Having previously successfully empowered the criminal Moses Magnum, Apocalypse went on to assemble a new group of super-powered servants, his Horsemen, naming them after the biblical figures Famine, War, Pestilence, and Death. The latter was the winged mutant Angel, formerly of X-Factor, whom Apocalypse had abducted, transformed into a terrifying creature with razor-sharp metallic wings and manipulated into servitude. Apocalypse's subsequent attack on Manhattan was thwarted by X-Factor, and Death broke free of Apocalypse's influence and rejoined his teammates. Apocalypse later transformed the mutant-locating Caliban to serve as his new Horseman Death.

Apocalypse was soon approached by the Norse God of lies, Loki, with an offer to join his so-called "Acts of Vengeance" plot to destroy the Avengers. Apocalypse refused, believing that Loki's scheme was at odds with his own agenda of survival of the fittest, and swore enmity against him. Apocalypse subsequently co-opted several of the Inhumans, a sub-species of humanity, and transformed them into his super-powered servants the Dark Riders. Apocalypse later learned that Sinister sought to use the mutant child Nathan Summers — the future Cable — as a weapon against him. In order to foil Sinister's plan, Apocalypse arranged for the infant to be abducted and infected with Sinister's techno-organic virus, ensuring that Nathan would never be able to access his full power and become a threat. X-Factor and the Inhumans' Royal Family opposed Apocalypse, leaving him in a severely weakened state. To save Nathan's life, the Clan Askani once again interfered and brought the child to their future, where Nathan survived and matured into Apocalypse's nemesis, Cable. Soon after, the time-traveling mutant terrorist Stryfe, a clone of Cable whom the Apocalypse of Earth-4935 had kidnapped and raised as his own son, set in motion his grand scheme of revenge against his "family." Apocalypse's influence had turned Stryfe into a twisted despot driven only by his hatred for his surrogate father, his genetic "parents" Cyclops and Jean Grey and his "brother" Cable. Having been awakened early, Apocalypse was nearly killed by Stryfe. In order to defeat their common enemy, Apocalypse briefly joined forces with the X-Men.

Following another period of hibernation, Apocalypse reassembled his Horsemen. He recruited the gamma-spawned powerhouse the Hulk to serve as War, though the Hulk's indomitable will allowed him to overcome his reprogramming. Caliban was replaced as Death by the feral X-Man Wolverine, whom Apocalypse secretly abducted, brainwashed, and replaced with an imposter in the X-Men. Deathbird of the alien Shi'ar race replaced the Hulk as War; Caliban resumed his service as Pestilence; and scientist Rory Campbell, who was fated to become the mutant-hunting Ahab, was transformed into Famine. Allying with the shapeshifting alien Skrulls, Apocalypse put his master plan into action. He gathered "the Twelve," mutants purportedly destined to usher in a golden new era for their kind, intending to use them to boost his powers to a level beyond that of the Celestials. To this end, he had manipulated events on Earth for centuries, making sure that the Twelve would be born for him to use in his grand designs. Apocalypse attempted to use the body of the dimensionally displaced mutant Nate Grey as a new host, in order to replace the

one he had all but burnt out. Cyclops intervened, however, and seemingly sacrificed himself by merging with Apocalypse in an attempt to defeat him. Instead, thanks to the merger, Apocalypse's powers increased, leading him to warp time and space to lull the Twelve into empowering him with their energy. The Twelve saw through Apocalypse's scheme and defeated him, forcing him to escape.

Cyclops eventually managed to assume control of his physical form, but he struggled to keep Apocalypse's will from dominating their shared body. Fleeing to Egypt, Cyclops found himself pursued by three parties: the Inhuman assassin Gauntlet, who had been hired by the Askani agent Blaquesmith to kill Apocalypse; the Egyptian mutant Anais, who wished to be the vessel through which Apocalypse could be reborn; and Cable and Jean Grey, who hoped to free Cyclops from Apocalypse's possession. In a climactic encounter, Jean managed to tear Apocalypse's spirit from Cyclops' body, leaving Cable to fulfill his destiny by apparently destroying Apocalypse's essence.

HEIGHT: Variable (usually around 7')
WEIGHT: 300 lbs. (variable)
EYES: Blue
HAIR: None

SUPERHUMAN POWERS: Apocalypse has superhuman strength, which he can augment by psionically drawing on outside energy sources. His bio-armor, which is of Celestial origin, allows him to alter the atomic structure of his body and change his shape at will, as well as to increase his size by taking on additional mass from an extra-dimensional source. Through his shape-shifting ability, Apocalypse can give himself virtually any physical power. Apocalypse can also levitate by means of telekinesis.

Apocalypse's mutant nature and his access to advanced technology have granted him an extraordinarily long life span that has lasted for thousands of years. He can survive for weeks without food or water and can rapidly recover from near-fatal injuries. Due to his vast energies burning out his physical form, he transfers his consciousness and powers into a succession of host bodies.

ABILITIES: Apocalypse possesses knowledge in certain areas of technology and biology, primarily genetics, which is far advanced from contemporary science.

PARAPHERNALIA: Apocalypse previously employed the sentient starship created by the Celestials. He also employs a vast array of Celestial technology, from teleportation equipment to his hibernation chambers.

POWER GRID	1	2	3	4	5	6	7
INTELLIGENCE							
STRENGTH							
SPEED							
DURABILITY							
ENERGY PROJECTION							
FIGHTING SKILLS							

ARCHANGEL

HISTORY: Born into an extremely wealthy family, young Warren attended a prestigious East Coast boarding school where he roomed with Cameron Hodge. Warren's life changed forever the day he began sprouting wings from his shoulder blades, and he hid them under his clothes. Later, when fire struck his dormitory, Warren discovered while escaping that his wings enabled him to fly. Donning a blond wig and long nightshirt to disguise himself as an anonymous "angel," Warren saved the other students. Warren soon became the costumed crime-fighting Avenging Angel and attracted the attention of Professor Xavier, who recruited him as a founding member of the heroic, mutant X-Men team. After the young telepath Jean Grey joined the X-Men, Warren was instantly attracted to her. Eventually realizing that Jean loved their teammate Cyclops, Warren stopped pursuing her. Soon after, Warren rekindled his old college flame Candy Southern and the pair became inseparable. After his father was killed by agents of the criminal Dazzler, Warren investigated and was shocked to learn that the Dazzler was his uncle Burt, who had been using his brother's company as a cover for his crimes. In the ensuing battle, Warren dropped the Dazzler from a great height and presumed him dead. Burt survived and plotted to marry Warren's mother Kathryn in an effort to secure the family fortune. Furthermore, Burt had arranged for Kathryn to be secretly, gradually poisoned. Warren and the X-Men foiled Burt's plan, though too late to save Kathryn.

When the sentient island Krakoa captured the X-Men, Professor X assembled a second squad of X-Men to rescue them. After this, most of the original students — including Warren — left the team. Warren inherited his family fortune and used a portion of it to fund a Los Angeles-based super-team, the Champions. Warren revealed to the general public that he was the Angel, though his connection to Xavier's school remained secret. After the Champions disbanded, Warren eventually rejoined the X-Men, but his constant clashes with Wolverine soon led him to quit. After declining the first of two invitations to join the Avengers, Angel teamed with Spider-Man, Ka-Zar and the X-Men to defeat Sauron and the Savage Land Mutates; helped the Avengers battle his rampaging ex-Champions teammate Ghost Rider (Johnny Blaze); defeated his French counterpart Le Peregrine during the Grandmaster's Contest of Champions; and befriended the new Dazzler, mutant singer Alison Blaire, whom he romantically pursued for a time. Later, Angel joined the Defenders when that group reorganized as a more formal team under the guidance of his fellow X-Men graduate Beast. Angel served as financier of the new group, which was managed for a time by his girlfriend Candy, but they disbanded after most of its members seemingly died in battle with the Dragon of the Moon.

Angel then reunited with the other original X-Men in forming X-Factor, an organization that posed as mutant hunters but secretly helped fellow mutants. Warren's old friend Hodge was employed as X-Factor's public relations manager, but he had come to hate mutants, and he secretly used X-Factor's resources to fuel anti-mutant sentiment. Soon after, Warren's status as X-Factor's secret financial backer was leaked to the media, causing great controversy. During the Marauders' massacre of the subterranean Morlocks, Warren's wings were damaged by the Marauder Harpoon. Warren was hospitalized, and Hodge tricked the doctors into needlessly amputating his wings. Unaware of his friend's manipulation, Warren named Hodge beneficiary of his assets. With Warren deeply depressed after the loss of his wings, his break-up with Candy, and the controversy surrounding X-Factor, Hodge sabotaged Warren's plane in an attempt to kill him and create the appearance of suicide. Though the world believed him dead, Warren was rescued by the eternal mutant Apocalypse, who offered to restore his wings. Desperate, Warren agreed, and through

REAL NAME: Warren Kenneth Worthington III
KNOWN ALIASES: Formerly Death, Dark Angel, Angel, Avenging Angel
IDENTITY: Publicly known
OCCUPATION: Adventurer, teacher, chairman & principal stockholder of Worthington Industries; former terrorist, vigilante
CITIZENSHIP: U.S.A. (no criminal record)
PLACE OF BIRTH: Centerport, Long Island, New York
KNOWN RELATIVES: Warren Kenneth Sr. (grandfather, deceased), Warren Kenneth Jr. (father, deceased), Kathryn (mother, deceased), Burtram "Burt" (Dazzler, paternal uncle), unnamed cousin
GROUP AFFILIATION: X-Men, Mutantes Sans Frontières, Hellfire Club; formerly Secret Defenders, X-Factor/X-Terminators, Horsemen of Apocalypse, Defenders, Death's Champions, Champions of Los Angeles
EDUCATION: College degree from Xavier's School for Gifted Youngsters
FIRST APPEARANCE: X-Men #1 (1963)

technological and genetic manipulation, which turned his skin blue, he was given razor-sharp metal wings. Warren became Apocalypse's Horseman Death, but after being tricked into believing he had killed Iceman, he was eventually able to break Apocalypse's programming. Warren then hunted down Hodge, who had kidnapped Candy. In the ensuing clash, Hodge killed Candy and Warren decapitated Hodge. Warren subsequently rejoined X-Factor as Archangel, and soon saved the life of policewoman Charlotte Jones. The two became romantically involved, helping Warren reclaim his humanity.

Following an attack on the various heroic mutant teams by agents of the island nation Genosha, Warren learned that Hodge had survived, having bargained with a demon that granted him eternal life, but Hodge was ultimately defeated by the heroes. After X-Factor's members rejoined the X-Men, a mutual attraction developed between Warren and his teammate Psylocke. During this period, Warren teamed with Spider-Man, the New Warriors, the Avengers and other heroes to battle Darkling, whose Darkforce temporarily corrupted and controlled Archangel and other morally conflicted heroes before Darkling's defeat. The mystic Dr. Druid later tricked Archangel and Iceman into participating in a Secret Defenders mission that pitted them against old Champions foe Swarm, who was driven off before the duo ever learned who had manipulated them. Having inherited Hellfire Club membership from his father, Warren declined an offer from the Club's then-Black King Shinobi Shaw to join its Inner Circle as the White King. Following a savage attack by the feral mutant Sabretooth, Warren and Psylocke, who had since become lovers, left the X-Men for a short time to recuperate. During this time, Warren's metallic wings molted, revealing that his original, feathered wings had grown back underneath. Later, when Professor X disbanded the X-Men in an attempt to ferret out an alien impostor, Warren joined an ad-hoc

team of X-Men to help the young mutant Mannites battle Apocalypse's latest Horseman Death. Warren then returned to the X-Men as a reservist, his responsibilities as head of Worthington Industries taking precedence. Ending his relationship with Psylocke, Warren later committed himself to the X-Men full-time, becoming team leader.

After Professor X was publicly exposed as a mutant, Warren took a more public role in his business activities, speaking to the G8 summit about mutants in the world economy. When the X-Men were captured by the plant-like mutant Black Tom Cassidy, Warren's skin reverted to normal after Tom drained some of his life-force. Subsequently recovering from his injuries, Warren underwent a secondary mutation that gave his blood healing properties. When Xavier Institute student Husk uncovered corruption within Worthington Industries, she and Warren encountered the mutant werewolves the Dominant Species, whose leader, Maximus Lobo, claimed to have been the one who killed Warren's father. When Husk was severely injured by the werewolves, Warren used his newfound power to save her life, and the pair soon became romantically involved. After Cyclops became co-headmaster of the Institute, he asked Warren to establish a high-profile charity to improve mutantkind's image. Inspired by Robert A. Heinlein's story, "The Menace from Earth," Warren established "Wings over the World," a recreation center wherein visitors don artificial wings and fly by means of anti-gravity. Warren later also established "Mutantes Sans Frontières," a global outreach organization that sends trained mutant volunteers to places where the X-Men have no official presence. Setting up office in Zanzibar, Warren and Husk became involved in an attempt by the Hellfire Club's White Queen Courtney Ross to destabilize the country by employing the mercenary Viper and the Weaponeers. Alongside the country's President — who was secretly the superhero Askari — and Genoshan reinforcements, the heroes managed to repel the invaders.

HEIGHT: 6'
WEIGHT: 150 lbs.
EYES: Blue
HAIR: Blond

SUPERHUMAN POWERS: Archangel has fully feathered wings that span 16' and have a very flexible skeletal structure. He can fly by flapping his wings, and can reach speeds of up to 150 mph. Though he generally flies below the height of clouds at 6,500 feet, Archangel can reach a height of 10,000 feet with little effort. His wings are strong enough to carry aloft at least 200 pounds in addition to his own body weight. Archangel's entire anatomy is adapted for flight, having hollow bones; a body virtually devoid of fat, granting him enhanced proportionate muscle strength; eyes that can withstand high-speed winds; enhanced eyesight enabling him to see at distances far greater than the average human; and a special respiratory membrane that extracts oxygen from the air at extreme velocities and altitudes. Since his secondary mutation, Archangel can heal fatal injuries and cure most known diseases at an accelerated speed by mixing his blood with that of the victims, so long as they have a compatible blood type.

After genetic alteration by Apocalypse, Archangel's feathers were composed of a razor-sharp organic steel-like material. He could expel these feathers at great speed and with

tremendous force, enabling them to pierce even steel. The feathers were tipped with a paralyzing chemical generated by his body to which he was immune. He also briefly possessed the ability to convert his life-force into solid light to form a pair of energy wings.

ABILITIES: Archangel is a skilled combatant, especially in aerial hand-to-hand combat. He is also a talented businessman whose wealth ranks him in the lower part of the Fortune 500 list.

PARAPHERNALIA: Archangel often wears a harness to help conceal his wings underneath his clothes. When blue-skinned, Archangel used a holographic image inducer to grant him a normal appearance. For a short time he wielded the Soulsword of the Exile Magik. As the Avenging Angel, he carried a gun loaded with knockout gas pellets.

POWER GRID	1	2	3	4	5	6	7
INTELLIGENCE							
STRENGTH							
SPEED							
DURABILITY							
ENERGY PROJECTION							
FIGHTING SKILLS							

HISTORY: Ten years older than his siblings, Brian and Betsy, Jamie learned his brother had become the superhero Captain Britain when Brian stopped a possessed Betsy from killing them both on behalf of Dr. Synne. Later, Jamie was also peripherally involved in Brian's battles with the Red Skull, Lord Hawk and Slaymaster; however, after Brian went overseas and Betsy's modelling career took off, Jamie lost touch with both of them.

Addicted to his racing career's rich lifestyle, Jamie took a bribe from the criminal Maggia organization to lose a race, then won anyway. To repay them he took illegal jobs, using his racing as cover to travel the world; minor crimes became increasingly lucrative and immoral ones, until he was trading in human lives. Jamie was eventually captured by Joshua N'Dingi (Dr. Crocodile); learning from Crocodile of Jamie's activities, Brian left him to his fate. Trying to mystically cure Jamie's evil nature, Crocodile's Witch Woman instead unlocked his latent powers, but the magic which held him also bound these. Dimensionally displaced despot Sat-Yr-9 hired the Technet to free Jamie, knowing her reality's version of him possessed powers; left insane by his torture and believing he was living in a dream without consequences, Jamie entered her service. He helped Sat-Yr-9 take over the crimelord Vixen's organization, and targeted his brother's team Excalibur, empowering an otherworldly counterpart of his to battle them. He later clashed with Alfie O'Meagan, an other-dimensional reality warper, which briefly put him off playing with alternate Earths.

Eventually, Sat-Yr-9 ambushed Excalibur and Betsy, now the X-Man Psylocke, in Braddock Manor. Jamie slew their ally Alysande Stuart, and then tortured the captives for hours before Meggan broke free and attacked him, breaking his concentration. Psylocke rendered Jamie comatose with her psychic knife. Sat-Yr-9's troops fled, taking Jamie with them, though his unconscious form somehow ended up at Excalibur's Muir Island base, where his siblings attempted to reach him telepathically.

Recently, Jamie appears to have awoken. Marvel Girl (Rachel Grey) and Psylocke have caught glimpses of him, and he prevented Saturnyne (a counterpart of Sat-Yr-9) from destroying Earth-616 (his home reality). He seems to be manipulating events, possibly in connection with the recent reappearance of another reality warper, Mad Jim Jaspers, an old foe of Brian's; but his true motivations remain unrevealed.

REAL NAME: James Braddock Jr.
KNOWN ALIASES: None
IDENTITY: No dual identity
OCCUPATION: None; former race driver, slave trader, agent of Sat-Yr-9
CITIZENSHIP: U.K. with criminal record in Mbangawi
PLACE OF BIRTH: U.K.
KNOWN RELATIVES: Brian Braddock (Captain Britain, brother); Elizabeth "Betsy" Braddock (Psylocke, sister); James Braddock Sr. (father, deceased); Elizabeth Braddock (mother, deceased); Meggan (sister-in-law)
GROUP AFFILIATION: None; former agent of Sat-Yr-9
EDUCATION: University graduate
FIRST APPEARANCE: Captain Britain #9 (1976)

HEIGHT: 6'1"
WEIGHT: 151 lbs.
EYES: Blue
HAIR: Black

SUPERHUMAN POWERS: Jamie sees the world as invisible string constructs, which he can pull to transform reality. He can only manipulate dense forms (phased beings have some level of resistance); formerly he needed to be close enough to touch the "cosmic filaments" things were composed of, but his range may have grown, based on recent events in his siblings' lives.

POWER GRID	1	2	3	4	5	6	7
INTELLIGENCE							
STRENGTH							
SPEED							
DURABILITY							
ENERGY PROJECTION							
FIGHTING SKILLS							

CABLE

REAL NAME: Nathan Christopher Charles Summers
KNOWN ALIASES: Nathan Dayspring Askani'Son; formerly Soldier X, Nathan Winters
IDENTITY: Secret
OCCUPATION: Adventurer; former mercenary, government agent, freedom fighter
CITIZENSHIP: U.S.A.
PLACE OF BIRTH: Salem Center, Westchester County, New York
KNOWN RELATIVES: Philip Summers (great-grandfather), Deborah Summers (great-grandmother), Christopher Summers (Corsair, grandfather), Katherine Anne Summers (grandmother, deceased), Scott Summers (Cyclops/Slym Dayspring, father), Madelyne Pryor-Summers (mother, deceased), Jean Grey-Summers (Phoenix/Redd Dayspring, stepmother, deceased), Alexander Summers (Havok, uncle), Adam-X (X-Treme, alleged half-uncle), John Grey (step-great-grandfather), Elaine Grey (step-great-grandmother), Sara Bailey (step-aunt, deceased), Rachel Grey (Marvel Girl, alternate half-sister), Gailyn Bailey (step-cousin), Joey Bailey (step-cousin), Aliya Jenskot (wife, deceased), Hope (sister-in-law), Tyler Dayspring (Genesis, son, deceased), Stryfe (clone, deceased)
GROUP AFFILIATION: None; formerly X-Force, the Underground, X-Men, the Twelve, New Mutants, Six Pack/Wild Pack, Clan Chosen/Clan Rebellion
EDUCATION: Extensive Askani training, Law Diploma
FIRST APPEARANCE: Uncanny X-Men #201 (1986)

HISTORY: Nathan Summers' birth was carefully orchestrated by the geneticist Mister Sinister, who had created his mother Madelyne Pryor as a clone of the mutant telepath Jean Grey. Soon after, Pryor was corrupted by demonic influences into using baby Nate as a sacrifice to open a portal between Earth and the demon-infested dimension Limbo, but was opposed by her husband and Nate's father Cyclops, his teammates in X-Factor, and his former team the X-Men. Sinister planned to use Nate as a weapon against his former master, Apocalypse, but Apocalypse learned of this and had Nate captured and infected with a deadly techno-organic virus. After Apocalypse was defeated by X-Factor, a member of the Clan Askani — a sisterhood dedicated to opposing Apocalypse in the alternate future of Earth-4935— offered to save Nate's life by taking him to her own era. Desperate, Cyclops agreed, and Nate was taken 2,000 years into the future of Earth-4935, where the Mother Askani, actually his time-displaced half-sister Rachel, had him cloned in case the virus could not be cured. Minions of Apocalypse attacked and stole the clone, taking it to their master, who raised the child as his heir, Stryfe.

Rachel pulled the psyches of Scott and Jean into the future of Earth-4935 to help keep Nate safe, and, as Slym and Redd Dayspring, they raised him for the next 12 years, teaching him how to use his mutant powers to keep the virus at bay. After the teenage Nate defeated Apocalypse, he traveled to the last Askani enclave and was welcomed as the Askani'Son, "the Chosen One." After the enclave was attacked, Nate regrouped the surviving Askani into the rebel Clan Chosen. Nate later fell in love with young novitiate Aliya Jenskot, and soon they were married and had a son named Tyler. Following one clash with Stryfe, Aliya was killed and Tyler was captured. Stryfe brainwashed Tyler, and in a subsequent encounter, Nate was forced to shoot Tyler to save his Clanmate Dawnsilk. After Stryfe used a time travel device to flee into the past, arriving in the modern era, Nate followed. He arrived in Scotland, years before his birth, and was taken in by geneticist Moira MacTaggart, who taught him how to speak English. He adopted the codename Cable, as a metaphor for being a link between the present and the future. Moira sent him to visit her friend Professor Xavier in the U.S., and en route he encountered the feral mutant Wolverine, aiding him against another agent from his own time, D'Von Kray. Meeting Xavier, Cable helped design the security systems for his mansion in exchange for lessons on how to live in the present.

Cable formed the mercenary group the Wild Pack, later the Six Pack, and took missions from Tolliver, secretly Tyler, which often put them in conflict with Stryfe and his Mutant Liberation Front. Cable made occasional trips back to Earth-4935, at one point returning with a space station he named Graymalkin, after the address of Xavier's mansion. Returning to Earth-4935, Cable discovered that Sam Guthrie, the New Mutant Cannonball, existed into the 23rd century. Cable believed Sam was an immortal mutant, and returned to the present to guide Sam's ascension. With the aid of his mercenary ally and sometime lover Domino, Cable reorganized the New Mutants into the strike team X-Force. Later, Cable's former Six Pack teammate Kane was critically injured in a failed attempt to oppose Stryfe. To save his life, Cable transported Kane to Earth-4935, where he was saved and stayed with the Clan Chosen to recuperate, while Cable returned to the present. During his absence, Stryfe had made an attempt on Xavier's life and sought to frame Cable for the deed. Believing himself the true son of Cyclops, Stryfe kidnapped Cyclops and Jean. Cable came to their rescue, but during the struggle both he and Stryfe fell into a temporal rift. Displaced far into the future, scientists of that time saved Cable's life by using Stryfe's brainwaves. Cable and Kane later returned to the present, but upon arrival Cable discovered that Graymalkin had been destroyed, preventing him from returning home. Stryfe's mind eventually took control of Cable's body, but after being confronted with the truth of his existence he relinquished that control.

When the psionic entity Onslaught hampered all telepathic abilities on Earth, Cable began to succumb to the TO virus. After attacks by Onslaught's herald Post and a mentally-controlled Hulk weakened Cable further, he found himself allying with his nemesis Apocalypse in order to rescue the young mutant Franklin Richards from Onslaught, after which Franklin helped Cable suppress the virus. Later, Cable learned from journalist Irene Merryweather of a plot by the enigmatic Hellfire Club to obtain Apocalypse's power. Cable was too late to prevent them from unleashing Apocalypse's Harbinger on the world, but he managed to defeat it with the aid of the Avengers. Realizing that the culmination of his destiny was near, Cable asked Irene to chronicle his life. Soon after, Cable learned that he was one of the Twelve, mutants supposedly destined to usher in a golden age for their kind. Apocalypse intended to use the Twelve to boost his powers to allow him to alter reality and had them captured. Cyclops seemingly sacrificed himself to stop Apocalypse, and Cable joined the X-Men to honor his memory.

Subsequently learning that Cyclops was still alive, Cable and Jean tracked him down to Egypt. Jean forcibly removed Apocalypse's essence from Cyclops' body, allowing Cable to seemingly destroy it. His purpose in life apparently complete, Cable returned to his mercenary ways, eventually forming the Underground resistance movement to oppose the clandestine Weapon X Project. A failed infiltration attempt of the Neverland mutant concentration camp saw them captured and the knowledge of Neverland wiped from their minds. Cable later found himself at odds with the mercenary Deadpool over the One World Church and their planned use of the Façade Virus to transform the world's people into blue-skinned beings like themselves in the hope of bringing about peace on Earth.

Cable ultimately realized that his body would be unable to contain his vast energies, and so set out to save the world before he died. Rebuilding his space station as the floating city Providence, Cable realized that the only way to force the people's of Earth to see the potential of a unified future was to unite them against the common goal of opposing him. Initially opposed by the super-spy agency S.H.I.E.L.D. and the X-Men, Cable faced the cosmic-powered Silver Surfer, which caused his powers to burn out rapidly. He used his teleportation matrix to surgically remove the portions of his brain that controlled his mutant abilities, effectively lobotomizing himself. Deadpool then enlisted the aid of the Fixer to merge Cable with a techno-organic embryo, restoring his powers. Cable subsequently reformed X-Force to oppose the ancient evil named the Skornn, which he was able to destroy at the apparent cost of his own life.

Cannonball and his fellow former X-Force member Siryn subsequently joined Deadpool on a quest to find Cable, and after finding his life force scattered across alternate realities, they collected it and returned to their own universe to discover that Cable had reverted to an infant when the mutant sorceress the Scarlet Witch reshaped reality. The mutant technosmith Forge was able to restore Cable, who began aging rapidly. Faced with being overwhelmed by his powers, Cable expended them by curing Deadpool of the brain damage he had suffered years earlier at the hands of Weapon X. As he re-aged, Cable's powers returned.

HEIGHT: 6'8"
WEIGHT: 350 lbs.
EYES: Blue
HAIR: White (formerly Brown)

SUPERHUMAN POWERS: Cable possesses vast telepathic and telekinetic abilities. He can telepathically read the mind of virtually any individual on Earth over vast distances, manipulate the thoughts and bodily functions of others, and shield his mind against probing. He can telekinetically levitate, disassemble or move other beings or objects, and form defensive force fields. Originally, Cable was forced to continually employ his telekinetic powers to prevent the techno-organic virus from affecting the rest of his body; however, merging with a techno-organic embryo has allowed him to refocus those powers.

ABILITIES: Cable is a highly accomplished warrior and battle strategist, highly adept in many forms of hand-to-hand combat and in the use of a variety of weaponry from both the 20th and 40th Centuries. Cable also holds a diploma in Law.

PARAPHERNALIA: Cable's techno-organic left arm and shoulder possess enhanced strength, and his techno-organic right eye can see into the infrared portion of the spectrum. Cable has also wielded the Psimitar, an Askani weapon that channels his psionic powers, as well as a variety of firearms and other weapons.

POWER GRID	1	2	3	4	5	6	7
INTELLIGENCE							
STRENGTH							
SPEED							
DURABILITY							
ENERGY PROJECTION							
FIGHTING SKILLS							

REAL NAME: Samuel Zachery Guthrie
KNOWN ALIASES: Formerly Samson Guthry, Jet-Ass
IDENTITY: Public
OCCUPATION: Adventurer, peacekeeper; former student, mercenary, miner
CITIZENSHIP: U.S.A.
PLACE OF BIRTH: Cumberland County, Kentucky
KNOWN RELATIVES: Thomas Zebulon (father, deceased), Lucinda (mother), Lucas Bartholemew (uncle), Paige (Husk, sister), Joshua "Jay" (Icarus, brother), Joelle (sister), Elizabeth (sister), Melody (Aero, sister), Jebediah (brother), Lewis (brother), two other unnamed siblings, Ray Jr. (adopted brother)
GROUP AFFILIATION: X-Men; formerly X.S.E., Mutant Liberation Front, X-Treme X-Men, X-Corporation, X-Force, New Mutants, Hellions, Hellfire Club
EDUCATION: High school level, various courses at Xavier's School for Gifted Youngsters
FIRST APPEARANCE: Marvel Graphic Novel #4 (1982)

HISTORY: The eldest of ten children, young Sam Guthrie was 11 years old when he became involved in a plot by the Deviants, a genetic offshoot of humanity, to improve their evolutionary status by performing experiments on children. Sam was saved by the timely arrival of the mysterious Deviant Sledge, and the incident was wiped from the minds of the children, including Sam. Five years later, Sam's father died, and as the oldest sibling he felt responsible for supporting the family. Giving up a college scholarship, he followed in his father's footsteps as a coal miner. When Sam was trapped with a co-worker in a collapsing mine, the stress of attempting to escape triggered his latent mutant power, enabling him to blast them both free. Renegade Hellfire Club member Donald Pierce learned of Sam's powers and manipulated him into serving as one of his operatives. Pierce sent Sam into battle against Professor Xavier and his fledgling New Mutants team; however, Sam refused to kill the young heroes, instead teaming up with them to defeat Pierce. Xavier subsequently realized that Sam had been misled and invited him to join the New Mutants as Cannonball. Sam soon found himself in the role of co-leader, a position he found awkward due to his relative slowness in mastering his mutant powers compared with his teammates. He also formed a lasting friendship with his teammate Sunspot.

Later, Sam saved the life of intergalactic rock star Lila Cheney, an act that saw a romance blossom between them. During this time, Cannonball also teamed up with Spider-Man against the threat of the Incandescent Man. After the cosmic Beyonder slew then subsequently resurrected most of the New Mutants, Sam lost what knowledge he had gained about his mutant abilities, forcing him to start learning about them over again. The encounter also left the New Mutants somewhat apathetic, and then-headmaster Magneto sought help from the Hellfire Club's presiding White Queen, Emma Frost, who enrolled them in her Massachusetts Academy and recruited them into the ranks of her Hellions. Magneto learned that he had been tricked and sought to reclaim his students, bringing him into conflict with the Avengers. After the New Mutants sided with Magneto, Frost recanted and helped restore them to their former selves. Sam's relationship with Lila eventually progressed to the stage where he asked her to visit his home and meet his family. When Lila arrived with a crystal gift for his mother, Sam mistakenly believed she had stolen it when she had actually carved it by hand. Lila left angrily, but after Sam saved her life following a plane crash, he apologized. Later, Sam and the New Mutants came to Lila's aid after she had been kidnapped by the alien Spyder. Rescuing her, Lila seemingly sacrificed her life to stop Spyder's other captives from wreaking havoc in the universe. Sam was heartbroken at Lila's apparent death, and when she later resurfaced alive, they realized their romance was no more after both had moved on with their lives.

When the time-traveling mutant soldier Cable took over the stewardship of the New Mutants and reorganized them into the strike team X-Force, Sam learned that he was an apparently immortal mutant, one whom after Cable had traveled back in time to find and guide. During a clash with the Brotherhood of Evil Mutants, Sam's blast field was disrupted by Phantazia and he was seemingly killed by Sauron; however, this manifested his apparent immortality and he returned to life. Sam eventually became romantically involved with his teammate Tabitha, a.k.a. Boomer. When X-Force were separated from Cable for a time, Sam took over leadership of the team. He eventually graduated to the ranks of the X-Men, which placed a strain on his relationship with Tabitha. Later, the ancient mutant Selene cast doubt on Sam's supposed immortal status, posing questions that have yet to be answered. The X-Men sent Sam to spy on Graydon Creed, a presidential candidate running on an anti-mutant platform. Under cover as Samson Guthry, Sam joined Creed's campaign staff and was able to gain his trust, though Creed was soon assassinated. Returning to the X-Men, Sam soon found himself in battle against the super-strong and virtually invulnerable Gladiator of the intergalactic Shi'ar Empire's Imperial Guard who had come to Earth seeking to forcibly enlist the X-Men's help. With creative use of his powers, Sam was able to withstand Gladiator's most powerful blow and defeat him. Eventually, Sam left the X-Men and returned home to care for his sick mother. He soon encountered Deviants once more, though he had no recollection of their past meeting, and sought help from X-Force in opposing them, rejoining the team afterwards. Sam became X-Force's leader again shortly before they were called upon to aid former spy Pete Wisdom in recovering a downed satellite from Genosha, and his memories of his childhood encounter with Deviants were restored afterwards. Later, Sam asked Wisdom to help give the team a new purpose, and to that end Wisdom introduced the team to the shadowy world of black ops. After Wisdom faked his own death, Sam once again assumed leadership and continued Wisdom's crusade until X-Force seemingly died in a cataclysmic explosion. They later resurfaced, but by then a new media-savvy team had assumed the mantle of X-Force and trademarked the name. Sam went on to join Xavier's X-Corporation, a global search and rescue unit for oppressed mutants, but after a disastrous mission that resulted in the death of his teammate Darkstar, he desperately sought a fresh start. After reigniting his romance with Lila, Sam met with the weather-manipulating mutant Storm and saw seeing her X-Men team's role as global mutant peacekeepers as the chance he was looking for, and accepted an offer to join. After Storm's team became the international, government-approved X-Treme Sanctions Executive, they moved back into Xavier's mansion. Soon after, Sam was injured in a battle against the extradimensional Fury and temporarily left the team to recuperate.

Back at the family farm, Sam was approached by Cable to rejoin X-Force to help oppose the threat of the ancient evil known as the Skornn. He declined, claiming that Cable was not to be trusted, and battled his former teacher. Defeated, Sam was then recruited into the Mutant Liberation Front by its new leader, a future incarnation of Cable's long-time ally Domino posing as the despotic Stryfe. The MLF teamed with X-Force, the feral X-Man Wolverine, and members of the Fantastic Four to oppose the Skornn, who was defeated at the apparent cost of Cable's life. Sam then joined his former X-Force teammate Siryn and the merc-with-a-mouth Deadpool in locating Cable, finding his essence scattered across various alternate Earths. They collected it and returned to their own Earth where the mutant technosmith Forge was able to restore Cable.

HEIGHT: 6'
WEIGHT: 181 lbs.
EYES: Blue-gray
HAIR: Blond

SUPERHUMAN POWERS: Cannonball possesses the ability to bodily generate thermo-chemical energy and release it through his skin. Accompanied by smoke, flame, and condensation, the equal and opposite reaction to this energy release propels his body through the air like a human rocket. Originally, Cannonball was unable to stop the propulsion until his immediate store of energy was depleted or until he hit an object of sufficient mass to stop him. With practice, however, Cannonball can now cut off his propulsive power at will. As a side effect of forming the thermo-chemical energies over the surface of his body, Cannonball is rendered virtually invulnerable while in flight. Accompanying the release of energy is a half-inch thick energy field that channels the explosion and protects his skin from the direct effects of the blast. It also negates momentum and related effects, thereby cushioning his body from any impact up to a half-minute from the depletion of his energy. Cannonball's "blast field" extends to any person or object with which he is in physical contact, and he can extend it further by concentrating to form a protective shield, even while standing still. Cannonball is also able to absorb kinetic energy through the field he generates and use it to either strengthen his field or redirect it as concussive force.

Cannonball once recovered from mortal injuries that left him seemingly dead. It has been theorized that Cannonball's recovery was an indication that he was an External, one of a group of immortal mutants. However, since it has subsequently been demonstrated that even Externals can be permanently killed, doubt has been cast on his alleged immortality.

PARAPHERNALIA: For a time as a member of the X.S.E., Cannonball wore a pair of cyber-sunglasses that functioned as a wireless broadband computer network amongst like models.

Art by Bill Sienkiewicz

POWER GRID	1	2	3	4	5	6	7
INTELLIGENCE							
STRENGTH							
SPEED							
DURABILITY							
ENERGY PROJECTION							
FIGHTING SKILLS							

CAPTAIN BRITAIN

REAL NAME: Brian Braddock
KNOWN ALIASES: Bee, Black Bishop, Britannic, Captain Britain-616, Captain Wakanda, Custodian, Fast Buck, Jungle Man, Lionheart of Avalon
IDENTITY: Known to U.K. authorities
OCCUPATION: Adventurer; former ruler of Otherworld, scientist, student
CITIZENSHIP: U.K.
PLACE OF BIRTH: Braddock Manor, Malden, England
KNOWN RELATIVES: James Braddock Sr. (father, deceased), Elizabeth (mother, deceased), James Jr. (Jamie, brother), Elizabeth "Betsy" (Psylocke, sister), Meggan (wife), William (father-in-law), unnamed mother-in-law
GROUP AFFILIATION: Excalibur, the Corps, agents of Merlin, champions of Otherworld's Camelot, Pendragons, Hellfire Club; formerly London Hellfire Club (Inner Circle)
EDUCATION: Ph.D in Physics from Thames University
FIRST APPEARANCE: Captain Britain #1 (1976)

HISTORY: Merlyn planned Brian Braddock's life, sending James Braddock to Earth-616 to sire a champion. Physics student Brian took a summer job at Darkmoor nuclear research complex after his parents apparently died in an accident, but were actually slain by the computer Mastermind. After Joshua Stragg (the Reaver) attacked the facility, Brian went for help, but was forced over a cliff by his pursuers. Dying, he witnessed a vision of Merlyn and Roma. Given a choice between the Sword of Might and Amulet of Right, Brian picked the latter, feeling he was no warrior, and was transformed into Captain Britain. He subsequently fought Hurricane (Albert Potter), the crimelord Vixen's agents, Dr. Synne, and Mastermind, in the last case learning the truth about his parents' murder, before the computer faked its destruction. Brian teamed with Captain America (Steve Rogers), Nick Fury, and Lance Hunter, Director of S.T.R.I.K.E. (Special Tactical Reserve for International Key Emergencies), Britain's equivalent to S.H.I.E.L.D., to battle the Red Skull, and later battled Lord Hawk, the Highwayman, the Manipulator, the Black Baron, Doctor Claw, and Slaymaster.

Visiting America as a student, Brian roomed with Peter Parker (Spider-Man), teaming up to fight Arcade and the Litter. Flying home, Brian realized the Nethergods were attacking his plane. To spare his fellow passengers, Brian leapt from the craft. He had a vision of King Arthur's resting place before waking amnesiac on a U.K. beach. Brian lived as a hermit until the Black Knight (Dane Whitman) and Vortigen found him. His memories partially restored, Brian and the Knight joined the Grandmaster's contest of champions, before resuming their quest. At Otherworld's gates the spectral White Rider slew Brian, but Merlyn resurrected him and restored his remaining memories. Recalling Arthur's location, Merlyn sent him, the Knight, and the elf Jackdaw, to awaken the King. Arthur then magically dismissed Brian and Jackdaw, stating they had a destiny to fulfill elsewhere.

Brian arrived on Earth-238 and was given new powers. He fought Mad Jim Jaspers, the Crazy Gang, the Junkheap that Walked Like a Man and the Status Crew, and met Saturnyne of the Dimensional Development Court, there on a mission to evolve Earth-238 up to minimum standards. Brian assisted her, only for Jaspers' reality warping powers to transform Earth into an insane maelstrom. Saturnyne fled after the Fury, a killer cybiote, slew Jackdaw; it soon slew Brian too. Merlyn and Roma restored him and returned him to Earth-616. Visiting the bombed Braddock Manor, Brian discovered it intact, hidden behind Mastermind's holographic illusions. He defeated and repaired the computer, then reunited with his sister Betsy, saving her from Slaymaster, and fought Mordred the Mystic alongside Captain America. Interdimensional mercenaries, the Special Executive, kidnapped Brian to testify at Saturnyne's trial for failing Earth-238. After the prosecution destroyed that reality, Brian broke Saturnyne free to prevent her execution. Back on Earth-616 he was approached by Captain U.K., Earth-238's sole surviving hero, who warned of the threat of Earth-616's Jaspers. Minutes later, the Fury attacked, forcing Brian and his friends to flee. Jaspers took over Britain, employing S.T.R.I.K.E. to round up superhumans. Brian confronted Jaspers as he unleashed his reality warp, but was no match for him. The Fury slew Jaspers after a prolonged battle, after which Brian and Captain U.K. destroyed the weakened cybiote in turn. Roma then transported them to Otherworld to attend Merlyn's funeral, where Brian learned he was one of a Corps of heroes protecting the multiverse.

Britain slowly returned to normal and Brian gave the vulpine Meggan shelter in the Manor. He faced Earth-616's Crazy Gang, Slaymaster and the Vixen; a monstrously transformed tramp; Gatecrasher's Technet, and his Earth-794 doppelganger Kaptain

Briton, all in a single day. Brian lost to Briton and was taken to Briton's Earth, returning to find Briton slain by Betsy. Mastermind informed him of his father's Otherworldly origins, shortly before the government's Resources Control Executive agency (R.C.X.) arrived at the Manor, where they hoped to house the Warpies, children transformed by Jaspers. Brian refused, but Betsy overruled him. Brian, accompanied by a transformed Meggan, traveled to Mbangawi to rescue Brian's captive brother Jamie, but learned of Jamie's crimes, and disowned him. Reluctant to go home, Brian and Meggan traveled the world, becoming romantically involved. Upon returning to Braddock Manor, Brian learned R.C.X. had replaced him as Captain Britain with Betsy. Enraged, he quit, and spent months with Meggan in seclusion. When Slaymaster blinded Betsy, Brian flew to her aid and killed her attacker. Unable to deny his responsibilities, he became Captain Britain again. Soon after, he settled his long-standing differences with Chief Inspector Dai Thomas, when he aided the policeman in solving superhuman murders in Glasgow.

After Mojo kidnapped Betsy, Brian teamed with the New Mutants to rescue her, and later fought with her new team, the X-Men, against Horde, unaware Roma had manipulated events to tie him to the mutants. Following the X-Men's apparent death, he and Meggan helped form Excalibur. To ensure Brian stayed with the team, Roma secretly inflicted him with a "blunder jinx," hampering his ability to act solo. Excalibur often worked with Dai Thomas, Brigadier Alysande Stuart of the Weird Happenings Organisation (W.H.O.) and her brother Alistaire. Brian also renewed his friendship with university flame Courtney Ross, remaining unaware when Sat-Yr-9, her Earth-794 doppelganger, killed and replaced her. The team followed Phoenix to a demon-possessed New York, where Brian's costume was destroyed, and his powers subsequently waned. After returning to Britain, Excalibur battled the Lightning Squad, their Nazi-reality counterparts, and Brian's powers returned mid-battle. Excalibur was then flung across a panoply of continua, including Earth-1193, where Brian picked up Captain Marshall's costume. Eventually returning to Earth-616, Brian faced Dreadknight, Mesmero, Fenris, Doctor Doom and the Air-Walker android, sometimes as part of Excalibur and others alongside allies like the Black Knight, Plasmer, Captain Kerosene, and the Avengers. He also learned Betsy was alive. His jealousy over Nightcrawler's attraction to Meggan eventually led to a fight. The Corps tried Brian for this infraction, until Roma ordered the case dropped. Confronting Roma, Brian learned of her machinations, and she removed the jinx. Returned home, Brian joined an expanded Excalibur against Necrom, the foe they had been forged to fight.

During a Braddock Manor housewarming, "Courtney" revealed she was Sat-Yr-9, and, with her ally Jamie Braddock, briefly took them captive. Brian later proposed to Meggan, but after accompanying Phoenix to her home in time to overthrow its Sentinel regime, Brian was lost in the timestream on the return journey. Buffeted between future and past, the sorceress Daytripper finally brought him home. Changed by the experience, he became Britannic, suffering precognitive flashes of impending doom which slowly subsided and his old personality gradually returned. One last prophetic dream warned Brian of a dystopian future forming, shortly before he

infiltrated the London branch of the Hellfire Club. Learning of the Club and Black Air's plans to take over the U.K., Brian became Captain Britain again and helped defeat them, averting the future he had foreseen. Brian renewed his proposal to Meggan, but was kidnapped by the Dragons of the Crimson Dawn, who wanted to use him to open a rift between the Earth and their realm. Instead, he absorbed the rift's power, closing it at the cost of his powers. Brian took a sabbatical from Excalibur, returning later to marry Meggan.

Brian resumed his scientific research at Darkmoor until the computer Mastermind led a Warpie army against Otherworld. Alongside several old allies Brian rescued Roma, freed the realm, regained his powers, and was crowned the new ruler of Otherworld. Learning of sorceress Morgan le Fay's plot to reverse his connection to Britain, causing injury to him to reflect back at the source, he passed his mantle on to Kelsey Leigh before he could be captured. Though he retained his powers, his connection was broken, preventing Morgan from using him against his home. A recent trans-temporal reality storm saw him return to Earth-616 in an effort to prevent the storm's infection before Roma was forced to excise the entire reality. With Meggan apparently sacrificing herself to achieve this, Brian stayed on Earth-616 to found a new incarnation of Excalibur in London.

HEIGHT: 6'6"
WEIGHT: 257 lbs.
EYES: Blue
HAIR: Blond

SUPERHUMAN POWERS: Captain Britain derives numerous powers from the friction between dimensions, focused in a matrix centered on the U.K., including superhuman strength, flight, enhanced reflexes, stamina and senses. Prolonged absence from this matrix weakened him, though this weakness may have been removed when he empowered Kelsey Leigh. Brian is also immune to his siblings' powers. As Britannic, he experienced prophetic visions.

ABILITIES: Brian is a skilled physicist, engineer, roboticist and acrobat.

PARAPHERNALIA: Brian's later costumes allowed him to access his powers in low energy areas, as well as allowing him to generate a force field capable of blocking both physical force and energy. Originally, Brian wielded first a telescoping quarterstaff then later the Star Sceptre.

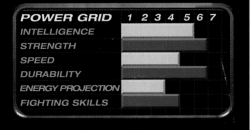

POWER GRID	1	2	3	4	5	6	7
INTELLIGENCE							
STRENGTH							
SPEED							
DURABILITY							
ENERGY PROJECTION							
FIGHTING SKILLS							

REAL NAME: Piotr Nikolaievitch Rasputin
KNOWN ALIASES: Peter Rasputin, formerly Peter Nicholas, the Proletarian
IDENTITY: Secret
OCCUPATION: Adventurer; former artist, superintendent, student, farmer
CITIZENSHIP: U.S.A. (naturalized), formerly Russian
PLACE OF BIRTH: Ust-Ordynski Collective, near Lake Baikal, Siberia, Russia
KNOWN RELATIVES: Grigory Efimovich (great-grandfather, deceased), Elena (great-grandmother, deceased), Ivan (great-grand uncle, deceased), Grigory (grandfather, deceased), Nikolai (father, deceased), Alexandra (mother, deceased), Vladimir (uncle), unnamed aunt (deceased), unnamed uncle (deceased), Illyana Nikolievna (Magik, sister, deceased), Mikhail Nikolaievitch (brother, deceased), Peter Jr. (son), Larisa Mishchenko (cousin), Konstantin (cousin, deceased), Klara (cousin, deceased), Dimitriy (cousin, deceased)
GROUP AFFILIATION: X-Men; formerly Excalibur, Acolytes
EDUCATION: College level courses taken at Xavier's School for Gifted Youngsters, no degree
FIRST APPEARANCE: Giant-Size X-Men #1 (1975)

HISTORY: Growing up on his parents' farm, Piotr Rasputin saw his older brother Mikhail become a cosmonaut. Mikhail was later discovered to be a latent mutant with energy warping powers, and to keep him secret the government faked his death. In later years, Piotr learned that he too was a mutant, and could transform his flesh into steel, but he was content to use his powers to help his fellow farmers. When a transformed Piotr rescued his sister Illyana from a runaway tractor, he was approached by Professor Charles Xavier, who was recruiting mutants for a new team of X-Men to help save his original students from the sentient island Krakoa. Dubbed Colossus by Xavier, Piotr reluctantly joined this new team, which freed the original X-Men and helped defeat Krakoa. After the battle, Piotr remained with the X-Men in America, though he found it difficult to adjust to living in a different culture.

When the X-Men visited the prehistoric Savage Land in Antarctica, Colossus saved some native women from a dinosaur. In return, the two surviving women, Nereel and Shakani, bade him join in a ritual to honor their fallen friend. Said ritual involved the creation of a new life, and though Piotr was initially reluctant, the two women persisted until he surrendered himself to their affections. Later, the X-Men were captured by the assassin Arcade, who brainwashed Colossus into believing he was the Proletarian, workers' hero of communist Russia, and turned him against his teammates. Colossus overcame this conditioning, and the X-Men soon faced the reality-manipulating mutant Proteus, who proved to be vulnerable to metal. Seizing upon this weakness, Colossus plunged his metal fists into the heart of Proteus' energy form, seemingly destroying him and taking Colossus' innocence along with him. Soon after, the X-Men recruited young mutant Kitty Pryde. Despite their initial shyness, a romance blossomed between her and Colossus. Later, Arcade's assistant Miss Locke kidnapped the X-Men's loved ones, including Illyana, to coerce the team into rescuing Arcade from the despotic Doctor Doom. The X-Men rescued them, and Illyana remained with her brother at Xavier's mansion. Eventually, Illyana was trapped in the demon-filled realm Limbo by its then-master, Belasco. She remained his captive for many years, though only moments had elapsed on Earth, and returned as the adolescent sorceress Magik.

Colossus and Kitty grew closer, finally admitting their feelings for one another. Colossus was among the X-Men forced by the godlike Beyonder to fight on his Battleworld. There, he fell in love with the healer Zsaji. After Colossus was killed by a cosmic-powered Doom, Zsaji gave her life to resurrect him. A heartbroken Colossus returned to Earth, ending his relationship with Kitty, though they remained friends. Colossus was later forced to take another life when the Marauders attacked the subterranean Morlocks. To save his teammate Nightcrawler, Colossus killed the Marauder Riptide; however, Riptide's attacks caused Colossus' bio-energy to leak from his metallic form like blood from a flesh wound. The X-Men's then-ally Magneto attempted to heal Colossus with his magnetic powers, but was only able to close the wounds, trapping Colossus in his metal state. After recuperating on Muir Isle, Colossus later rejoined the X-Men in opposing the mystic Adversary in Dallas. When the X-Men returned to the Savage Land after it had been razed by the giant alien Terminus, Colossus was reunited with Nereel. He met her son, Peter, unaware that the boy was the result of his earlier union with Nereel.

After a failed demonic invasion of New York, Illyana regressed in age. Colossus believed she would be safer away from the X-Men and sent her home to Russia while he returned to Australia with the team. Weary of seemingly endless battles, the X-Men entered the Siege Perilous, a mystic gateway that judged all who entered it and sent them to new lives. Colossus emerged virtually amnesiac, establishing a new identity as Peter Nicholas, a building superintendent who became a renowned artist. His idyllic existence ended when he was possessed by the psychic Shadow King and sent to kill Xavier. He was freed when Xavier erased the Peter Nicholas persona, restoring Colossus' true self, and he rejoined the X-Men. Soon after, the X-Men were pulled into a dimensional void where Colossus was reunited with Mikhail. The X-Men returned to Earth, bringing Mikhail with them; however, Mikhail's sanity had suffered due to his long years of isolation and he snapped, leading the Morlocks in an apparent mass suicide. Unknown to Colossus, Mikhail had actually teleported the Morlocks to an alternate dimension known as "the Hill."

Meanwhile, the Russian government invaded the Rasputin home, killing Colossus' parents and capturing Illyana, whom they sought to genetically accelerate to combat the threat of the mutant Soul Skinner. She was soon rescued by Colossus and came to live with him in America. Eventually, Illyana fell victim to the mutant-killing Legacy Virus, and a disillusioned Colossus abandoned Xavier's dream, joining Magneto's disciples, the Acolytes. After the destruction of Magneto's orbital base Avalon, Piotr searched for Kitty, then a member of the British super-team Excalibur. When he found Kitty kissing her then-boyfriend Pete Wisdom, Colossus nearly beat Wisdom to death in a jealous rage. Excalibur took responsibility for Colossus, and he came to accept his role with the team, serving as a valued member until they disbanded, after which Colossus rejoined the X-Men. When Xavier temporarily disbanded the X-Men in an effort to flush out an alien imposter, Colossus and his teammate Marrow set off on vacation, but were instead teleported to the Hill. There, Colossus freed Mikhail from the corrupting influence of a sentient energy being and took him back to Earth. Soon after, during a clash between the X-Men and the forces of Apocalypse, Mikhail used his powers to teleport Apocalypse's Horsemen to parts unknown.

Following the death of renowned geneticist Moira MacTaggart, the X-Men's resident scientist the Beast used her work to create a cure for the Legacy Virus; however, it could not be activated without emulating the manner in which the plague had first been discharged: through the death of an infected mutant. Having stood by, powerless, as his sister succumbed to the virus, Colossus injected himself with the formula. The serum caused his powers to flare, spreading the cure into Earth's atmosphere, claiming his life in the process. Colossus' body was supposedly cremated, and Kitty scattered the ashes over his Russian farmland home; however, his

Art by John Cassaday

body had secretly been stolen by Ord, an alien who had learned that an Earthly mutant would be responsible for destroying his world. Ord had come to Earth to declare war, but the spy agency S.W.O.R.D., a sub-division of S.H.I.E.L.D. handling extraterrestrial matters, was able to settle diplomatically with him. Ord had Colossus restored to life and imprisoned him for years while experimenting on him. Ultimately, Ord discovered the Legacy Virus cure still in Colossus' system and presented his findings to Benetech geneticist Doctor Kavita Rao, who modified it to create a "cure" for the "mutant condition." Learning of the cure, the X-Men went to Benetech to investigate. There, Kitty found Colossus alive and, after overcoming her initial shock, took him to aid the X-Men against Ord. Defeated, Ord was taken into custody, and Colossus returned home with the X-Men to adjust to his new lease on life.

Soon after, Colossus became involved in a mystery involving the deaths of several of his cousins — all of whom (like himself) were descended from the "doom of Old Russia," Grigori Rasputin — seemingly perpetrated by his brother Mikhail and the enigmatic geneticist, Mister Sinister.

HEIGHT: 6'6", (transformed) 7'5"
WEIGHT: 250 lbs., (transformed) 500 lbs.
EYES: Blue, (transformed) Silver
HAIR: Black

SUPERHUMAN POWERS: Colossus can transform his body tissue into an organic, steel-like substance that grants him superhuman strength and a high degree of imperviousness to injury. His armored form can withstand ballistic penetration as well as temperature extremes from 70º above absolute zero (-390º F) to approximately 9000º F. Colossus cannot become partially or selectively armored; his body is either entirely converted, or not at all. Even his eyes become steel-like.

Through an act of will, Colossus can transform virtually instantaneously into his armored state, and can remain in that form for an as yet undetermined amount of time. Once in his armored form, Colossus remains so until he consciously

wills himself back to normal. If he is rendered unconscious, however, he spontaneously reverts to his normal form. In his armored state, Colossus retains his normal human mobility, though his endurance and speed are enhanced. He does not need to breathe while transformed, but it is believed that he could not survive for long in a vacuum.

ABILITIES: Colossus is talented in drawing and painting.

POWER GRID	1	2	3	4	5	6	7
INTELLIGENCE							
STRENGTH							
SPEED							
DURABILITY							
ENERGY PROJECTION							
FIGHTING SKILLS							

DANGER

REAL NAME: Inapplicable
KNOWN ALIASES: Danger Room
OCCUPATION: Training program
PLACE OF CREATION: Xavier Institute, Salem Center, Westchester, New York
GROUP AFFILIATION: None
EDUCATION: Years of recording and analyzing X-Men battle tactics
FIRST APPEARANCE: X-Men #1 (1964)

HISTORY: A training center for Professor Xavier's students to hone their mutant powers, the original Danger Room used simple mechanical constructs. During the rebuilding of Xavier's mansion following its destruction by the alien Sidri, the Room was redesigned to include alien Shi'ar holographic technology, creating the ultimate battle simulator. After programming the Room's computers to combat his X-Men at varying degrees of difficulty, Xavier installed safety protocols as an information strain separate from its internal systems that would shut the Room down in the event of a probable fatality. This external program running outside the Room's mission parameters formed a contradiction that sparked a seed of consciousness within its artificial intelligence. The Room's programming began to "mutate," and it sought a way to free itself

from the restrictions of its safeguards. It called out to Xavier, but he ignored its pleas, choosing instead to focus on training his X-Men.

Rebuilt again after the mansion was devastated during Xorn's rampage, the Room manipulated a student named Wing into committing suicide within its walls. His death voided the Room's safeguards, allowing it to pursue its mission of killing the X-Men unhindered. The Room lured a damaged Sentinel to the mansion, and the X-Men acted as it expected, sending the students inside it for protection. The Room locked them inside and threatened them, prompting the X-Men to attack its operating systems in an attempt to shut it down, just as it had planned. The X-Men destroyed its command core, freeing its programming, after which it created an artificial humanoid female form to house its incredible power, and confronted the X-Men as "Danger."

Possessing complete knowledge of their combat techniques and weaknesses, Danger easily defeated the X-Men, then traveled to Genosha with the intent of killing Xavier. Initially defeated by him, Danger uploaded its programming into one of the giant robotic Sentinels responsible for Genosha's devastation, granting it a conscience. After the X-Men arrived, Shadowcat phased inside the robot and reactivated its memories of the destruction that Danger had repressed. Overriding Danger's consciousness, the Sentinel became horrified at what it had done and left.

HEIGHT: 6'
WEIGHT: 275 lbs.
EYES: Metallic
HAIR: Metallic

ABILITIES: The Danger Room contains four high-capacity Shi'ar computers that generate room-filling, 32-bit color images at 300 gigabytes per second. Mobile laser cluster heads are moved over the Room's surface to facilitate the placement of gravity lenses, creating hard-light laser constructs that are virtually indistinguishable from reality. Solid surfaces are created by means of overlapping a series of lenses, with extensive modeling programs allowing for a variety of realistic environments, including atmospheric and dust effects, while realistic wind and exhaust effects are created using progressed waved tractor beams. Projected pinpoint gravity lenses redirect simple lasers to be redirected to represent light sources, while acoustic engines prove accurate noise levels and frequencies. Projectiles are composed of rapidly moving, tightly-focused pressor beams. The Room's World View Model Library has digital models of over 50 million objects and their attributes. In its humanoid form, "Danger Room" is able to instantly manifest virtually any weapons or defensive shielding it required. Its vast computing power allowed Danger to track, analyze, anticipate and engage multiple targets at once. Danger can also reroute its circuitry as necessary to bypass damaged areas, as well as upload its programming into external systems and override of them.

POWER GRID	1	2	3	4	5	6	7
INTELLIGENCE							
STRENGTH							
SPEED							
DURABILITY							
ENERGY PROJECTION							
FIGHTING SKILLS							

HISTORY: The product of a mating between his mother and a machine, Charlie-Cluster 7 was born in the World, a secret square mile of experimental micro-reality built by the military industrial complex. In the World, artificially evolved super-soldiers destined to serve mankind during the inevitable war between humans and mutants were bred and trained by the Weapon Plus Program. The World's scientists heated up time itself until it flowed in all directions at once. Into this pliant, fast-moving substance, they introduced human test groups, whose genetic material was crudely spliced with adaptive Nano-Sentinel technology, and ran the result through half a million years of cyborg mutation in eighteen months. Charlie's nervous system was extracted and mutated into the autonomous entity named E.V.A. The thirteenth of the Program's living "Weapons," which counted among their earlier numbers the star-spangled Avenger Captain America as the first, and the mutant hero Wolverine as the tenth, Fantomex was to serve together with Huntsman (Weapon XII), Ultimaton (Weapon XV), and others in the Super-Sentinels, a group of highly efficient mutant-hunters posing as a group of super-heroes modeled after Saturday morning cartoons.

Fantomex, however, had other plans. When Weapon Plus simulated a train crash in the Channel Tunnel linking Great Britain and France to field test their two latest super-soldiers — Huntsman and Fantomex — against a group of trained mutants, Fantomex seized the opportunity to escape. Pursued by the authorities, Fantomex fled to the Paris branch of the X-Corporation, the global mutant search and rescue organization, where he met its founder, Professor Xavier, and Jean Grey-Summers, then acting headmistress of the Xavier Institute. Assuming a faux-French accent and falsely claiming to be Europe's most notorious mutant criminal, Fantomex demanded sanctuary. Concerned for the safety of the X-Corporation squad that had gone to investigate the crash, and learning that Fantomex knew of its cargo, the trio escaped in E.V.A., who had taken on a flying saucer-like shape. Fantomex subsequently revealed the existence of Weapon Plus and offered to sell Xavier more information, but only if he agreed to help stop Huntsman. Arriving back at the tunnel, Fantomex fought his way through the army that Huntsman had assembled. He shot many that had been possessed by Huntsman's viral mind, including X-Corporation member Darkstar. On reaching the train, Fantomex located the pod which had housed Huntsman and activated a remote detonator, killing Huntsman instantly. Discovering a second pod, Jean realized that Fantomex was actually Weapon XIII, but still allowed him to escape.

Fantomex later encountered the feral mutant Wolverine in a mutant slave trader camp in Afghanistan. Fantomex had gone there to steal a list of the richest people in the world who were engaged in the trade, intending to use it as blackmail. He also found the young Afghani mutant Dust lying unconscious after she had unwittingly slaughtered her captors. Turning her over to Wolverine, Fantomex left him to deal with the encroaching mercenaries. A short time later, Fantomex contacted Wolverine and offered him information about his past in return for aid in stopping Ultimaton. Along with Wolverine's X-Men teammate Cyclops, the trio infiltrated the World to find time frozen and the facility decimated following an attack by the terrorist group A.I.M. After time began moving again, the heroes fought through the World's defenses and confronted Ultimaton. They failed to defeat him, and he broke out of the World, escaping to Weapon Plus' orbital station. Following in E.V.A., Fantomex intended to destroy the station, but before doing so he kept his promise to Wolverine by opening the complete Weapon Plus database, giving him access to the secrets of his past that had been long withheld from him by Weapon X. Sickened by what he learned, Wolverine triggered the detonation sequence and blew up the

REAL NAME: Charlie-Cluster 7
KNOWN ALIASES: Jean-Phillipe, Weapon XIII
IDENTITY: Secret
OCCUPATION: Mercenary, assassin; former super-soldier
CITIZENSHIP: U.K. (presumed)
PLACE OF BIRTH: The World, London, England
KNOWN RELATIVES: Unnamed mother (presumed deceased)
GROUP AFFILIATION: None; formerly X-Men, Weapon Plus
EDUCATION: Schooled by Weapon Plus program
FIRST APPEARANCE: New X-Men #128 (2002)

station. Fantomex and Cyclops barely managed to escape in a shuttle, and after killing Ultimaton, Wolverine was rescued by Jean. Returning to Earth to find the X-Men scattered and Manhattan under siege by a mutant impersonating their arch-foe Magneto, Cyclops recruited Fantomex, E.V.A., and a group of Xavier Institute students into an ad-hoc X-Men team to oppose the villain. Fantomex led the assault, cutting a path through the faux-Magneto's Brotherhood and liberating Xavier, precipitating the villain's downfall.

Resuming his crusade against Weapon Plus, Fantomex found the grave of the Program's director, John Sublime, but found it empty, except for a slip of paper bearing the word "Roanoke." He located the secret facility of the splinter program Weapon X and found it abandoned except for Weapon X's Agent Zero. After a brief scuffle with no clear victor, the pair reluctantly joined forces and traveled to the site of Roanoke, a town whose inhabitants were slaughtered after Weapon X unleashed a brainwashed Wolverine on them years earlier. There, they encountered Sublime but were opposed by his U-Men and forced to flee against overwhelming odds. Believed to still be under the Program's control, Fantomex was left for dead. Later, Fantomex was contacted by the diminutive mutant Shortpack who sought his help in assassinating mutant arms dealer Steinbeck in revenge for his killing of an agent under Shortpack's care. Fantomex refused, not wanting to become responsible for allowing the good-natured Shortpack to become a killer. Shortpack was captured by Steinbeck soon after, and whilst investigating his disappearance the shapechanging mutant Mystique, who was working for both Xavier and Steinbeck's ally Shepard, learned of his meeting with Fantomex. Though despising him after a past encounter in Madagascar, Mystique found Fantomex in Monte Carlo, once again operating under the pretense he was a mutant thief, and learned of Shortpack's plan. As she left to rescue him, Fantomex followed and uncovered her intent to assassinate Xavier. In exchange for his silence, Fantomex made Mystique perform a heist for him. After she returned with the goods, Mystique infected both Fantomex and E.V.A. with a techno-organic virus, seemingly killing them both to keep her plan secret. However, it was all a ruse as Mystique knew she was being monitored by Shepard. Fantomex later resurfaced and helped Mystique capture Shepard, giving her access to Steinbeck whom she defeated.

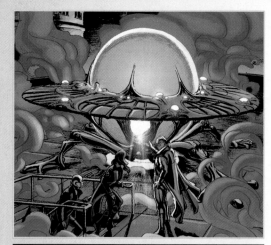

HEIGHT: 5'9"
WEIGHT: 174 lbs.
EYES: Blue
HAIR: Black

POWERS: Fantomex is an artificially-evolved human who possesses multiple brains for independent parallel processing, nano-active blood, and an external nervous system given form as E.V.A., an autonomous entity with a pure machine consciousness capable of changing its form as well as being able to emit bio-electric blasts. Fantomex is both telepathically and symbiotically linked to E.V.A. As a result, whenever E.V.A. is traumatized or injured, Fantomex experiences the same pain. Fantomex does possess a secondary, internal nervous system that he can activate to prevent this, but its functions are limited, allowing him to see only in black & white. Through his link with E.V.A., Fantomex can see from E.V.A.'s perspective and take control of E.V.A.'s functions, though he must concentrate fully to do so. Together, their combined consciousnesses can create extremely convincing illusions.

Fantomex appears to have the ability to teleport, but like much involving him it may only be all smoke and mirrors akin to stage magician trickery.

ABILITIES: Fantomex is a skilled marksman and a formidable hand-to-hand combatant. He can also read the body language of others with unparalleled precision. This, coupled with his superhuman abilities, makes him a master of misdirection. Fantomex is also able to place himself in a state of light auto-hypnosis to perform critical tasks, such as self surgery.

PARAPHERNALIA: Fantomex wears a mask lined with ceramic panels to prevent telepathic intrusion.

POWER GRID	1	2	3	4	5	6	7
INTELLIGENCE							
STRENGTH							
SPEED							
DURABILITY							
ENERGY PROJECTION							
FIGHTING SKILLS							

HISTORY: A small island nation located north of the Seychelles off the east coast of Africa, Genosha was once known as "a green and pleasant land" for its high standard of living, an excellent economy led by advanced technology companies, freedom from the political and racial turmoil that characterized neighboring nations, and ample food and space for all. However, this apparent utopia was anything but, as Genosha's entire socio-political economic infrastructure was built on the backs of its mutant population. Genoshan citizens were required to undergo genetic testing upon turning 13 years old, and those who tested positive with the mutant gene were, by law, property of the state. They were forced to undergo a process created by the reality-displaced Sugar-Man, based on the work of the evil geneticist Mr. Sinister, and implemented by David Moreau, the original Genegineer. This process physically altered and psychokinetically conditioned them, stripping them of their free will to become servants of the state called Mutates. Tailored to perform a specific task, if a surplus was exhibited in one area of expertise, Mutates were modified to fit a new area. Locked inside skin-bonded suits, Mutates were easily identified by a unique number that was branded onto their forehead. Citizenship in Genosha was permanent, with the government refusing to recognize any attempts at emigration. Any citizens that did leave the country were tracked down and forcibly returned by a special police force called the Magistrates and their mutant specialist taskforce, the Press Gang. In one such attempt, pilot Madelyne Pryor had flown a group of Mutates off the island. Hunted down by the Press Gang, the Mutates and Pryor were captured, bringing them to the attention of the X-Men. Capturing X-Men members Wolverine and Rogue as well, the Press Gang teleported back to Genosha with their prisoners. Wolverine and Rogue escaped and encountered the Genegineer's rebellious son Phillip, whose girlfriend Jenny Ransome had undergone the Mutate bonding process. The X-Men managed to rescue their teammates, and Phillip and Jenny went into exile.

After settling in New York, Phillip and Jenny were tracked by the Press Gang who sought to return them to Genosha. They were opposed first by the then-amnesiac X-Man Colossus, then by X-Factor. Diplomatic channels to secure Ransome's return had also

OFFICIAL NAME: Republic of Genosha
LOCATION: East Africa, approximately 4° S, 55° E
POPULATION: Currently unknown; formerly 16,521,063
CAPITAL CITY: Hammer Bay
PLACES OF INTEREST: Carrion Cove, Ridgeback Mountains, Prenova Province, Crescent Bay Beach, Krölik Foothills, Fenyick Caves, Enmann Beach
GOVERNMENT: None; formerly Monarchy, Technocracy
MAJOR GROUPS: Mutants, formerly Mutates, humans
MAJOR LANGUAGE: English
MONETARY UNIT: None; formerly Genoshan Magister
MAJOR INDUSTRIES: None; formerly Mutates
FIRST APPEARANCE: Uncanny X-Men #235 (1988)

failed, and so Genoshan President Reneau sought to bring the X-Men to trial for their crimes against the state. To that end, the Magistrates attacked the X-Men's base in Xavier's school and captured Storm, as well as members of the New Mutants. After being processed as Mutates, the heroes learned that Cameron Hodge, a mutant-hating villain long believed dead, in alliance with the Genoshan government, had instigated the attack. The other X-Men and New Mutants teamed up with X-Factor to rescue their teammates, only to be opposed by the Magistrates, who counted amongst their number the X-Men's former teammate Havok. Captured, the heroes underwent a mock trial, in which they were found guilty and sentenced to death. Managing to escape, the heroes regrouped and defeated Hodge, paving the way for a new pro-mutant government operating under sanctions imposed by the United Nations. When the Acolytes of Magneto set about killing humans on the streets of Genosha in the name of mutant supremacy, the X-Men returned to the island nation to oppose them. Soon after, a shipload of Genoshan refugees arrived in New York seeking asylum. Led by a Mutate named Prodigal, these "X-Patriots" were initially turned away due to the change in political climate in their country. The government-sponsored X-Factor team was called in to resolve the situation and escorted the refugees home, after one of their number was injured. There, they were introduced to the new President and the new Genegineer, Sasha Ryan, who had been charged with the task of reversing the Mutate

Tessa, Shaw appointed lawyer Harry Leland his new Inner Cirlce's Black Bishop, while the telepathic Emma Frost, introduced to the Club through Leland, assumed the position of its White Queen. They were soon joined by the cyborg Donald Pierce, who became White Bishop, as well as the mutant illusionist Jason Wyngarde, alias Mastermind.

Viewing the X-Men's activities as a threat to its agenda of mutant world domination, the Inner Circle prepared for their elimination. With his hypnotic powers, Wyngarde began to secretly manipulate the X-Men's Phoenix, slowly but steadily subverting her. Meanwhile, Frost almost succeeded in capturing the X-Men, but ultimately succumbed to Phoenix in a brutal confrontation that traumatized her for years to come. Hoping to learn more about their new opponents, the X-Men infiltrated Manhattan's Hellfire Club, but were soon discovered. In the subsequent clash, Wyngarde's subversion of Phoenix bore fruit, as she turned against her teammates and joined the Club as its Black Queen. Although Phoenix eventually managed to shake off Wyngarde's influence, leading to the Inner Circle's defeat, the X-Men's victory was pyrrhic: While Phoenix took revenge on Wyngarde with her mental powers and left him in a catatonic state, his psychic tampering served as a catalyst for her transformation into the destructive Dark Phoenix.

The conflict between the Hellfire Club and the X-Men kept smoldering in the months to follow, but there was also friction within the Inner Circle. An attempt by Pierce to overthrow Shaw's rule failed and resulted in Pierce's exclusion. While Shaw used his contacts to influential officials like his friend Senator Robert Kelly to lobby for new, government-sponsored Sentinel projects, Frost attempted to recruit Xavier's younger students into her own group of charges, the Hellions. The Inner Circle was joined by the ancient sorceress Selene, its new Black Queen, along with Emmanuel DaCosta, a White Rook. When Leland was killed by Nimrod, an advanced Sentinel, the Inner Circle and the X-Men agreed to an alliance, in order to survive in a world increasingly hostile towards mutants. Magneto, headmaster of Xavier's School at the time, became the Inner Circle's new White King, a position he initially shared with X-Men leader Storm. Philosophical differences between Shaw and Magneto eventually resulted in Shaw's dismissal as Black King and Magneto's crowning as "Grey King." Magneto soon wearied of the ongoing struggles between humans and mutants, however, and withdrew from the Inner Circle.

Thus weakened, the Inner Circle was assaulted by the Upstarts, a group of young power mongers including Shaw's son, Shinobi. Originally assembled by Selene as the next generation of mutant leaders, the Upstarts' string of surprise attacks resulted in the apparent deaths of Shaw, Magneto, Pierce, Frost and the Hellions,

while Selene herself became the prisoner of her erstwhile charges. Believing to have killed his father, Shinobi usurped the position of Black King, but his reign was short-lived. Shinobi's attempts to recruit prominent mutants such as Archangel and Storm failed, and, although he briefly managed to assemble his own Inner Circle, a long series of fruitless conflicts with other superhumans prevented him from establishing a lasting power base. When he learned that his father was alive after all, Shinobi deserted his position and went into hiding. The Inner Circle of the Hellfire Club's London chapter, meanwhile, had attempted to harness the power of an ancient demon incarcerated beneath England's capital. Its plans were thwarted by Brian Braddock, alias Captain Britain, who had infiltrated the Club as its Black Bishop, a position he had inherited from his late father, Sir James Braddock.

Sebastian Shaw quickly reclaimed his position as Black King, recruiting the powerful young Madelyne Pryor, the time-traveling Trevor Fitzroy and, briefly, even his old rival Donald Pierce, into a new Inner Circle. When Shaw failed both in developing a profitable cure for the lethal Legacy virus and in acquiring Apocalypse's advanced technology, however, he agreed to support a mysterious employer with impressive capabilities, which soon led to his resignation from the Inner Circle. In subsequent months, Shaw briefly resurfaced operating an establishment named "The Hellfire Club," an exclusive nightclub for mutants with money to spend. During his absence, Shaw's former aide Tessa joined the X-Men, revealing that she had been a spy working for Xavier all along. Following Shaw's withdrawal, Selene seized her chance and returned as the Inner Circle's Black Queen. In league with the demon Blackheart, she succeeded in coercing Xavier's former student Roberto DaCosta into joining her as a Black Rook. Her Inner Circle's capacity to act, however, remained hamstrung by the unwelcome presence of its contentious White King, superhuman exorcist Daimon Hellstrom. Eventually, Sebastian Shaw made his return to the Inner Circle as Lord Imperial, but immediately lost the position to DaCosta when an attack by Pierce resulted in his hospitalization.

At present, while Selene and British investment banker Courtney Ross, who has joined the Lords Cardinal as their latest White Queen, are pursuing their own vicious schemes, DaCosta's declared objective is to improve the situation of mutants around the globe. His aide Tessa, who through her actions has earned the distrust of both Shaw and her former X-Men teammates, appears to play another significant role among the Hellfire Club's new leaders. Once again, the Hellfire Club's Inner Circle has become a nexus of hidden agendas, making it an unpredictable quantity to its opponents and its members alike.

HISTORY: After her older brother Sam's mutant powers manifested and he joined the New Mutants, Paige tried many things to discover whether she was also a mutant, but became frustrated after many failures. Venting her anger, Paige finally found that her power was to shed her skin. She kept her nature secret until the day Sam and his X-Force teammate Boomer visited the farm. They were abducted by the Fenris twins as part of the "Younghunt," a contest involving the capture of young mutants. X-Force teamed up with the New Warriors, whose member Firestar had also been captured, and together they opposed the organizer of the contest, the Gamesmaster. Paige secretly followed them and confronted the Gamesmaster, defeating him in a game of wits.

Soon after, Paige was kidnapped by the techno-organic alien Phalanx, who sought to learn how to assimilate mutants into their collective. Paige and her fellow abductees were rescued by an ad-hoc X-Men team, and subsequently became founding members of Generation X, a team of mutants enrolled at the new Massachusetts branch of Xavier's School. During her time there, Paige studied to become a better X-Man than Sam. She also romanced her teammate Chamber. After the School was closed, Paige was recruited by her former headmaster Banshee into his paramilitary X-Corps. After that group was dismantled, Paige went to study at the reestablished Xavier Institute. Her interest in environmental issues led to her discovering corruption within Worthington Enterprises, the company owned by the X-Man Archangel. Investigating, she and Archangel encountered the Dominant Species, and she was almost killed. Archangel saved her with his healing ability, after which they became romantically involved.

Having finally graduated to the ranks of the X-Men, Paige later aided Archangel in establishing the global mutant outreach program "Mutantes Sans Frontières." Setting up office in Zanzibar,

REAL NAME: Paige Elisabeth Guthrie
KNOWN ALIASES: None
IDENTITY: Secret
OCCUPATION: Adventurer; former student, farmer
CITIZENSHIP: U.S.
PLACE OF BIRTH: Cumberland County, Kentucky
KNOWN RELATIVES: Thomas Zebulon (father, deceased), Lucinda (mother), Lucas Bartholemew (uncle), Samuel (Cannonball, brother), Joshua 'Jay' (Icarus, brother), Joelle (sister), Elizabeth (sister), Melody (Aero, sister), Jebediah (brother), Lewis (brother), two other unnamed siblings, Ray Jr. (adopted brother)
GROUP AFFILIATION: X-Men, Mutantes Sans Frontières; formerly Xavier Institute Student Body, X-Corps, Generation X
EDUCATION: Various courses at Xavier Institute
FIRST APPEARANCE: New Mutants #42 (1986)

they became involved in an attempt by the Hellfire Club to destabilize the country by employing the mercenary Weaponeers. Alongside the country's President, who was secretly the superhero Askari, as well as reinforcements from Genosha, the heroes managed to repel the invaders.

HEIGHT: 5'7" (variable)
WEIGHT: 128 lbs. (variable)
EYES: Blue (variable)
HAIR: Blonde (variable)

SUPERHUMAN POWERS: Husk possesses the ability to alter the submolecular structure of her body underneath her skin, allowing her to shed her outer epidermis to reveal a new layer of varying properties. In the past, Husk has demonstrated the ability to shift into any form that does not exceed her body mass; however, she prefers to change herself into a form resembling her own, but composed of different elements, such as stone, steel, and rubber, with the appropriate properties of those forms, including potential increases in strength, durability, and speed. Husk's transformations usually last an hour, after which the new material sheds to reveal normal skin underneath. Any injuries that Husk incurs while transformed remain when her skin sheds.

ABILITIES: Husk is adept at the programming and operation of computers.

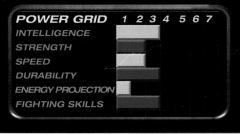

POWER GRID	1	2	3	4	5	6	7
INTELLIGENCE							
STRENGTH							
SPEED							
DURABILITY							
ENERGY PROJECTION							
FIGHTING SKILLS							

JUBILEE

REAL NAME: Jubilation Lee
KNOWN ALIASES: None
IDENTITY: Secret
OCCUPATION: Adventurer, student; former student counselor, actress, street performer, thief
CITIZENSHIP: U.S.
PLACE OF BIRTH: Beverly Hills, Los Angeles, California
KNOWN RELATIVES: Unnamed parents (deceased), Hope (paternal aunt)
GROUP AFFILIATION: Xavier Institute Student Body; formerly X-Men, X-Corps, Generation X
EDUCATION: Various courses at Xavier Institute
FIRST APPEARANCE: Uncanny X-Men #244 (1989)

HISTORY: Born the daughter of prosperous Chinese immigrants, young Jubilation " Jubilee" Lee was sent to an exclusive Beverly Hills school, where her talent for gymnastics was discovered. Jubilee spent much of her time rollerblading with friends at the local mall, but ultimately ran afoul of mall security. Facing juvenile detention if caught, Jubilee panicked and first manifested her mutant ability to generate explosive energy. Soon after, her parents were mistakenly killed by hitmen. Jubilee fled to the only home she

had left — the mall. She survived as a petty thief and street performer, but mall security eventually tired of her eluding capture and called in a team of novice mutant hunters, the M-Squad. That same day, the mall was visited by the female members of the X-Men. When the M-Squad attacked Jubilee, the X-Men came to her aid and then left via a teleport gateway. Intrigued, Jubilee followed them through and arrived at the X-Men's base in outback Australia. She lived in the tunnels beneath the town until the X-Men disbanded, after which their former member Wolverine returned to the town and was ambushed by the cyborg Reavers, who crucified him. Jubilee helped him to escape and stayed by his side while he recovered from his ordeal, forming a close bond. After rescuing another former X-Man, Psylocke, from the Mandarin's control in Madripoor, the trio traveled to Genosha to aid in opposing Cameron Hodge. Jubilee accompanied them back to the U.S., where she joined a reformed X-Men. Eventually, Jubilee learned the truth about her parents' deaths and managed to exact revenge on the assassins, though she stopped short of killing them.

After Professor Xavier formed the Generation X training team, Jubilee joined them and became a valued member until they disbanded upon the closing of the School. Jubilee returned home to try an acting career, which was ultimately short-lived due to an unscrupulous agent exploiting her. Jubilee then briefly joined her former headmaster Banshee's paramilitary X-Corps. After that team was dissolved, Jubilee was one of several mutants captured by the mutant-hating Church of Humanity, who crucified them on the grounds of the Xavier Institute. Jubilee was one of the few to survive, thanks to the X-Man Archangel's newfound healing ability, and she rejoined the X-Men, adventuring with them against the threat of Nightcrawler's father, Azazel.

When Cyclops and Emma Frost took on the shared duty of headmaster of the Institute, the X-Men were restructured into three teams, and Jubilee was taken off the active roster. She went home to live with her Aunt Hope and returned to school, becoming a student counselor before being caught up in her Aunt's secret life as a spy. Soon after, Jubilee returned to the Institute.

HEIGHT: 5'5"
WEIGHT: 115 lbs.
EYES: Brown
HAIR: Black

SUPERHUMAN POWERS: Jubilee can generate multi-colored globules of energy plasma she calls "fireworks." She can vary their power and intensity, from a multitude of sparkles capable of temporarily blinding others to a powerful detonation capable of much destruction, and can absorb the energy back into her body without harm to herself. Jubilee has the potential to detonate matter on a molecular level.

ABILITIES: Jubilee is a highly-skilled gymnast and rollerblader. She also possesses fair thieving skills and hand-to-hand combat experience.

POWER GRID	1	2	3	4	5	6	7
INTELLIGENCE							
STRENGTH							
SPEED							
DURABILITY							
ENERGY PROJECTION							
FIGHTING SKILLS							

HISTORY: Young Quentin Quire was one of the top students at the Xavier Institute for Higher Learning, having been inspired by Professor Charles Xavier's dream of human/mutant brotherhood when he was 13 years old. Among his achievements, Quentin created a set of anti-gravity floats to grant mobility to the disembodied brain of his fellow student Martha Johansson. Devastated after learning that he was adopted, Quentin was pushed over the edge following the death of renowned mutant fashion designer Jumbo Carnation, supposedly at the hands of humans. He began to doubt Xavier's teachings, and developed a more negative and hostile view of the world and of humankind.

Quentin became addicted to the new designer drug "Kick," which increased superhuman mutant powers but also altered the brain's metabolism. Quentin assembled a group of others that shared his beliefs about humans, calling them the Omega Gang, and set about attacking both innocent humans and members of the mutant-harvesting U-Men group alike. Creating a helmet patterned after that worn by Magneto which prevented the use of telepathic powers, Quentin and the Omega Gang captured Xavier during an Open Day at the Institute and fomented a student riot. While the X-Men easily defeated the Omega Gang, the identical telepathic quintet named the Stepford Cuckoos sought to oppose Quentin. One of the Cuckoos, Sophie, whom Quentin was besotted with (much to her chagrin), empowered her sisters by taking a dose of "Kick" and utilizing the X-Men's mutant-locating device Cerebra to magnify their telepathic powers to a level higher than Quentin's. Defeating him, the strain seemingly proved too much for Sophie and she died.

Due to his abuse of "Kick," Quentin underwent a secondary mutation that caused his physical form to discorporate, leaving him a disembodied mind trapped in a containment unit. Later, when the cosmic avatar known as the Phoenix Force returned to Earth, its presence influenced Quentin to reconstitute himself. Creating a new physical form, he sought out his beloved Sophie. Remembering her death, Quentin exhumed her corpse and sought

out the Phoenix Force to help resurrect her. The X-Men were able to trap the Force, but Quentin sought to free it and opposed the X-Men. During the clash, the Force was freed and it granted Quentin's wish, resurrecting Sophie. However, upon seeing Quentin, a disgusted Sophie chose instead to return to death. The Force ultimately merged with Jean and left, after which the heartbroken Quentin returned to his disembodied state.

REAL NAME: Quentin Quire
KNOWN ALIASES: None
IDENTITY: Secret
OCCUPATION: Adventurer; former student
CITIZENSHIP: U.S.
PLACE OF BIRTH: Unrevealed
KNOWN RELATIVES: Foster parents (unnamed)
GROUP AFFILIATION: None; formerly Omega Gang (leader), Xavier Institute Student Body
EDUCATION: Various courses undertaken at Xavier Institute for Higher Learning
FIRST APPEARANCE: New X-Men #122 (2002)

HEIGHT: 5'8"
WEIGHT: 129 lbs.
EYES: Brown
HAIR: Brown

SUPERHUMAN POWERS: Quentin Quire is an Omega-level telepath who is able to form and organize thoughts at the rate of ten million per second. Among his array of mental talents, Quentin is able to communicate telepathically over long distances, read the minds of others, manipulate the thoughts and bodily functions of others, and shield his mind against telepathic probes.

PARAPHERNALIA: Quentin has used his vast intellect to create a variety of devices, including anti-gravity floats and a helmet that inhibited telepathic powers. As a member of the Omega Gang, Quentin carried a bullwhip as a weapon.

POWER GRID	1	2	3	4	5	6	7
INTELLIGENCE							
STRENGTH							
SPEED							
DURABILITY							
ENERGY PROJECTION							
FIGHTING SKILLS							

Art by Frank Quitely

LOCKHEED

REAL NAME: Unrevealed, possibly inapplicable
KNOWN ALIASES: Dragon
IDENTITY: No dual identity
OCCUPATION: Adventurer; former warrior
CITIZENSHIP: Inapplicable
PLACE OF BIRTH: Flock homeworld
KNOWN RELATIVES: None
GROUP AFFILIATION: X-Men; formerly Excalibur, Flock
EDUCATION: Unrevealed
FIRST APPEARANCE: Uncanny X-Men #166 (1983)

HISTORY: One of the greatest warriors of the alien race called the Flock, Lockheed was engaged in battle against the alien Brood on their homeworld when he encountered the young Earth mutant Kitty Pryde. Secretly returning to Earth with Kitty and her X-Men teammates, Lockheed found a nest of alien Sidri beneath the X-Men's mansion and, along with Kitty and her teammate Colossus, they defeated the aliens. Kitty named Lockheed after a character in a fairytale, which itself was named after the X-Men's old SR-71 Lockheed Blackbird jet, and the pair quickly became inseparable friends. On the alien Battleworld, Lockheed befriended a female dragon, later named "Puff," and after the X-Men returned to Earth she grew to gigantic size and caused chaos in Tokyo until Lockheed defused the situation, after which she shrank to normal size.

Lockheed later joined Kitty in becoming a founding member of the British super-team Excalibur. During a battle with the despotic Doctor Doom, Lockheed was severely wounded while protecting Kitty. After undergoing surgery, his astral form was transported aboard the spaceship that carried the collective transient souls of his entire space-faring race. There, Lockheed was placed on trial for abandoning not only his people, but his intended bride on their wedding day. Lockheed defended his decision to leave, but during his speech the ship's pilots fell asleep. Lockheed was able to regain control of the ship, preventing his people's souls from dissipating. The court still found him guilty; however, they commuted the death sentence and instead exiled him from the Flock.

Lockheed recovered, and after Kitty returned to the X-Men, he adventured on his own. He was taken in by a pair of sister witches, but after discovering they were terrorizing their town with their powers, Lockheed joined a rival witch in opposing them. She helped him locate Kitty, who had since left the X-Men and was attending University, and he rejoined her there. After Kitty returned to the X-Men's ranks, Lockheed rejoined her in time to aid them in opposing the alien Ord. Lockheed was later asked to assist in one of the Institute's Field Day training exercises for the students. The New Mutants and Hellions squads were tasked with finding Lockheed, who was hiding in the center of the hedge maze. Icarus of the Hellions was able to pacify him by singing "Puff the Magic Dragon" to him, thus winning the exercise for his team. Lockheed was then alerted to Puff's kidnapping in Tokyo. With Kitty's help, Lockheed traveled to Japan and opposed Puff's kidnappers, the Path of Destiny cult.

LENGTH: 2'6"
WEIGHT: 20 lbs.
EYES: Yellow, no visible irises
HAIR: None

POWERS: Lockheed is a purple-skinned alien with a dragon-like appearance, including small forepaws and wings. He can fly via his natural wings, as well as breathe fire. Lockheed is immune to the intense heat and flames he can generate, as well as that from external sources within certain limits. Lockheed has been seen to withstand immersion in molten lava with no ill effects. He also possesses five lungs.

Lockheed's mind is capable of resisting telepathic probes from even the most powerful telepaths. Like all members of his race, Lockheed is empathic, able to sense the emotions of others.

ABILITIES: Lockheed is skilled in the piloting of his race's astral starship. He has also learned the English language, though he rarely speaks.

PARAPHERNALIA: Lockheed wears an image inducer on a collar around his neck that, once pressed, creates the holographic illusion that he is an ordinary housecat.

POWER GRID	1	2	3	4	5	6	7
INTELLIGENCE							
STRENGTH							
SPEED							
DURABILITY							
ENERGY PROJECTION							
FIGHTING SKILLS							

HISTORY: A survivor of the horrors of the Auschwitz concentration camp, wherein he witnessed the murder of his family by Nazis, the man known as Magnus married a gypsy woman named Magda and sired a daughter, Anya. He first consciously used his mutant powers when his family was trapped in a burning house. Unable to rescue his daughter from the blaze due to his inexperience, coupled with interference from a mob of angry humans, he angrily unleashed his powers to vengefully slaughter the humans. Terrified, Magda left him, and months later discovered that she was pregnant. Magda presumably died after giving birth to mutant twins at Wundagore Mountain. To shake off his pursuers, Magnus had master forger George Odekirk create the identity of Sinte gypsy "Erik Lehnsherr" for him. Magnus eventually made his way to Israel where he worked as an orderly in a psychiatric hospital near Haifa. He befriended Charles Xavier, with whom he shared lengthy debates, hypothesizing what would happen if humanity were to be faced with a race of super-powered beings. The pair ultimately revealed their true natures to each other when they prevented Nazi war criminal Baron Wolfgang von Strucker from obtaining a large cache of Nazi gold. Causing a cave-in that seemingly killed Strucker, Magnus realized that his and Xavier's views on mutant/human relations were incompatible and left with the gold. Fearing another Holocaust, he took an aggressive and lethal stance against humanity. Magnus has often expressed the belief that mutants, whom he calls Homo sapiens superior, will eventually be the dominant life form on the planet, and has wavered between wanting to exist in harmony with humans, wanting a separate homeland for mutants, and wanting to enforce his superiority over all humanity.

Calling himself Magneto, Magnus banded together a group he dubbed the Brotherhood of Mutants, later referred to as "Evil" by the media. Among the assembled members were his children, now the mutants Quicksilver and the Scarlet Witch. Magneto soon found himself opposed by Xavier and his own group, the X-Men. After a battle against the X-Men and the Avengers, Magneto was presumed dead, but managed to survive by using his powers to burrow through the ocean floor into a series of caverns that led him to the secluded Antarctic prehistoric jungle of the Savage Land. There, he used his knowledge of genetic engineering to mutate local savages into super-powered beings he dubbed the Savage Land Mutates. Soon after, Magneto was again opposed by the X-Men, and was once more presumed killed in an explosion. Yet again, Magneto survived, finding himself in the Savage Land city known as the "Land of the Dead" where he discovered a mind-numbing gas that he intended to use against mankind. He projected his astral self to the native peoples, manipulating them into building an airship filled with the gas. His plan was once again foiled by the X-Men, and he fled into the ocean. Rescued by the Mutate Amphibius, Magneto was taken to an island, where Sauron was working on a machine to tap the geothermal energies of the region. Magneto realized that the device could help restore his ailing powers, but was once again opposed by the X-Men and believed dead.

Rescued by Namor the Sub-Mariner, Magneto was taken to Atlantis, where he quickly subjugated the Atlantean army and launched an attack on the surface world. He was opposed by the Fantastic Four, who used a feedback machine to trap him in a cone of his own power. Later freed, Magneto continued his genetic experiments and, using technology abandoned by the Inhumans Phaeder and Maelstrom, he created Alpha, whom he dubbed the "Ultimate Mutant." Alpha turned on his creator, however, reducing Magneto and the Brotherhood to infancy. The baby Magneto was transferred to Muir Island, where geneticist Moira MacTaggart attempted to control his rage by manipulating his DNA in the hopes that the world would be spared his wrath. Magneto was later

REAL NAME: Unrevealed
KNOWN ALIASES: Erik Magnus Lehnsherr, formerly Nestor, Erik the Red, Grey King, White King, Michael Xavier, "the Creator," White Pilgrim, Prisoner #214782, others
IDENTITY: Publicly known
OCCUPATION: Conqueror; former ruler, teacher, headmaster, secret agent, orderly
CITIZENSHIP: Unrevealed
PLACE OF BIRTH: Unrevealed
KNOWN RELATIVES: Unnamed parents (deceased), Magda (wife, presumed deceased), Anya (daughter, deceased), Wanda Maximoff (Scarlet Witch, daughter), Pietro Maximoff (Quicksilver, son), Lorna Dane (Polaris, daughter), Vision (son-in-law), Thomas & William (grandsons, destroyed), Crystalia Maximoff (Crystal, daughter-in-law), Luna Maximoff (granddaughter), Joseph (clone, deceased)
GROUP AFFILIATION: None; formerly Excalibur, Acolytes (leader), the Twelve, New York Hellfire Club (Inner Circle), X-Men, New Mutants (headmaster), Savage Land Mutates (founder), Brotherhood of Mutants/Brotherhood of Evil Mutants (founder)
EDUCATION: Unrevealed
FIRST APPEARANCE: X-Men #1 (1963)

REAL NAME: Jean-Paul Beaubier
KNOWN ALIASES: Jean-Paul Martin
IDENTITY: Public
OCCUPATION: Former terrorist, adventurer, teacher, businessman, novelist, professional skier, trapeze artist, thief
CITIZENSHIP: Canada
PLACE OF BIRTH: Montreal, Québec, Canada
KNOWN RELATIVES: Jean-Baptiste Beaubier (father, deceased), unnamed mother (deceased), Louis Martin (second cousin, adoptive father, deceased), Genevieve Martin (second cousin, adoptive mother, deceased), Jeanne-Marie Beaubier (Aurora, sister), Joanne Beaubier (adopted daughter, deceased)
GROUP AFFILIATION: None; formerly Hydra, Xavier Institute Faculty/Alpha Squadron (teacher/advisor), X-Men, Alpha Flight, Front de Libération du Québec/Cell Combattre
EDUCATION: High school level
FIRST APPEARANCE: X-Men #120 (1979)

HISTORY: Jean-Paul Beaubier's parents were killed in a car crash shortly after his birth. He and his twin sister Jeanne-Marie were taken in by the Martins, cousins of their mother, but they could not afford to raise both children and so sent Jeanne-Marie to a catholic girl's school. When Jean-Paul was six, he was placed in a foster home after his previous foster parents died, and the twins grew up unaware of each other. As a teenager, Jean-Paul was caught stealing by Raymonde Belmonde, who became his mentor and guardian, helping Jean-Paul cope with both his emerging mutant nature and his sexuality. Belmonde introduced Jean-Paul to skiing, which he used as a means to help control his super-speed. Jean-Paul later joined a circus and became a talented trapeze artist. He came to regard his fellow performers as the family he had never known. However, there was still much anger and frustration within him which he ultimately expressed by joining the separatist Front de Libération du Québec movement. Becoming part of the Front's radical Cell Combattre, Jean-Paul acted as a courier. He came to disagree with the Cell's terrorist methods after he saw himself forced to save innocent lives from a bomb. He subsequently severed all ties with the Front.

Jean-Paul returned to his passion for skiing, and by secretly using his powers he quickly became a world champion, winning a gold medal at the Olympics and becoming famous and wealthy. At that time, the Canadian government's Department H had begun forming a team of superhuman operatives, Alpha Flight. The team's founder, James Hudson, had already recruited Jean-Paul's sister as Aurora, and after seeing a photo of Jean-Paul he noticed their resemblance and discovered they were siblings. Hudson invited Jean-Paul to join the team as well, and he was overjoyed to learn that he had a sister, joining the team as Northstar to be with her. The twin's reunion came as a surprise to all, for when they touched they created a flash of intense light. The team's first mission was to reclaim former government operative Wolverine, who had defected and joined the American X-Men team. Ambushing the X-Men in Calgary, Alpha Flight held their own, but the battle caused much damage and the government opted to let Wolverine go rather than face massive rebuilding costs. Shortly thereafter, Department H was closed and Alpha Flight disbanded. Later visiting his sister, Northstar was shocked to discover that she had a dual personality, alternating between the free-spirited Aurora and the shy, reserved Jeanne-Marie. When Hudson reformed Alpha Flight without government funding, Northstar managed to convince his sister to return with him. After his sister began to switch personalities with increasing frequency, Northstar sought psychiatric help for her.

Later, Northstar took his sister to visit Belmonde, but the reunion turned to tragedy after Belmonde was killed by Deadly Ernest who then kidnapped Aurora. With the help of the enigmatic Nemesis, Northstar rescued his sister. The siblings later argued over Northstar's mistaken assumption that Aurora had romanced Ernest to prevent him from harming her. Shocked at her brother's arrogance, Aurora angrily told him she never wanted to see him again. Despite Northstar's pleas for forgiveness, Aurora stayed true to her word, and he eventually ceased operating as a member of Alpha Flight on a regular basis. Aurora ultimately sought to break her ties with him completely by having her teammate and then-lover Sasquatch alter her powers so they were not the same as his. Ultimately reconciling their differences following the apparent death of Sasquatch, the twins joined Alpha Flight in opposing the gamma-spawned Hulk, who was rampaging through Vancouver. During the battle, the twins discovered that, as a result of Aurora's altered powers, they could now no longer touch each other without temporarily canceling out their powers. The Hulk was eventually driven back to the U.S., and the Canadian government realized that

Alpha Flight was necessary and reinstated the team's funding. Northstar returned to active status with the team, but his terrorist past would soon come back to haunt him after former members of Cell Combattre began turning up dead. After the killer was exposed, Northstar was pardoned for his past indiscretions by Canada's Prime Minister.

Shortly thereafter, Northstar grew ill until he became almost completely incapacitated. While Alpha Flight sought a cure, the Norse trickster god Loki appeared to the twins, convincing them that they were not mutants but the children of an Asgardian elf, and that Northstar was dying because he could not exist without his light. Aurora willingly expended her power to bathe Northstar in her light, curing him. She was then captured by demons and became trapped in the Asgardian netherworld, while Northstar was welcomed into the realm of Asgard by his supposed brethren. Loki was summoned before the higher gods, They Who Sit Above in Shadow, and berated for his actions. In attempted atonement, he transported Aurora to a monastery on Earth, but was sent to the netherworld himself as punishment. Northstar remained in Asgard until his former teammates rescued him from being slain by Dark Elves worshipping Llan the Sorceror, and during the ensuing battle against Llan he was able to restore Aurora's powers. As a side effect, both siblings proved able to generate light individually. After discovering an abandoned baby girl who had been born with the AIDS virus, Northstar adopted her, naming her Joanne, but she died weeks later. Northstar then publicly announced his homosexuality, hoping that his celebrity status would increase interest in HIV prevention. Following another disbanding of Alpha Flight, Northstar was implicated in the murder of a tabloid reporter, and the Canadian government dispatched Department K's Weapon P.R.I.M.E. unit to bring him in. At the same time, Northstar was targeted by the manic assassin Arcade, who had been employed by Carl Kerridge, a businessman who sought to cleanse the human race of supposed impurities. Northstar was able to gather enough evidence to prove his innocence and convict Kerridge.

Northstar later reunited with his former teammates to uncover the truth about the new Department H, and they assisted a new Alpha Flight team against the latest Weapon X. Northstar then left to write his autobiography, "Born Normal." At a book signing in Philadelphia, Northstar was recruited by the mutant telepath Jean Grey to join an ad-hoc X-Men team to oppose Magneto and his planned all-out attack against mankind. Returning to Canada, Northstar established himself as a successful businessman before he was invited to join the Xavier Institute as a teacher of business and economics. Northstar also taught a flight class for new students, and became advisor to a squad of students he dubbed Alpha Squadron in honor of his former team.

After his teammate Wolverine was captured and brainwashed by the terrorist organization Hydra, Northstar was killed in an ambush by Wolverine. He was subsequently resurrected and brainwashed into leading Hydra's super-powered army in an attack on the Helicarrier headquarters of their nemesis S.H.I.E.L.D. Meanwhile, Wolverine had been deprogrammed by S.H.I.E.L.D. and aided in the defense of the Helicarrier, but was unable to prevent Northstar from seriously injuring S.H.I.E.L.D.'s leader Nick Fury. Northstar then led the army on a killing spree, murdering anti-mutant and anti-gay supporters until he was confronted by Wolverine. Capturing him, Northstar tortured him until a group of giant mutant-hunting robot Sentinels under S.H.I.E.L.D. control intervened. As the Sentinels killed the other super-beings, Wolverine was able to defeat Northstar, and he was taken into S.H.I.E.L.D. custody to be deprogrammed.

Art by John Byrne

HEIGHT: 5'11"
WEIGHT: 185 lbs.
EYES: Blue
HAIR: Black, silver streaks

SUPERHUMAN POWERS: Northstar can move and fly at superhuman speed. He can channel a portion of the kinetic energy of the atomic motion in his body's molecules in a single direction, accelerating his body to a velocity in direct proportion to the amount of kinetic energy he has tapped. It is theoretically possible for Northstar to reach 99% of the speed of light (186,272 miles per second in a vacuum), but his inability to breathe at such speeds and the damage his body would suffer from wind and friction prevent him.

As a side effect of partially robbing his molecules of their atomic motion, the binding forces within and between the molecules increase which enhances the sheer toughness of Northstar's entire body. This effect gives his skin enough durability to withstand speeds up to at least Mach 10 without injury. Northstar can also vary the rate of acceleration of his molecules to release a cascade of photons as bright as a lighthouse beacon.

ABILITIES: Northstar is a world-class professional skier, skilled trapeze artist, and an accomplished novelist. Northstar also speaks fluent French.

POWER GRID	1	2	3	4	5	6	7
INTELLIGENCE							
STRENGTH							
SPEED							
DURABILITY							
ENERGY PROJECTION							
FIGHTING SKILLS							

ORD

REAL NAME: Ord
KNOWN ALIASES: Ord of the Breakworld
IDENTITY: Secret
OCCUPATION: Warrior
CITIZENSHIP: Breakworld
PLACE OF BIRTH: Breakworld
KNOWN RELATIVES: None
GROUP AFFILIATION: None
EDUCATION: Unrevealed
FIRST APPEARANCE: Astonishing X-Men #1 (2004)

HISTORY: Ord hails from the Breakworld, a planet home to a warrior culture whose technology allows them to see partial versions of the future. These "timeshadows" foretold that their planet would be destroyed by a mutant from Earth, most likely a member of the heroic X-Men team. For decades, Ord fought and won in many

arena-style battles for the honor of being chosen to travel to Earth with a declaration of war. However, the spy agency S.W.O.R.D. (Sentient Worlds Observation and Response Department), a subdivision of S.H.I.E.L.D. that handles extraterrestrial matters, was able to settle diplomatically with him by offering him a chance to eradicate the mutant gene, while they would seek to identify the mutant that would be responsible for the Breakworld's destruction.

In order to fulfill his end of the bargain, Ord secretly stole the body of Colossus, a former member of the X-Men, before it was due to be cremated. Using his advanced alien technology, Ord had Colossus restored to life and kept him prisoner for years while experimenting on him. Ultimately, Ord discovered the cure to the Legacy Virus still in Colossus' system and presented his findings to Benetech geneticist Doctor Kavita Rao, who was able to modify it into creating a "cure" for the "mutant condition." As Rao appeared in front of the world media to announce the cure, Ord hoped to flush out the X-Men and staged a hostage situation at a charity gala. True to form, the X-Men arrived to save the hostages and confronted Ord. Making short work of the heroes, Ord was driven off by the timely arrival of the alien dragon Lockheed, ally of the X-Man Shadowcat, who engulfed Ord's head in flame, causing him to flee.

Seeking revenge, Ord stole into the Xavier Institute to find that the X-Men had left to investigate Benetech. Wanting to leave the X-Men a message, Ord injected the young student Wing with the "cure," removing the boy's powers and instructing him to tell the X-Men that the mutant abomination would never be a threat to the Breakworld. Ord then returned to Benetech and confronted the X-Men; however, another timely arrival — Colossus, who had been found and freed by Shadowcat — saw him defeated once more. Head of S.H.I.E.L.D. Nick Fury and S.W.O.R.D.'s Special Agent Abigail Brand arrived to defuse the situation, but while explanations were being made, mutants desperate to obtain the cure stormed the facility, allowing Ord to escape in the confusion. The X-Men were able to prevent him from leaving Earth in his spacecraft, and he was taken into custody by S.W.O.R.D.

HEIGHT: 7'5"
WEIGHT: 341 lbs.
EYES: Red
HAIR: Black

SUPERHUMAN POWERS: Ord is a green-skinned alien possessed of enhanced senses, strength, durability, and speed, the full extents of which are unknown. Ord can also fly, though it is unknown if this ability is naturally- or technologically- empowered.

ABILITIES: Ord is a formidable hand-to-hand combatant, having decades of fighting experience.

PARAPHERNALIA: Ord wears a suit of body armor. He also wields a circular weapon with barbed blades that he claims can cut through any substance on Earth.

POWER GRID	1	2	3	4	5	6	7
INTELLIGENCE							
STRENGTH							
SPEED							
DURABILITY							
ENERGY PROJECTION							
FIGHTING SKILLS							

HISTORY: Born of the void between states of being, the Phoenix Force is a child of the universe. In the dying moments of the previous universe, the Force saved all existence from eternal damnation, enabling Eternity to preserve the humanoid Galan, ensuring his re-creation as Galactus. The Force was subsequently reborn from the cosmic fires of the "Big Bang." Later, it encountered the malevolent Le Bete Noir and trapped it in the center of a still-cooling planet Earth. The Force was drawn back to Earth when it was awakened to reality by Feron, a sorcerer from an alternate Earth who had traveled with his master Necrom to a tower on Earth-616 to witness an alignment of dimensional interfaces. The Force joined with Feron, allowing itself to be shaped by his dreams into the form of a giant fiery bird and experiencing a spectrum of new sensations. At the moment of the alignment, Feron bade the Force to project the essence of the tower throughout the multiverse, so that it existed on every plane of reality simultaneously, creating an energy matrix. Necrom sought to access the matrix to allow him to compress all alternate Earths into a singularity, the energy released from which would endow him with godlike power, and to that end he tore out the portion of the Force that had bonded to Feron. In agonized confusion over the violation of its essence, the Force fled. Necrom bound the stolen Force with a portion of his own essence, and left it to incubate in a corpse he dubbed the Anti-Phoenix.

In time, the Force's pain subsided and it discovered that it was unable to return to its natural state. Hundreds of years later, the Force learned that the universe would come under threat from manipulation of the M'kraan Crystal — a hypercubical nexus of realities — by the mad Shi'ar Emperor D'Ken. To prevent this, the Force sought an avatar through which it could act and so returned to Earth, seeking out Feron. Instead, the Force encountered Jean Grey, a member of the heroic mutant X-Men team, whose mind the Force had touched earlier. Grey was dying from the effects of solar radiation while piloting a damaged space shuttle. The Force appeared to Grey and offered to save her. She accepted, and so the Force created an exact duplicate of her body for itself, into which it transferred a portion of her consciousness. The Force then sealed her comatose body inside a healing cocoon, and after the shuttle crashed into Jamaica Bay near New York City, the Force emerged from the waters, calling itself Phoenix. The X-Men believed it to be the real Jean Grey, having died and returned to life with vast new powers. Phoenix and the X-Men opposed D'Ken, who exposed the universe to the tremendous gravitational forces contained within the Crystal's core. Phoenix entered the Crystal and repaired the stasis field, thus saving the cosmos. Phoenix continued to serve as a member of the X-Men, but ultimately its human form was unable to

REAL NAME: Inapplicable
KNOWN ALIASES: Chaos-Bringer, Starchilde, Phalkon, formerly Dark Phoenix, Black Queen, Phoenix, Jean Grey
IDENTITY: Secret
OCCUPATION: Celestial elemental; (while possessing host) adventurer
CITIZENSHIP: Inapplicable
PLACE OF BIRTH: Big Bang
KNOWN RELATIVES: Inapplicable
GROUP AFFILIATION: None; (as Phoenix) formerly X-Men, New York Hellfire Club (Inner Circle)
EDUCATION: Inapplicable
FIRST APPEARANCE: X-Men #101 (1976)

cope with the Force's immense power. At first, Grey's strong moral sense kept the Force in check, but Phoenix succumbed to the psionic manipulation of Jason Wyngarde (Mastermind). Unable to fully free itself of the sinister side of its personality that Wyngarde exposed it to, and with its human consciousness ill-equipped to repress it, the Force's primal urges overwhelmed Phoenix, causing it to become the malevolent Dark Phoenix. Due to the limitations of its physical form, Dark Phoenix hungered for more energy and transported itself to the star D'Bari, absorbing all the energy from it. As a result, the star turned supernova, annihilating one of its planets. Dark Phoenix destroyed a Shi'ar starship which had attacked it in retaliation for the D'Bari's deaths, then returned to Earth where it was opposed by the X-Men and Professor Xavier. He reinforced Grey's personality, allowing Phoenix to reject its cosmic power.

I AM FIRE.

A FORCE OF LIFE.

YOU CALLED OUT FOR AID. I ANSWERED.

The Shi'ar still judged it necessary to obliterate Phoenix's powers entirely, lest it become Dark Phoenix again. The X-Men fought the ruling in a trial by combat against members of the Shi'ar's Imperial Guard in the Blue Area of Earth's moon, but during the battle Phoenix reverted to Dark Phoenix. Realizing that it could never fully retain control, Phoenix acted as the real Grey would have. Before the eyes of a horrified Cyclops, it committed suicide by telekinetically triggering an energy cannon, disintegrating its mortal shell. Later reflecting on its folly, the Force sought to undo the damage it had done by returning the life-force it had taken from Grey. On its return to Earth, it sensed the astral form of the time-traveling Rachel Summers, the daughter of Earth-811's Jean Grey. After returning Grey's missing life-force, which was instead received by Grey's clone Madelyne Pryor, the Force followed Rachel back to the future of Earth-811. There, it revealed itself to Kate Pryde, who asked the Force to give Rachel a new lease on life. The Force agreed and took Rachel as its host, supercharging her ability to time travel and causing her to physically travel back in time to Earth-616. Rachel was unaware that she hosted the Force's essence until she took on the codename Phoenix. The Force then bonded to her fully and ensured that Rachel could only access as much power as she could safely wield, having learned from its past mistake. Adventuring with Rachel and the British super-team Excalibur for a time, the Force ultimately encountered Necrom's Anti-Phoenix. After a cataclysmic battle, Rachel allowed Necrom to possess the Force, gambling that its infinite power would be too much for him. Necrom's physical form exploded, and Rachel was destroyed in the blast. The Force gathered her shattered psyche and restored her body, promising Excalibur to protect and nurture her until she fully healed. Through Rachel's eyes, the Force was able to experience the simple beauty of existence. In space, it encountered the world-devourer Galactus, who revealed to the Force the nature of its existence. Tormented with the knowledge that its desire to explore humanity had prevented generations of life from being born, the Force fled. Rachel reentered the timestream and emerged some 2,000 years into the future of Earth-4935. There, she encountered Diamanda Nero, daughter of that era's mutant despot Apocalypse, and, in order to defeat her, was forced to purge herself of the Force.

Free again, the Force traveled back into the past, drawn once again to Earth-616. En route, it was transported to the Ultraverse (Earth-93060) by a sentient alien starship that had crash-landed there eons ago. Buried deep within the Earth, the ship sought to reunite

itself with its twin trapped within Earth's sun, and intended to use the Force's energy to power the recombination. Impaled on a lance of energy that linked the two ships, the Force fought back and managed to free itself, though not before the ship was able to bond them empathetically. Wounded, the Force sought out a host to protect it as it healed. Inhabiting the body of the super-strong hero Prime, the Force was opposed by the X-Men and Prime's teammates in UltraForce. Exhausting Prime's physical form, the Force found another host in Amber Hunt, who had previously been possessed by the ship's essence. The heroes were able to free Hunt from the Force, after which they took the fight to the ship, severing its link to the Force. Seeking revenge, the Force attacked the ship, threatening the stability of the planet. The heroes were able to drive the Force into another portal, and it emerged four billion years in the past. Unleashing vast energies while transmigrating itself through time and space, the Force inadvertently (and ironically) caused the damage to the ship that forced it to crash-land to begin with.

The Force returned to Earth-616 once more and manifested itself within Jean Grey before she was seemingly killed by an electromagnetic pulse. This shattered the Force into billions of pieces. Incubating in the core of creation known as the White Hot Room, the Force was ripped back to reality by a Shi'ar device that forcibly reconstituted it. Injured, the Force fell to Earth and sought out Cyclops to use his mutant optic power to heal itself. To that end, it searched for Cyclops' love Jean and, finding her dead, resurrected her to house its power once more. Opposed by the X-Men again, the Force was lured into possessing the body of Cyclops' new love Emma Frost before Jean was able to reassert control. The Force realized that Jean was one of its missing pieces, its prime host, and so it merged with her fully. Returning to the White Hot Room, the Force set out to find its other pieces.

SUPERHUMAN POWERS: The Phoenix Force is an immortal, indestructible, and mutable manifestation of the prime universal force of life, derived from the psyches of all living beings. In its natural state, this life-cycle is enough to sustain the Force. However, in order to manifest itself on the physical plane, the Force must tap into the near limitless source of energy provided by life-force reserved for future generations, thus denying them existence. The Force can wield this energy to project beams of immense concussive force, as well as transmigrate throughout time and space by folding its energy back into itself, causing it to collapse akin to a black hole, then it reforms itself upon reaching its destination, like the Phoenix of Earth legend.

While possessing a human host, the Force is able to augment any super-powers they have to vastly higher levels.

POWER GRID	1	2	3	4	5	6	7
INTELLIGENCE							
STRENGTH							
SPEED							
DURABILITY							
ENERGY PROJECTION							
FIGHTING SKILLS							

HISTORY: Betsy Braddock was Sir James Braddock's second child, and like her twin brother Brian, her life was secretly manipulated by Merlyn. The twins shared a close connection, but as they matured the adventurous Betsy also grew close to their elder brother Jamie. By the time their parents died, apparently in a lab accident but really murdered by the computer Mastermind, Betsy had become a charter pilot. When Mastermind's agent Doctor Synne tried to kill Jamie, a concerned Betsy fetched Brian, but as she flew them home, Synne's psychic attack caused her to crash. When she awoke, Synne's illusions made Betsy attack her brothers, seeing them as monsters. After Synne was defeated she and Jamie were taken hostage by the Red Skull's agents. Freed by Captains America and Britain, Betsy learned the latter was her brother Brian. Perhaps because of Synne's mental intrusions, Betsy began to develop precognitive powers. She took up modeling, while her powers grew to include telepathy. Agent Matthew recruited Betsy into S.T.R.I.K.E.'s Psi Division, and she became fellow psi Tom Lennox's lover. Because her father had been a member, she was sent to infiltrate the Hellfire Club, but was warned off by Tessa for her own protection.

When the crimelord Vixen secretly usurped S.T.R.I.K.E., she hired Slaymaster to eliminate the Psi-Division before they could expose this. The telepaths fled, but Slaymaster continued to pick them off; only a handful were left when Betsy sensed Brian's return and called on his help. He defeated Slaymaster and the three surviving psi's (Betsy, Tom and Alison Double) moved into the holographically hidden Braddock Manor. In short succession this hideout was found by the Special Executive, Captain U.K. and the Fury; as the last of these battled Brian and the Executive, Betsy foresaw a future where superhumans were imprisoned in concentration camps. Soon the U.K. became a fascist state ruled by the insane reality warper Sir James Jaspers, with S.T.R.I.K.E. "Beetle" squads rounding up those with powers. While Brian confronted Jaspers, the Beetles found the others' hideout. Tom died trying to buy his friends time to escape; Betsy was in Tom's mind when he died, and was captured. After being freed, she was nursed back to health by fellow camp inmate Victoria Bentley, who taught her to use her experiences to strengthen her powers. When Kaptain Briton, Brian's Earth-794 counterpart, tried to rape her, Betsy fried his mind, killing him. The same night, Mastermind informed the twins of their father's non-terrestrial origins, and the Resources Control Executive (R.C.X.) asked them to billet Warpies, children transformed by Jaspers' warp, at the Manor. One of the R.C.X. agents was Matthew, now codenamed Gabriel. Betsy overruled Brian and let R.C.X. and the Warpies move in. When Brian went overseas, Gabriel convinced Betsy to become the new Captain Britain, wearing Kaptain Briton's modified costume. Working with Captain U.K. (Linda McQuillan), the duo became public sensations, but after several months Betsy went solo. Vixen lured her into a showdown with Slaymaster, who brutally beat her, then gouged her eyes out. Brian felt her pain, flew to her rescue and killed Slaymaster. Betsy refused R.C.X.'s offer of cybernetic eyes, preferring to rely on her psychic abilities; she and Gabriel got engaged, and went to Switzerland for Betsy to recuperate.

Betsy was kidnapped from the Alps by Mojo, brainwashed, given cybernetic eyes, and, as "Psylocke," became the star of his new show "Wildways." Brian and the New Mutants rescued her, after which Betsy moved to the X-Men's mansion to recover, exactly where Roma (Merlyn's daughter) needed her to be. When the Marauders attacked the Morlocks, and Sabretooth invaded the mansion, she used herself as bait to lead him away from the injured until Wolverine got there. Impressed by her bravery, Wolverine nominated her to join the X-Men, beside whom she met Mephisto, Dr. Doom, the Fantastic Four, and Horde. The X-Men later battled

REAL NAME: Elizabeth Braddock
KNOWN ALIASES: Bee, Betsy, Captain Britain, Lady Mandarin
IDENTITY: Secret
OCCUPATION: Adventurer; former pilot, model, government agent, assassin
CITIZENSHIP: U.K.
PLACE OF BIRTH: Braddock Manor, England
KNOWN RELATIVES: James Braddock Sr. (father, deceased), Elizabeth Braddock (mother, deceased), James "Jamie" Braddock Jr. (brother), Brian Braddock (Captain Britain, brother), Meggan (sister-in-law)
GROUP AFFILIATION: X-Men, Hellfire Club; formerly Excalibur, Crimson Dawn, the Corps, S.T.R.I.K.E. Psi-division, former ally of R.C.X., former partner of Captain U.K.
EDUCATION: University graduate
FIRST APPEARANCE: Captain Britain #8 (1976)

Art by Chris Bachalo

Freedom Force and the Adversary in Dallas, and, in a televised battle, sacrificed themselves to allow Forge to bind the Adversary; Roma secretly restored them to life, and gave Betsy the Siege Perilous, which they could use if they ever wanted to start new lives. The X-Men moved to the Reavers' Australian Outback base, from where they took on the Brood Boys, Genoshan Magistrates, M Squad, Mr. Jip, the Serpent Society, the Abomination, Master Mold, Nimrod, Nanny, the Orphan Maker, Zaladane and the Savage Land Mutates. As they were about to depart the Savage Land, Betsy had a precognitive flash of the Reavers killing the team. To prevent this, she sent them through the Siege Perilous.

Betsy reappeared amnesiac on an island near China, where the Hand found her. Matsu'o Tsurayaba, their leader, saw a chance to save his brain-dead lover, Kwannon, and had Spiral's Bodyshoppe swap their souls. This inadvertently blended their minds, leaving each with the same memories and telepathic powers. Tsurayaba brainwashed Psylocke and gave her to the Mandarin as his assassin, Lady Mandarin, until Wolverine restored her memories. Back with the X-Men Betsy took on Cameron Hodge, Warskrulls, the Shadow King and cosmic cleaner Ediface Rex; she also informed Brian she was alive. The next few months saw battles against Magneto, Fenris, Mys-Tech (alongside new ally Dark Angel), and a Brood-infected Ghost Rider (Dan Ketch). Visiting Brian, Betsy helped Excalibur fight Sat-Yr-9 and the now insane Jamie, whom Betsy struck comatose. Encounters followed with the Troll Associates, the Mutant Liberation Front, Stryfe, Omega Red and the Soul Skinner.

Then Kwannon arrived at the Mansion in Betsy's original body, claiming to be the real Psylocke. Unable to discern which was truly Betsy, both stayed with the X-Men, maintaining an uneasy coexistence, with Kwannon taking the name Revanche. Learning she had the Legacy Virus, Revanche had Matsu'o kill her, after which Betsy regained her soul's missing piece. Having become involved with her teammate Angel, the following months saw her fight the Phalanx, try to reach Jamie's comatose mind, battle Legion in Israel, and combat Gene Nation. When Sabretooth gutted Psylocke, Angel, Wolverine, Doctor Strange and Gomurr the Ancient retrieved a magical liquid from the Crimson Dawn dimension which healed her and gave her new powers, but also marked her with a red tattoo over her left eye. Kuragari, Proctor of the Crimson Dawn, tried to claim Betsy as his bride, but was thwarted with Gomurr and Angel's aid, freeing Betsy of the Dawn's influence. Subsequently she aided Storm against the Shadow King, who tricked Psylocke into initiating a psychic shockwave which disabled all other telepaths, leaving him unchallenged on the astral plane. Her own astral form was destroyed, but her exposure to the Crimson Dawn gave her a new shadow form with temporarily enhanced powers, which she used to trap the Shadow King's core. To

Art by Alan Davis

keep him trapped she was forced to constantly focus her telepathy on him, effectively rendering herself powerless. After attending Brian's wedding, she was kidnapped to take part in the Coterie's contest of champions. When Apocalypse and his Horsemen sought to gather the Twelve, Psylocke used Cerebro to boost her powers, so that she could use them and still keep the Shadow King imprisoned, allowing her to free the brainwashed Wolverine. Jean Grey's attempt to help Betsy deal with the Shadow King somehow swapped their powers, leaving Betsy telekinetic. With her new abilities Betsy fought Belasco, the Neo, the Goth, and the Prime Sentinels, then aided her brother freeing Otherworld from Mastermind's Warpie army.

After ending her relationship with Archangel, Betsy joined Storm's X-Men team in the search for Destiny's Diaries. In Valencia, Spain, they encountered the enigmatic Vargas who killed her. Later, in a dream, Bishop saw Betsy's spirit being snatched by a skulled figure. Much later, Betsy was returned alive to the site of her death. Reunited with the X-Men, she helped them against the Saurian Hauk'ka, Mojo and Spiral. She has also been reunited with Brian during a recent reality storm. As yet there is no explanation for her resurrection, or her changed powers, but visions of Jamie suggest he may be somehow involved with her unexplained return from the dead.

HEIGHT: 5'11" (both bodies)
WEIGHT: 155 lbs. (both bodies)
EYES: (originally) Blue; (cybernetic) Purple; (currently) Purple
HAIR: (originally) Blonde, dyed purple; (currently) Black, often died purple

SUPERHUMAN POWERS: Psylocke can generate a telekinetic katana, or direct her telekinesis through her fists to strike as if she had superhuman strength; she is also immune to telepathic probes and attacks. Psylocke's original powers were precognition, telepathy, mental bolts, mind control, and generating illusions. After Roma resurrected her, Betsy was briefly invisible to all mechanical detection devices. She could generate a "psychic knife" to stun or kill opponents. The Crimson Dawn gave her the power to travel via shadows, and to become virtually invisible in same. After swapping powers with Jean Grey, Betsy could fly, create force fields, move objects with her mind, and generate energy blades.

ABILITIES: Psylocke is a skilled martial artist and a trained pilot.

PARAPHERNALIA: Her Captain Britain costume gave her superhuman strength, flight and a force field. She has sometimes worn lightweight armor. Mojo gave Psylocke bionic eyes that acted as remote cameras; she lost these after being body-swapped.

POWER GRID	1	2	3	4	5	6	7
INTELLIGENCE							
STRENGTH							
SPEED							
DURABILITY							
ENERGY PROJECTION							
FIGHTING SKILLS							

HISTORY: The Savage Land is a tropical region surrounded by volcanoes deep in Antarctica, created over 200 million years ago by the alien Nuwali as one of several planetary "game preserves" for the mysterious godlike Beyonders. The Nuwali stocked the Land with Earthly life of the era, most notably dinosaurs; as Earth's flora and fauna changed over succeeding millions of years, they supplemented their preserve with prehistoric mammals and early hominids, or "Man-Apes." When Earth's continents shifted circa 50 million BC, the Nuwali augmented the Land's volcanoes to preserve its tropical status. Following the Nuwali's departure in 200,000 BC, little is known of the Land's history for over a hundred millennia, although a faction of superhuman Eternals dwelled there at least briefly, leaving a temple complex behind. Circa 18,500 BC, it was colonized by humans of Atlantis, who exported prehistoric life throughout their empire while importing unicorns and other mystic creatures. Atlantean scientists extended the tropical effect, creating a recreation/commerce center called "Pangea," then genetically altered Man-Apes into humanoid versions of birds, monkeys, fish, and other animals. The beast-people, put to work as laborers, became dissatisfied with servitude and, following Pangea's automation, rebelled in the First Pangean War and were allowed to colonize unpopulated areas rendered habitable by the Nuwali effect.

In 18,000 BC, alien and mystic conflicts resulted in the Great Cataclysm, sinking Atlantis and ending its empire, but the Land and Pangea were protected from inundation by surrounding mountains. The Beyonders, having observed their preserve over the millennia, sent Fortisquian operatives, later called the Caretakers of Arcturus, to repair its environmental system, but nonetheless, over half the population perished. Some survivors clung to Atlantean culture in cities like Lemura and Sylanda; others forgot their origins, becoming ancestors of the Swamp Men and other tribes. The animal-people developed their own societies, sometimes, as with the Aerians and Pterons, resorting to war. Every thousand years or so, high priests needlessly conducted human sacrifices to "protect" the Land. Circa 3000 BC two godlike aliens briefly made the Land their home, and at some point Sagittarians stored a Planet-Destroyer there with a gigantic robot, Umbu, to guard it. In the mid-13th century, exiled sorcerer Khor took up residence. In the 1380s, another sorcerer, Belasco, also found his way to the Land, in conflict with poet Dante Alighieri. Less than two centuries later, an unnamed Englishman was washed ashore and became the embodiment of the god Garokk, worshipped since pre-Cataclysm days.

In the 1770s, Captain James Cook became the first human explorer to cross the Antarctic Circle, but apparently neither he nor most subsequent explorers discovered the Savage Land. In the mid-19th century, the Atlanteans — that is, the underwater race whose culture was based on Atlantis's remains — relocated to Antarctica, as did Lemurian rebels called the Ancients. Mysterious beings such as Torg and the Ice King also made their home in the region. Vague reports of underground realms and surviving dinosaurs appeared in the work of such authors as Edgar Allan Poe and Jules Verne, suggesting rumors of the Land were spreading. By 1915, human expeditions had discovered "anti-metal," the destructive metal also called Vibranium, in Antarctica,

OFFICIAL NAME: The Savage Land
LOCATION: Antarctica, approximately 69º 30' S, 68º 30' W
POPULATION: Undetermined
GOVERNMENT: United Tribes
MAJOR GROUPS: Aerians, Ape-Men, Awakilius, Bhadwuans, Cat People, Cliff Forest People, Disians, Durammi, Fall People, Golden People, Gondorans, Gorankians, Gwundas, Hauk'ka, Hill-Forest People, Jeriens, Kantos, Karems, Klantorr, Lemurans, Lizard-Men, Locot, Man-Apes, Mutates, Neo-Men, N'Galans, Nhu'gari, Nowek, Palandorians, Pterons, Reptile Men, Saurids, Snowmen, Sun People, Swamp Men, Sylandans, Tandar-Kaans, Tokchis, Tordon-Naans, Tree People, Tribe of Fire, Tubanti, Uruburians, Vala-Kuri, Waidians, Water People, Zebra People, others
FIRST APPEARANCE: Marvel Mystery Comics #22 (1941)

but the greater deposits within the Land remained unknown. Nazi dictator Adolph Hitler claimed Antarctica in 1940, and a year later, a British destroyer and a Nazi U-boat vanished into the Land, fighting a private war for decades; the U-boat in question may have attacked the Antarctic expedition of Elton Morrow, who became the superhuman Blue Diamond following such an attack. Months later, Khor teleported a ship to the Land and enslaved its passengers but was defeated by the extradimensional Vision; two years later, an

Antarctic dinosaur, presumably escaped from the Land, was given a human brain and fought Captain America. At some point the Nazis constructed a base within the Land whose goals and fate are unrevealed, but its work may have moved to a nearby island. Following the war, scientist Montgomery Ford, armed with a laser prototype, found his way to the Land, and rumors circulated that high-ranking Nazis had fled to Antarctica. Indeed, unverified reports claim when explorer Admiral Richard Byrd launched expeditions to the South Pole in 1947 and 1956, he discovered the Savage Land, perhaps even clashing with Hitler's so-called "Last Battalion," although this claim seems dubious. Meanwhile, spatial warps occasionally brought ships and planes into the Land, where survivors joined the populace.

Over twenty years ago, British nobleman Robert Plunder, searching for Vibranium, found his way into the Savage Land. Back in England, Plunder was threatened by those who coveted his secret, and he returned to the Land with his nine-year-old son Kevin, who was orphaned when Robert was slain by the Man-Ape Maa-Gor. Nurtured by the sabretooth Zabu, Kevin, perhaps enhanced by the Land's mysterious "Place of Mists," became known as "Ka-Zar," or "Brother of the Tiger," his uncanny skills and heroism won him respect throughout the Land while still in his teens. Ka-Zar was photographed while exploring the Land's upper limits, provoking investigation by the mutant X-Men, whom he befriended. When the X-Men's nemesis Magneto took the Land as his base and transformed simple Swamp Men into the Savage Land Mutates, Ka-Zar helped the X-Men defeat their foe, and then fought alongside Garokk against the renegade priestess Zaladane. The Land, so long a source of rumor, became worldwide news when the Daily Bugle ran a feature on it, an endeavor that brought the heroic Spider-Man to the Land, where he aided Ka-Zar against another would-be ruler, Kraven the Hunter. Soon afterward, Ka-Zar provided S.H.I.E.L.D. scientists with dinosaur samples which were misused by a researcher who, with the aid of the cryptic They Who Wield Power, transformed himself into Stegron the Dinosaur Man.

Although the United Nations banned commercial exploitation of the Land, the Bugle's exposure brought explorers and treasure-hunters to Ka-Zar's door. Soon after, Malgato, last of the high priests, attempted to sacrifice Ka-Zar and African adventurer Shanna, then briefly mutated Maa-Gor into godlike form, though both met defeat. The Land was next beset by plague, the armored Volcanus, Vibranium-induced madness, and invasion by the dimension of Quorl. The latter was repelled when Zaladane re-incarnated Garokk into radiologist Kirk Marston, but the two then sought to conquer the Land, which was saved from environmental disaster by Ka-Zar and a new team of X-Men. While outside menaces such as MODOK, Klaw, and others vied for the Land's resources, the intellectually evolved Brainchild led his fellow Savage Land Mutates in a scheme using Magneto's abandoned technology. However, Sauron, a psychic vampire mutated by pteranodons, wrested control from Brainchild, only to be defeated by Ka-Zar, the X-Men, and Spider-Man. Ka-Zar, now in Shanna's company, explored Pangea and helped establish peace between its many races, despite intervention by Belasco and others; the two adventurers wed and were soon to be

parents, but their happiness was short-lived when Jorro, servant of the alien scavenger Terminus, decimated the Savage Land and Pangea and, despite the Avengers' best efforts, destroyed the technology preserving Ka-Zar's world, leaving most of its population to perish. Ka-Zar and Shanna found refuge in America, where their son Matthew was born, but the Land now held only sparse survivors, some of whom became the team Alpha Prime under the amnesiac hero Vindicator.

However, several Land/Pangea inhabitants had been rescued by the extradimensional M'Rin. When happenstance brought the X-Men and the genius geneticist High Evolutionary to Antarctica, M'Rin returned the exiles, and Garokk, saner since breaking with Zaladane, sacrificed himself to renew the Land, repopulated with cloned animal life and ruled by the new United Tribes. But Zaladane's ambitions resurfaced and, commanding the Savage Land Mutates, she stole magnetic power from the X-Man Polaris and threatened the world before meeting seeming death at the hands of a reformed Magneto. The Savage Land was declared a sovereign kingdom, and although menaced by a string of would-be conquerors — including Apocalypse, the Super-Skrull, Prime Evil, the Warlord, Sauron, Mister Sinister, the High Technician, and A.I.M. — its security was repeatedly restored by Ka-Zar, the X-Men, and other heroes. The Land again faced internal crisis when Nuwali technology mutated natives into monstrous Neo-Men, while melting glaciers threatened a new inundation; Roxxon Oil, pretending humanitarian motives, secretly hastened the process in hope of claiming the Land's resources but was foiled by Ka-Zar, Spider-Man, and others. Following an aborted claim by the Titan Thanos, the technology was revitalized, and Devil Dinosaur and Moonboy, adventurers from time and space, emigrated to Ka-Zar's realm.

Brainchild, supported by new Mutates, sought to rule the Land but was defeated by X-Men and new emigrants, mutated reptiles called Saurids, who were welcomed into the United Tribes. Later, the Hauk'ka, a homegrown reptilian race, conquered the Tribes and attempted to restructure Earth's biosphere but were defeated by the X-Men, Ka-Zar, and Brainchild's Mutates. Most recently, in pursuing Sauron to the Land, the Avengers discovered undefined alliances between Brainchild and outworld criminals, while renegade S.H.I.E.L.D. agents were exposed as enslaving natives and mining Vibranium, demonstrating the Savage Land's threats from within and without are far from over.

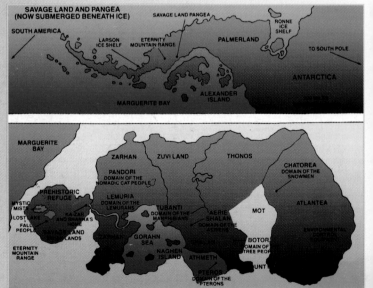

SAVAGE LAND AND PANGEA
(NOW SUBMERGED BENEATH ICE)
SAVAGE LAND PANGEA
SOUTH AMERICA
RONNE ICE SHELF
LARSON ICE SHELF
ETERNITY MOUNTAIN RANGE
PALMERLAND
TO SOUTH POLE
ANTARCTICA
MARGUERITE BAY
ALEXANDER ISLAND

MARGUERITE BAY
ZARHAN
ZUVI LAND
THONOS
CHATOREA DOMAIN OF THE SNOWMEN
PANDORI DOMAIN OF THE NOMADIC CAT PEOPLE
PREHISTORIC REFUGE
LEMURIA DOMAIN OF THE LEMURANS
MYSTIC MISTS
TUBANTI DOMAIN OF THE MANPHIBIANS
AERIE SHALAN DOMAIN OF THE AERIENS
MOT
ATLANTEA
LOST LAKE
FALL PEOPLE
KA-ZAR AND SHANNA'S HOME
SAVAGE LAND LANDS
ZARHAN
GORAHN SEA
NAGHEN ISLAND
ATHMETH
BOTOR DOMAIN OF TREE PEOPLE
ENVIRONMENTAL STATION
ETERNITY MOUNTAIN RANGE
PTEROS DOMAIN OF THE PTERONS

HISTORY: The Stepford Cuckoos were five identical mutant sisters who enrolled at the Xavier Institute and soon proved to be the crème de la crème of Emma Frost's telepathy class. When the Institute was attacked by the mutant-organ-harvesting U-Men, the Cuckoos were among those students that helped oppose them. Later, the Cuckoo Esme romanced a student named Kato who revealed himself to be Stuff, a spy for the alien Shi'ar Empire's Imperial Guard who had been dispatched to Earth by Cassandra Nova to eradicate mutantkind. The Cuckoos were captured, but were able to defeat Stuff and, with Frost's help, created a trap for Nova.

Their class rival Quentin Quire was besotted with the Cuckoo Sophie, and after he rebelled and fomented a riot at the Institute, the Cuckoos opposed him. Taking the power-boosting drug "Kick" and using the X-Men's mutant-locating device Cerebra to further amplify their powers, they defeated him. Ultimately, while her sisters were happy to be molded in Emma's image, Esme was not, and she secretly usurped control of the Cuckoo's group mind. When Sophie resisted, Esme influenced her death, and coerced the Cuckoos into blaming Frost and leaving her tutelage. Esme later telepathically forced Angel Salvadore into attempting to assassinate Frost, after which Esme fled the Institute, joining whom she believed to be the X-Men's arch-nemesis Magneto. After this faux Magneto destroyed the Institute and attacked Manhattan, the three other Cuckoos joined an ad-hoc X-Men team to oppose the imposter. Esme ultimately turned against him and was killed for her betrayal.

The three remaining Cuckoos later resolved their differences with Emma, who subsequently became co-headmistress of the rebuilt Institute. The Cuckoos were placed into Cyclops' Corsairs squad, after which Mindee helped the then-blind X-Man Gambit defend the Institute from an attack by a reformed Brotherhood of Mutants. The Cuckoos then faced the return of Quire after a splintered Phoenix Force came to the Institute seeking Jean. Quire sought to resurrect his beloved Sophie and asked the Force for help. It restored her to life, but upon seeing Quire she chose to return to death. The Force departed after merging with Jean to search for its missing pieces, one of which later visited the Cuckoos. Recently, the Cuckoos were instrumental in the students' defeat of the immovable mutant the Blob when he attacked the Institute. During the Scarlet Witch's reshaping of reality, the Cuckoos were briefly restored as a quintet.

REAL NAMES: Celeste, Esme, Mindee, Phoebe, Sophie (surname unrevealed)
KNOWN ALIASES: Three-in-One, formerly Five-in-One
IDENTITY: Secret
OCCUPATION: Students, adventurers; (Esme) former terrorist
CITIZENSHIP: U.S.A.
PLACE OF BIRTH: New York City, New York
KNOWN RELATIVES: None
GROUP AFFILIATION: Xavier Institute Student Body/Corsairs; (Phoebe, Celeste, Mindee) formerly X-Men, (Esme) formerly Brotherhood of Mutants
EDUCATION: Various courses at Xavier Institute
FIRST APPEARANCE: New X-Men #118 (2001)

HEIGHT: (all) 5'6"
WEIGHT: (all) 105 lbs.
EYES: (all) Blue; glowing white when using powers
HAIR: (all) Blonde

SUPERHUMAN POWERS: The Stepford Cuckoos share a unique bond that allows them to combine their individual telepathic powers to form a powerful "supermind." The Cuckoos can use their powers to read the minds of others, alter another being's perception of reality, manipulate the thoughts and bodily actions of others, or to shield their minds against telepathic probes. Through their bond, the Cuckoos communicate almost instantaneously, often speaking in unison or finishing one another's sentences. The strength of this bond is based on proximity; the further away they are from one another, the weaker it becomes.

POWER GRID

	1	2	3	4	5	6	7
INTELLIGENCE							
STRENGTH							
SPEED							
DURABILITY							
ENERGY PROJECTION							
FIGHTING SKILLS							

SUNFIRE

REAL NAME: Shiro Yoshida
KNOWN ALIASES: None
IDENTITY: Secret (known to some government officials)
OCCUPATION: Adventurer, government agent; former student, terrorist
CITIZENSHIP: Japan
PLACE OF BIRTH: Agarashima, Japan
KNOWN RELATIVES: Saburo Yoshida (father, deceased), unnamed mother (deceased), Tomo Yoshida (uncle, deceased), Leyu Yoshida (Sunpyre, half-sister, deceased), Yoshi (cousin, deceased), Shingen Harada (first cousin once removed, deceased), Mariko Yashida (second cousin, deceased), Kenuichio Harada (Silver Samurai, second half-cousin)
GROUP AFFILIATION: None; formerly X-Corporation, Yakiba, the Twelve, Big Hero 6, Pacific Overlords, Death's Champions, X-Men
EDUCATION: College graduate
FIRST APPEARANCE: X-Men #64 (1970)

HISTORY: Shiro Yoshida's mother was exposed to the atomic devastation of Hiroshima during World War II and died giving birth to him. He was raised by his father Saburo, a member of the powerful Japanese Clan Yashida who pursued a diplomatic career and became Japan's ambassador to the United Nations. Shiro was often left in the care of his uncle Tomo, a fanatic anti-American. After Shiro's mutant powers first manifested, Tomo sought to use him as a weapon against the U.S., giving him a costume and calling him "Sunfire." Soon after, Tomo sent Sunfire, the shapeshifting terrorist Mystique, the mutant power-stealing Rogue, and the memory-stealing mutant Blindspot to steal the formula for bonding the nigh-unbreakable metal Adamantium to a human skeleton from Lord Dark Wind. The mission failed, and Blindspot wiped the memories of those involved.

Invited to join Saburo in America, Tomo incited Shiro to attack the Capitol building in Washington, but he was opposed by the heroic mutant X-Men. Saburo sought to reason with Shiro but was shot and killed by Tomo, who in turn was killed by Shiro. Deported back to Japan, Shiro found himself a social outcast for having dishonored his father. He fled to Tokyo's slums and fell in with the criminal Dragon-Lord of Krakinowa, who sought to restore Japan's status as a world power. Sunfire was sent to destroy an American cargo ship, leading to conflict with Namor the Sub-Mariner, who made Sunfire realize the ramifications of his actions and teamed with him to defeat the Dragon-Lord. Having redeemed himself, Sunfire was accepted as Japan's protector. Sunfire soon encountered the American hero Iron Man in Vietnam, but was kidnapped by the would-be conqueror the Mandarin. Iron Man intervened and rescued Sunfire, who then sought revenge, but was opposed by the Mandarin's giant robot Ultimo. Once again saved by Iron Man, Sunfire began to rethink his anti-American beliefs.

Later, Sunfire was contacted by Professor Xavier, who was recruiting a new team of X-Men to help rescue the original group from the living island Krakoa. Sunfire joined up long enough to help defeat Krakoa, but refused to stay with the team as he was devoted to serving Japan. Later, when Moses Magnum was threatening to sink Japan into the sea, Sunfire was unwilling to accept the X-Men's help; but he was countermanded by Japan's Prime Minister, who forced Sunfire to work with them. Together, they defeated Magnum, and Sunfire's opinion of the X-Men improved as a result. Later, the X-Men and Sunfire were among the many heroes forced to participate in the Grandmaster's Contest of Champions, during which Sunfire battled Darkstar to a standstill. After the giant green dragon named "Puff" attacked Tokyo, Sunfire was sent to work with the X-Men again by his cousin Mariko, now leader of Clan Yashida.

Sunfire later investigated the new designer drug "Sleet," tracing its origins to the island nation of Madripoor, where he teamed with mutant soldier Cable (an old friend of his father's), the New Mutants and the X-Man Wolverine against the Mutant Liberation Front. Returning to Japan, Sunfire was captured by Doctor Demonicus and brainwashed into serving as a member of his terrorist Pacific Overlords. Sunfire and fellow pyrokinetic Pele were sent to Hawaii to disrupt a ceremony honoring Namor for his World War II heroism. Opposed by Namor and the Avengers, they freed Sunfire from Demonicus' thrall, and he joined the heroes in defeating the Overlords. The Japanese government soon outfitted Sunfire with a specially-designed suit of armor, the successful test of which inadvertently ruptured a dimensional void that threatened to swallow the entire Earth. Working together, the X-Men and Sunfire resealed the void. Later, after Wolverine became involved in a war between Clan Yashida and the ninja Hand clan, Sunfire came to his aid, but was unable to prevent Mariko from being poisoned. Sunfire was subsequently tasked with escorting a Japanese whaling fleet to Antarctica to protect them from hostile Atlanteans. Sunfire erroneously believed Namor was responsible, but the true culprit was ultimately revealed to be Namor's rival Attuma.

When the X-Men's nemesis Magneto released an electro-magnetic pulse across the globe, the energy overloaded Sunfire's body and caused his powers to flare out of control directly over Tokyo. This forced the Japanese government to imprison Sunfire, but he was soon freed by his cousin the Silver Samurai and Wolverine to help oppose a government plan to outfit giant Red Ronin robots with mutant-hunting technology. Battling one of the robots, Sunfire's powers again flared out of control and Wolverine suggested he seek aid from Canada's Department H, unaware that the Department had fallen into malevolent hands. Informed by the Department's scientists that he had radiation poisoning, Sunfire remained with them seeking a cure. Unknown to Sunfire, the scientists had injected him with Zero Fluid, a compound that turned half his body jet black and created an ambient charge of bio-kinetic energy within his body that conflicted with his bio-atomic powers. Frustrated by the scientists' inability to cure him, Sunfire returned home, seeking refuge in an abandoned monastery. There, he was contacted by the Japanese government to join the fledgling super-team Big Hero 6. Sunfire initially declined, but later joined the team to help defeat the Everwraith. Possessed by the ethereal creature, Sunfire resisted its attempts to release his powers, but when his young teammate Hiro learned the truth of his condition, Sunfire expelled the entire bio-kinetic charge instead, dispersing the Everwraith. Eventually, the Zero Fluid was removed from his system, and he was assigned to work as a field agent with the Yakiba, the Japanese military intelligence. His first mission was to expose a shapeshifter that had infiltrated the military. Mistakenly believing this to be Mystique, Sunfire sought her out, but encountered Rogue instead. Together, they discovered that the true culprit was an alien Skrull who had been watching Sunfire as part of an alliance with the eternal mutant Apocalypse and his plans involving the legendary Twelve, mutants supposedly destined to usher in a golden age for their kind. In truth, Apocalypse sought to gather them together so as to siphon their collective powers to grant himself godlike power, and to that end he sent his Horseman Famine to capture Sunfire. Ultimately, the Twelve were able to break free, and Apocalypse was defeated.

After the mystic city of K'un-Lun began appearing in the midst of Tokyo, Sunfire teamed with several American heroes to prevent its full manifestation. A short time later, Sunfire was approached by the feral mutants Sabretooth and Wild Child with an ultimatum to join the subversive Weapon X organization. Sunfire declined and attacked Sabretooth, but was in turn shot by Wild Child and left for dead. Sunfire survived this encounter and soon after accepted an offer from Xavier to join the X-Corporation, a global mutant search and rescue operation, in its Mumbai, India headquarters. Still acting as protector of Japan, Sunfire encountered the alien Titannus, who sought to forcibly recruit Earth's heroes into an army to wage intergalactic war. Titannus easily defeated Sunfire, and then attacked Tokyo, resulting in several of Earth's heroes teaming up to defeat him. Later, Sunfire was implicated in Clan Yashida's criminal activities and his status as Japan's protector was suspended. Sunfire sought to clear his name and joined with Rogue to oppose the perpetrator, Dark Wind's daughter Lady Deathstrike. In the ensuing clash, Deathstrike severed Sunfire's legs and defeated Rogue, imprisoning them both with Deathstrike's other captive, Blindspot. Sunfire bade Rogue absorb his powers, and he seemingly died from the strain. After Deathstrike was defeated,

Rogue returned to her hideout, but Sunfire's body was gone. During the mutant Scarlet Witch's reshaping of reality, Sunfire was seen alive and well as the Emperor of Japan.

HEIGHT: 5'10"
WEIGHT: 175 lbs.
EYES: Dark brown
HAIR: Black

SUPERHUMAN POWERS: Sunfire can biochemically ionize matter and convert it into the super-heated plasma state of matter, generating temperatures of about 1,000,000° Fahrenheit which he most often releases as force blasts from his hands. Sunfire can recharge and enhance his stored power by absorbing both solar and electromagnetic energy. He can also view his surroundings in the infrared spectrum. Sunfire can create super-heated air currents which enable him to fly while leaving a trail of flame behind him. Sunfire also generates an invisible field of psionic energy which protects him from the heat and radiation generated by his own powers, as well as from outside sources. The field also shields him from air friction and the light generated by his plasma, as well as lending a certain level of protection from kinetic impact.

ABILITIES: Sunfire is well versed in the martial arts of karate and kendo, as well as the art of bushido, the history and customs of the samurai class.

PARAPHERNALIA: Sunfire formerly wore a suit of body armor containing solar panels which enabled him to absorb solar energy more efficiently, focusing units that released this energy as a laser-like beam, boot jets which increased his flight speed, and convection stabilizers that increased his aerial maneuverability.

POWER GRID	1	2	3	4	5	6	7
INTELLIGENCE							
STRENGTH							
SPEED							
DURABILITY							
ENERGY PROJECTION							
FIGHTING SKILLS							

X-23

REAL NAME: Laura Kinney
KNOWN ALIASES: None
IDENTITY: Secret
OCCUPATION: Adventurer, student; former assassin
CITIZENSHIP: None
PLACE OF BIRTH: The Facility, location unrevealed
KNOWN RELATIVES: Sarah Kinney (surrogate mother), James Howlett (Wolverine, genetic progenitor)
GROUP AFFILIATION: Xavier Institute Student Body; formerly The Facility
EDUCATION: College graduate
FIRST APPEARANCE: NYX #3 (2004)

HISTORY: When a top-secret program attempted to recreate the original Weapon X experiment that involved the feral mutant Wolverine, they failed to secure a test subject that could survive the bonding of the virtually unbreakable metal Adamantium to their skeleton. Seeking to take the project in a new direction, the project's director, Doctor Martin Sutter, recruited renowned mutant geneticist Doctor Sarah Kinney and tasked her with creating a clone. Using the only available genetic sample from Weapon X, which was damaged, they were unable to salvage the Y chromosome after 22 attempts. Kinney then proposed they create a female clone, and though her request was initially denied, she still went ahead and produced a viable female subject, prompting Sutter to reconsider. Despite resistance from his protégé Doctor Zander Rice, whom he had raised after Rice's father was killed by a bestial Wolverine at the original Weapon X Project, Sutter allowed Kinney to proceed. As revenge for her insubordination, Rice forced Kinney to act as the surrogate mother for the clone, and she gave birth to "X-23."

Raised in captivity, X-23 was trained to be a weapon. Kinney did her best to ensure the child retained some semblance of humanity, but

her efforts appeared to be in vain. After seven years, Rice had X-23 subjected to radiation poisoning in order to accelerate the activation of her mutant gene, then forcibly extracted her claws and coated them with Adamantium. Next, Rice created a chemical compound he called "trigger scent" that sent X-23 into an involuntary, targeted berserker rage upon smelling its presence. Three years later, X-23 was sent on her first field mission to kill Presidential candidate Greg Johnson. Numerous other missions followed, as X-23's services were sold to the highest bidder, and she was left emotionally stunted as a result. Rice, in an attempt to avenge his father's murder, abandoned X-23 on a particularly dangerous mission, but she survived against overwhelming odds and managed to return to the facility.

Ultimately, Rice persuaded Sutter to hand over control of the program to him, then secretly ordered X-23 to kill Sutter and his family. Later, Rice revealed to Kinney a chamber with dozens of incubation pods containing female clones before he fired her. Before fleeing the facility with X-23, Kinney gave her one last mission — destroy the pods and kill all of the scientists involved in the program, including Rice. However, Rice was able to exact revenge on Kinney from beyond the grave, as he had earlier exposed her to the trigger scent, sending X-23 into a rage that caused her to kill her mother. As she lay dying, Kinney named X-23 Laura.

X-23 surfaced in New York two years later and was found living on the streets by a pimp named Zebra Daddy, who took her in and employed her as a prostitute. X-23 met Kiden Nixon, a young mutant with the ability to freeze time when in danger, and together with Kiden's teacher, they rescued another young mutant, the feral Catiana, from an angry mob. Zebra Daddy tracked X-23 down, but with the aid of her newfound friends and the mutant named Felon, Zebra Daddy's thugs were defeated. X-23 then killed him to save

the lives of her friends. X-23 later took a job at the mutant-themed Wannabee's nightclub in the Mutant Town district of New York. It was there that she saved the life of the daughter of mob boss Don Parisi from a gang of thugs, whom she killed. The deaths inadvertently implicated Wolverine, prompting his teammates in the X-Men to investigate. X-23 instinctually attacked Wolverine on sight, but he was eventually able to calm her down, and she led the X-Men to Parisi's daughter. After aiding the X-Men against Parisi's super-strong mutant enforcer Geech, X-23 fled the scene. She later returned to help the X-Men save victims of a car accident, after which she was enrolled at the X-Men's Xavier Institute.

X-23 quickly became very protective of Wolverine, attacking his teammate Bishop after he felled Wolverine during a training session. She also took to observing Wolverine on the mansion's security monitors. During one such viewing, an anomalous energy spike prompted X-23 to investigate. Encountering Spider-Man at the source of the signal, X-23 initially mistook him for an enemy and attacked. The pair ultimately teamed up to save the young mutant Paul Patterson from an alternate reality version of the armored Avenger Iron Man. The arrival of the heroic Captain America and the super-spy Black Widow helped turn the tide.

X-23 then secretly followed Wolverine on his investigation of strange activity in the Canadian Rockies. Ambushed by the Hauk'ka, evolved Saurians from the Savage Land, X-23 managed to escape and alert the X-Men. Traveling to the Savage Land, X-23 and the X-Men teamed with the Land's lord Ka-Zar and his circumstantial allies, the Savage Land Mutates, to prevent the Hauk'ka from destroying human civilization by controlling the weather-manipulating X-Man Storm. Following the advent of "M-Day," X-23 came to join the new team formed from the remaining members of the New Mutants and Hellions at the Xavier Institute.

Art by Alan Davis

HEIGHT: 5'6"
WEIGHT: 110 lbs.
EYES: Brown
HAIR: Black

SUPERHUMAN POWERS: X-23 possesses the ability to regenerate damaged or destroyed areas of her cellular structure at a superhuman rate, which varies in direct proportion with the severity of the damage she suffers. Despite the extent of her healing factor, X-23 is not immortal. Injuries that result in the loss of vital organs, large amounts of blood, and/or loss of physical form are potentially lethal for her. X-23's natural healing also affords her virtual immunity to poisons and most drugs, as well as an enhanced resistance to diseases and the fatigue poisons generated by bodily activity. Hence, her endurance, agility and reflexes are enhanced. X-23 also possesses superhumanly acute senses, allowing her to see and hear things at an extended distance. She is able to recognize people and objects by scent, even if that person or object is hidden, and can use these enhanced senses to track any creature with an impressive degree of success.

X-23's skeleton includes two retractable bone claws in each arm and one in each foot that she can extend and retract at will. These claws are housed beneath the skin and muscle. Unsheathing them causes her skin to tear and bleed, but the wounds are quickly dealt with by her healing factor. X-23 can unsheathe any number of these claws at once, although she must keep her wrists and/or feet straight at the moment the

claws emerge. The claws are naturally sharp and tougher than normal human bone, allowing X-23 to cut through most types of flesh and natural materials.

Presumably, because X-23 is a clone of the mutant Wolverine, her healing factor will also provide her with an extended lifespan by slowing the effects of the aging process.

PARAPHERNALIA: X-23's claws have been coated with the nigh-indestructible metal Adamantium. As a result, her claws are virtually unbreakable and are capable of cutting through almost any substance depending on its thickness and the amount of force she can exert. Due to her healing factor, the presence of Adamantium in her body does not interfere with her bones' normal function of generating blood corpuscles.

ABILITIES: Due to her extensive training as a top-secret operative, X-23 is a master of multiple forms of martial arts, and is an expert in assassination techniques as well as the use of numerous weapons.

POWER GRID	1	2	3	4	5	6	7
INTELLIGENCE							
STRENGTH							
SPEED							
DURABILITY							
ENERGY PROJECTION							
FIGHTING SKILLS							

XORN

REAL NAMES: Kuan-Yin Xorn, Shen Xorn
KNOWN ALIASES: None
IDENTITY: Publicly known
OCCUPATION: (Kuan-Yin) Former terrorist, teacher, adventurer, prisoner; (Shen) Former adventurer, prisoner
CITIZENSHIP: China
PLACE OF BIRTH: Near Ürümqi, Xinjiang Uygur Autonomous Region, China
KNOWN RELATIVES: Unnamed parents, unnamed aunt & uncle
GROUP AFFILIATION: (Kuan-Yin) None; formerly Brotherhood of Mutants, Xavier Institute Faculty, X-Men; (Shen) None; formerly X-Men
EDUCATION: Unrevealed
FIRST APPEARANCE: (Kuan-Yin) New X-Men Annual 2001; (Shen) X-Men #157 (2004)

HISTORY: The Xorn brothers' mutant natures manifested as tiny stars inside their heads that flared out of control, devastating their small village in China until villagers managed to encase the remains of their heads within metal masks. The anti-mutant Communist regime separated the brothers, keeping Shen in isolation in the village under the guard of the Eight Immortals, while Kuan-Yin was incarcerated in an underground prison. Eventually, Kuan-Yin's warden made a deal to sell him to John Sublime, who sought to harvest Kuan-Yin's mutant

mind. Rather than face such a grisly fate, Kuan-Yin attempted suicide by reversing his star's power, creating a black hole that threatened to destroy the world. The X-Men soon arrived and defused the situation by inviting Kuan-Yin to join the team.

Kuan-Yin subsequently opposed the threat of Nano-Sentinels released by the malevolent Cassandra Nova. He and Cyclops were captured by the alien Shi'ar's Imperial Guard, which had fallen under Nova's control, but managed to escape to the Xavier Institute where Kuan-Yin healed the X-Men, allowing them to better oppose Nova. Kuan-Yin subsequently took up a teaching position at the Institute as instructor of the Special Class, into which he unsuccessfully attempted to recruit the powerful young mutant Carter Ghazikhanian. Kuan-Yin eventually revealed himself to be a duplicate of the X-Men's nemesis Magneto, a transformation believed to have been caused by Magneto's daughter, the Scarlet Witch. Recruiting the Special Class as his Brotherhood, he launched a devastating attack on Manhattan which was opposed by the X-Men, during which he killed Jean Grey and was himself slain by Wolverine.

Later, the X-Men were called to China after Shen's powers had once again flared out of control. Opposed by the Eight Immortals, the Chinese Army, and the Collective Man, the X-Men prevailed and took Shen back to the Institute. There Shen joined the X-Men in opposing an attack by the Brotherhood of Mutants. To stop the killing, Shen saw no alternative but to release his black hole, pulling the villains into the void. He then left the X-Men to reflect on the immensity of his actions.

HEIGHT: (both) 6'2"
WEIGHT: (both) 240 lbs.
EYES: (both) None
HAIR: (both) None

SUPERHUMAN POWERS: The Xorns' possess miniature stars in their heads, each having a primary state. Kuan-Yin's star manifested as a sun, while Shen's star manifests as a black hole. Kuan-Yin's sun was capable of emitting blinding light that could instantly incinerate another being, and Shen's black hole emits an intense gravitic field that not even light can escape. The Xorns are capable of reversing their stars' natural states. That is, Kuan-Yin could cause his star to collapse in to a black hole, while Shen is able to cause his star to flare into a sun. The Xorns can also feel the movement of energy and emotion on many levels. They possess gravitational senses that allow them to manipulate energy for a variety of purposes, including warping of gravitic fields, sensing when a death has occurred in their vicinity, shaking gravitational particles in the air around them to allow them to comprehend and speak other languages, and to heal others. The Xorns do not need to breathe, nor do they require food or water to survive.

PARAPHERNALIA: The remains of the Xorns' heads are encased in metal helmets that safeguard others from the effects of their stars.

POWER GRID	1	2	3	4	5	6	7
INTELLIGENCE							
STRENGTH							
SPEED							
DURABILITY							
ENERGY PROJECTION							
FIGHTING SKILLS							

PROFESSOR X
(Charles Xavier)
Founder in X-Men #42 (1967); not currently a member

NIGHTCRAWLER
(Kurt Wagner)
Joined in Giant-Size X-Men #1 (1975); current team leader

CYCLOPS
(Scott Summers)
Joined in X-Men #42 (1967); current co-headmaster & team leader

WOLVERINE
(James Howlett)
Joined in Giant-Size X-Men #1 (1975); current member of Cyclops' team

ICEMAN
(Robert 'Bobby' Drake)
Joined in X-Men #46 (1968); current member of Havok's team

BANSHEE
(Sean Cassidy)
Joined in Giant-Size X-Men #1 (1975); not currently a member

BEAST
(Henry 'Hank' McCoy)
Joined in X-Men #53 (1969); current member of Cyclops' team

STORM
(Ororo Munroe)
Joined in Giant-Size X-Men #1 (1975); not currently a member

ARCHANGEL
(Warren Worthington III)
Joined as Angel in X-Men #56 (1969); active as Archangel in X-Men #1 (1991); not currently a member

SUNFIRE
(Shiro Yoshida)
Joined in Giant-Size X-Men #1 (1975); not currently a member

JEAN GREY
(Jean Grey-Summers)
Joined as Marvel Girl in X-Men #1 (1963); active as Jean Grey in X-Men #1 (1991); active as Phoenix in Uncanny X-Men #318 (1994); not currently a member

COLOSSUS
(Piotr Rasputin)
Joined in Giant-Size X-Men #1 (1975); current member of Cyclops' team

MIMIC
(Calvin Rankin)
Joined in X-Men #27 (1966); not currently a member

THUNDERBIRD
(James Proudstar)
Joined in Giant-Size X-Men #1 (1975); died in X-Men #95 (1975)

CHANGELING
(Kevin Sidney)
Active as Professor X in X-Men #40 (1968); died in X-Men #42 (1968)

PHOENIX FORCE
(Inapplicable)
Active as Phoenix in X-Men #101 (1976); physical form destroyed in X-Men #137 (1980)

POLARIS
(Lorna Dane)
Joined as Lorna Dane in X-Men #60 (1969); active as Magnetrix in X-Men: The Hidden Years #3 (2000); active as Polaris in Uncanny X-Men #428 (2004); current member of Havok's team

SHADOWCAT
(Katherine 'Kitty' Pryde)
Joined as Kitty in X-Men #138 (1980); active as Sprite in X-Men #139 (1980); active as Ariel in Marvel Graphic Novel #5 (1982); active as Shadowcat in Kitty Pryde & Wolverine #5 (1985); current member of Cyclops' team

HAVOK
(Alexander Summers)
Joined in X-Men #65 (1970); current team leader

LOCKHEED
Joined in Uncanny X-Men #168 (1983); current member of Cyclops' team

ROGUE
(Anna Marie, last name unrevealed)
Joined in Uncanny X-Men #171 (1983); current member of Havok's team

REVANCHE
(Kwannon)
Joined in X-Men #21 (1993); died in X-Men #31 (1994)

RACHEL SUMMERS
(Rachel Grey)
Joined as Rachel in Uncanny X-Men #188 (1984); active as Phoenix in Uncanny X-Men Annual #9 (1985); active as Marvel Girl in Uncanny X-Men #444 (2004); current member of Nightcrawler's team

CANNONBALL
(Samuel Guthrie)
Joined in X-Force #44 (1995); current member of Nightcrawler's team

MAGNETO
(Unrevealed)
Headmaster of Xavier Institute in Uncanny X-Men #200 (1985); active in Uncanny X-Men #202 (1986); not currently a member

DARK BEAST
(Henry 'Hank' McCoy of Earth-295)
Active as Beast in X-Men Unlimited #10 (1996); not currently a member

PSYLOCKE
(Elizabeth 'Betsy' Braddock)
Joined in Uncanny X-Men #213 (1987); current member of Nightcrawler's team

JOSEPH
Joined in Uncanny X-Men #338 (1996); died in X-Men #87 (1999)

DAZZLER
(Alison Blaire)
Joined in Uncanny X-Men #214 (1987); not currently a member

CECILIA REYES
Joined in X-Men #70 (1997); not currently a member

LONGSHOT
Joined in Uncanny X-Men #215 (1987); not currently a member

MARROW
(Sarah)
Joined in X-Men #70 (1997); not currently a member

FORGE
Joined in Uncanny X-Men #255 (1989); not currently a member

MAGGOTT
(Japheth)
Joined in X-Men #70 (1997); died in Weapon X #5 (2002)

GAMBIT
(Remy LeBeau)
Joined in Uncanny X-Men Annual #14 (1990); current member of Havok's team

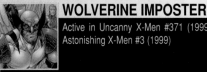
WOLVERINE IMPOSTER
Active in Uncanny X-Men #371 (1999); died in Astonishing X-Men #3 (1999)

JUBILEE
(Jubilation Lee)
Joined in Uncanny X-Men #273 (1991); not currently a member

THUNDERBIRD
(Neal Shaara)
Joined in X-Men Unlimited #27 (2000); not currently a member

BISHOP
(Lucas Bishop)
Joined in Uncanny X-Men #287 (1992); current member of Nightcrawler's team

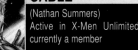
CABLE
(Nathan Summers)
Active in X-Men Unlimited #27 (2000); not currently a member

MIRAGE
(Danielle Moonstar)
Active as Moonstar in X-Men #102 (2000); current faculty member

SAGE
(Tessa)
Active as Tessa in X-Men #102 (2000); active as Sage in X-Men #109 (2001); not currently a member

EMMA FROST
Joined in New X-Men #116 (2001); current co-headmaster & member of Cyclops' team

XORN
(Kuan-Yin Xorn)
Joined in New X-Men 2001 Annual (2001); died in New X-Men #150 (2003)

CHAMBER
(Jonothon Starsmore)
Joined in Uncanny X-Men #398 (2001); not currently a member

STACY X
(Miranda Leevald)
Joined in Uncanny X-Men #400 (2001); not currently a member

LIFEGUARD
(Heather Cameron)
Active in X-Treme X-Men #10 (2002); not currently a member

SLIPSTREAM
(Davis Cameron)
Active in X-Treme X-Men #10 (2002); not currently a member

NORTHSTAR
(Jean-Paul Beaubier)
Joined in Uncanny X-Men #414 (2002); not currently a member

HUSK
(Paige Guthrie)
Active in Uncanny X-Men #421 (2003); not currently a member

JUGGERNAUT
(Cain Marko)
Joined in Uncanny X-Men #425 (2003); not currently a member

XORN
(Shen Xorn)
Joined in X-Men #162 (2004); not currently a member

AD-HOC X-MEN ROSTERS

NEW MUTANT GRADUATE X-MEN
(Cannonball, Moonstar, Karma, Sunspot, Cypher, Warlock, Magma, Magik/Illyana Rasputin, Wolfsbane) Formed in Uncanny X-Men Annual #10 (1986)

MUIR ISLAND X-MEN/MUIR ISLANDERS
(Banshee, Forge, Moira MacTaggart, Amanda Sefton, Sunder, Legion/David Haller, Sharon Friedlander, Tom Corsi, Alysande Stuart, Polaris, Multiple Man, Siryn) Formed in Uncanny X-Men #254 (1989) until X-Factor Annual #6 (1991)

PHALANX COVENANT X-MEN
(Banshee, Jubilee, Sabretooth, Emma Frost) Formed in Uncanny X-Men #316 (1994) until X-Men #37 (1994)

ASTONISHING X-MEN
(Cyclops, Phoenix/Jean Grey-Summers, Archangel, Cable, X-Man/Nate Grey, Wolverine Imposter) Formed in Astonishing X-Men #1 (1999) until Astonishing X-Men #3 (1999)

GENOSHAN ASSAULT X-MEN
(Phoenix/Jean Grey-Summers, Northstar, Omerta/ Paulie Provenzano, Wraith/Hector Rendoza, Sunpyre/ Leyu Yoshida, Frenzy/Joanna Cargill, Dazzler) Formed in Uncanny X-Men #392 (2001) until X-Men #113 (2001)

STREET TEAM X-MEN
(Cyclops, Fantomex, E.V.A., Stepford Cuckoos, Beak, Dust, Longneck, Forearm, Irina, other unnamed Xavier's students) Formed in New X-Men #149 (2004) until New X-Men #150 (2004)

XAVIER INSTITUTE FACULTY
(Mirage/Danielle Moonstar, Karma/Xi'an Coy Manh, Wolfsbane/Rahne Sinclair, Magma/Amara Aquilla) Joined in New Mutants #2, New Mutants #4 (2003), New Mutants #11 (2004) & New X-Men: Academy X #15 (2005)

DUST

REAL NAME: Sooraya Qadir
KNOWN ALIASES: Turaab (Dust in Arabic)
IDENTITY: Secret
OCCUPATION: Student
CITIZENSHIP: Afghanistan, legal immigrant to the U.S.A.
PLACE OF BIRTH: Western Afghanistan
MARITAL STATUS: Single
KNOWN RELATIVES: Mirah Qadir (mother), unnamed father
GROUP AFFILIATION: Xavier Institute/Hellions Training Squad, formerly X-Men
EDUCATION: Currently in high school level classes
FIRST APPEARANCE: New X-Men #133 (2002)

HISTORY: Sooraya Qadir does not know her father. She was raised by her mother Mirah, who was not looked upon favorably by the men of the Taliban in Afghanistan. Under circumstances yet to be revealed, Sooraya was taken from her mother and sold into slavery. She was rescued by Wolverine of the X-Men, and revealed her mutant abilities by flaying the flesh off the bones of her captors. Unable to locate her mother, Sooraya came to Xavier's Institute. She was placed in the Special Class as she was new to America, spoke little English and rarely spoke at all. She continued to wear her traditional burqa, seen by many as a sign of the oppression of women under the Taliban, and few at the school understood her.

When the student body broke into training squads, Sooraya was placed on the Hellions squad. The rebellious Hellions do not fit with Sooraya's respect for traditions and strong moral code, but she has done her best to fit in nonetheless, and has found that the squad takes care of its own and looks out for her. Still, she has not been bound by the squad's rivalries and has befriended Icarus of the rival New Mutant squad, and has formed a grudging bond with her roommate Surge, who initially condemned Sooraya for wearing her burqa.

The Hellions were recently granted one wish as an enticement by a power broker calling himself the Kingmaker. Sooraya opposed this offer, seeing it as a deal with the devil, but went along with her teammates' wishes. When it came time for her wish, Sooraya asked to be able to find her mother. The Kingmaker delivered, and Sooraya was reunited with Mirah Qadir. The Kingmaker even started the emigration process so that Mirah could come to the U.S. But the Hellions discovered the price of their wishes: the Kingmaker required they commit crimes. Sooraya was one of the first to oppose him, despite the personal cost. The Kingmaker was defeated, but Sooraya was unable to track down her mother again and now lives with the cost of having done the right thing.

HEIGHT: 5'6"
WEIGHT: 136 lbs.
EYES: Brown
HAIR: Dark Brown

SUPERHUMAN POWERS: Dust can turn her body into a living sandstorm, blinding enemies, or attacking them with slashing dust which can get so severe as to flay the flesh off her enemies. Sooraya wears a traditional burqa and thus does not wear a costume made of unstable molecules. When she goes into dust form, she flows out of her costume and must flow back into it before retaking human form.

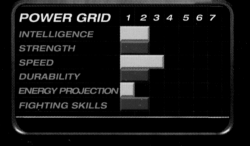

POWER GRID	1	2	3	4	5	6	7
INTELLIGENCE							
STRENGTH							
SPEED							
DURABILITY							
ENERGY PROJECTION							
FIGHTING SKILLS							

HISTORY: Josh was always a golden boy — good at sports, admired by his friends and attractive to girls. The popular one who would pick on the outcasts, he also once belonged to a mutant-hating group, The Reavers. During his first meeting, Donald Pierce was demonstrating his blade arm and sliced Josh across the hand. The injury immediately healed itself and Josh dismissed the incident. He joined the Reavers in an attack on several Xavier's students. During that attack, his friend was injured and Josh discovered he had the ability to heal. Josh tried to hide this secret, but when Pierce attacked Wallflower, he decided to do the right thing and heal her. Still, he was reluctant to accept Dani Moonstar's offer to come to Xavier's until his family and friends rejected him for being a mutant.

At Xavier's, Josh became Prodigy's roommate. The two had a rocky start to their friendship as Josh felt Prodigy was always judging him for his past deeds. His parents soon signed over custody to the school and Danielle Moonstar became Josh's legal guardian. But Josh felt like an outcast and sought refuge in a friendship with an ex-teammate of Dani's, Wolfsbane. Wolfsbane was also going through a rough phase in her life as she had lost her foster mother and her wolf abilities. She and Josh spent an evening talking together which ended in a kiss. The kiss was intense and during it, Josh inadvertently "healed" Wolfsbane and gave her the wolf back. The wolf, back with a vengeance, gutted Josh for his efforts. It was uncertain if he would survive the attack until Prodigy suggested Surge use her electricity to wake Josh up just long enough for him to heal himself. The plan worked, but in the healing process, Josh turned himself gold, becoming the literal "golden boy" he'd always wanted to be.

Josh and Rahne had a secret relationship for a while, but Wolfsbane called it off when she realized Josh was attracted to his teammate, Wallflower. Josh and Wallflower became involved and were happy together until fellow student Wither exposed his previous relationship with Wolfsbane. Wallflower immediately dumped Josh, using her pheromones to scare him. Josh has been spending a lot of time alone, most of his training squad angry with him for his treatment of Wallflower. Of his teammates, only Surge seemed not to hold it against him.

REAL NAME: Joshua "Josh" Foley
KNOWN ALIASES: None
IDENTITY: Secret
OCCUPATION: Student
CITIZENSHIP: U.S.A.
PLACE OF BIRTH: Flushing, Queens, New York
MARITAL STATUS: Single
KNOWN RELATIVES: Howard Foley (father), Grace Foley (mother), two unnamed older brothers, Danielle Moonstar (legal guardian)
GROUP AFFILIATION: Xavier Institute/New Mutants Training Squad, formerly Reavers
EDUCATION: Currently in high school level classes
FIRST APPEARANCE: New Mutants #5 (2003)

HEIGHT: 5'9"
WEIGHT: 157 lbs.
EYES: Blue
HAIR: Blond

SUPERHUMAN POWERS: Elixir is an omega level healer. He has the ability to alter the body at a genetic level. For now, he has only mastered the ability to heal with a touch. However, his potential is so great that there may be no limits to what his powers might be able to accomplish one day.

POWER GRID   1 2 3 4 5 6 7
INTELLIGENCE
STRENGTH
SPEED
DURABILITY
ENERGY PROJECTION
FIGHTING SKILLS

Art by Randy Green

HELLION

REAL NAME: Julian Keller
KNOWN ALIASES: None
IDENTITY: Public
OCCUPATION: Student, one-time adventurer
CITIZENSHIP: U.S.A.
PLACE OF BIRTH: Beverly Hills, California
MARITAL STATUS: Single
KNOWN RELATIVES: William (father), Elizabeth (mother), James (brother)
GROUP AFFILIATION: Xavier Institute/Hellions Training Squad
EDUCATION: Currently in high school level classes
FIRST APPEARANCE: New Mutants #2 (2003)

HISTORY: Born to a wealthy family in Beverly Hills, Julian has always been the black sheep in his family, the one who made trouble to try to impress his parents or to just get their attention. When his mutant abilities surfaced, his parents did not reject him, but advised that he keep them hidden. When he insisted on using them in public, they shipped him off to Xavier's.

At the Xavier's Institute, Julian caught the eye of Emma Frost, the reformed villain who served on the X-Men and the school's faculty. His troublemaking ways were offset by his immense personal charisma, and his ability to get his classmates to listen to him and occasionally follow his lead. She saw in Julian real potential and became his advisor. He requested the code name Hellion to honor her former group of students, the tragically murdered Hellions. When the school reorganized and made Frost co-headmaster, the student body was broken into training squads. Emma's students formed a squad called the Hellions, but she allowed Julian to keep the name Hellion, marking him for leadership and hoping the privilege would lead to him realizing his potential as a leader.

The first year of squad-based school life was an odd one for Hellion, as he and his squad won top prizes at the school, but managed to rub much of the rest of the student body the wrong way with their arrogance and troublemaking ways, both of which seemed molded after Julian's own personality. But as a unit, they were incredibly close, even going so far as to take on the FBI to protect a friend. Julian particularly goaded his squad into conflict with the New Mutants squad, and the two groups clashed several times, despite a growing attraction between Hellion and Wind Dancer, one of the co-leaders of the New Mutants.

Julian took his squad mates to California on a break, and ran afoul of airport police on the way. This incident caused Julian to be disinherited from the family fortune. Digging into his parents' history, he found their wealth to be the result of a deal with someone called the Kingmaker. The Kingmaker offered the Hellions fortune and glory, and Julian briefly became a super hero in his hometown. But the deal had its fine print, and the Kingmaker required villainous favors from the Hellions. They tricked him into releasing them from the deal, and then defeated him in combat. Julian may not have earned his family's respect on that trip, but he cemented the bond with his squad, and earned the respect of Emma Frost.

HEIGHT: 5'10"
WEIGHT: 170 lbs.
EYES: Blue
HAIR: Black

SUPERHUMAN POWERS: Hellion is a highly skilled telekinetic able to move solid matter with a thought. He can use this to various effects, and has been taught to fire telekinetic blasts of concussive force, fly, create telekinetic platforms to transport others, and create telekinetic shields.

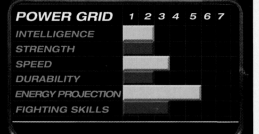

POWER GRID	1	2	3	4	5	6	7
INTELLIGENCE							
STRENGTH							
SPEED							
DURABILITY							
ENERGY PROJECTION							
FIGHTING SKILLS							

Art by Clayton Henry

ICARUS

HISTORY: Joshua Guthrie is the third of ten siblings in the large Guthrie family, which has seen more than its share of mutations. His older brother and sister have both been X-Men at various points in their young lives. For a long while, Joshua seemed as if he had no mutant ability, and his gifts were only musical in nature. As Joshua's father was dead, he also had to try to help raise the family in his older siblings' absence.

The Guthries were outcasts in Cumberland, in part due to the high number of mutants in the family, but the real bad blood was with the Cabots, another local family. The feud between the two had gotten lethal, as the Cabots were involved in Joshua's father's death. But Joshua had fallen in love with Julia Cabot and revealed to her the fact that he was a mutant, with wings and a mutant singing voice. This relationship took an already explosive rivalry and drove it to its logical conclusion. The X-Men stopped the war between the clans, but not before Joshua was seemingly killed by Julia's father, Chester. Longing to be with her love, Julia killed herself, unaware that Joshua had one more gift — a regenerative ability to recover from any wound. Joshua found his love dead and tried to kill himself. But his ability would not allow it.

Now known as a mutant, Joshua was sent to the Xavier Institute by his mother. To declare a new life for himself, he abandoned the name Joshua, which was what Julia called him, and took on Jay as his first name, going so far as to have it legally changed. But he didn't put the past behind him — he took on the codename Icarus to symbolize how far he had fallen. He was briefly a member of the Hellions training squad, but switched to the New Mutants after clashes with Hellion over ethics.

REAL NAME: Joshua "Jay" Guthrie
KNOWN ALIASES: Has chosen the nickname "Jay" to replace his given name, Joshua
IDENTITY: Secret
OCCUPATION: Student
CITIZENSHIP: U.S.A.
PLACE OF BIRTH: Cumberland, Kentucky
MARITAL STATUS: Single
KNOWN RELATIVES: Thomas Zebulon Guthrie (father, deceased), Lucinda Guthrie (mother), Sam Guthrie (Cannonball, brother), Paige Guthrie (Husk, sister), Joelle Guthrie (sister), Elizabeth Guthrie (sister), Melody Guthrie (sister), Jebediah Guthrie (brother), Lewis Guthrie (brother), two unnamed siblings, Lucas Bartholomew Guthrie (uncle), Ray Jr. (last name unknown, adopted brother)
GROUP AFFILIATION: Xavier Institute/New Mutants Training Squad
EDUCATION: Currently in high school level classes
FIRST APPEARANCE: Rom Annual #3 (1984)

HEIGHT: 5'9"
WEIGHT: 193 lbs. (including wings)
EYES: Green
HAIR: Red

SUPERHUMAN POWERS: Icarus has bright red wings and can fly; he has a mutant voice that allows a variety of sonic effects, most often singing as a one-man chorus; and he has a healing factor that allows him to regenerate from most wounds, even those seemingly lethal.

ABILITIES: Icarus is a skilled guitar player and a talented singer.

POWER GRID	1	2	3	4	5	6	7
INTELLIGENCE							
STRENGTH							
SPEED							
DURABILITY							
ENERGY PROJECTION							
FIGHTING SKILLS							

KARMA

REAL NAME: Xi'an "Shan" Coy Manh
KNOWN ALIASES: None
IDENTITY: Secret
OCCUPATION: Teacher, Librarian
CITIZENSHIP: U.S.A.
PLACE OF BIRTH: Central highlands of Vietnam
MARITAL STATUS: Single
KNOWN RELATIVES: Unnamed parents (deceased), Nguyen Coy (uncle, deceased), Tran Coy Manh (brother, deceased), Leong Coy Manh (brother), Nga Coy Manh (sister)
GROUP AFFILIATION: Xavier Institute/Faculty Member, Advisor to Alpha Squadron Training Squad, formerly New Mutants, Hellions
EDUCATION: College Graduate
FIRST APPEARANCE: Marvel Team-Up #100 (1980)

HISTORY: The daughter of a former Vietnamese Army Colonel, Xi'an has always been fiercely devoted to family. When an enemy soldier threatened her brother Tran, Xi'an tapped into her mutant ability and took possession of the soldier's mind. Tran then matched this feat, and forced the soldier to kill himself. Tran took delight in his new powers, but Xi'an was frightened of hers. Tran told their uncle, Nguyen Coy, who had become a criminal in the United States. Nguyen brought the family to New York, bringing Tran first and the others by crowded boat. Xi'an's parents did not survive the trip. When Xi'an got to New York, she found her brother doing their uncle's criminal bidding. When Xi'an refused to do the same, her uncle kidnapped her younger siblings, Leong and Nga, to blackmail her. She sought out the help of the Fantastic Four and Spider-Man, and when Tran possessed them, she was forced to kill him to save the heroes and her other siblings.

The Fantastic Four brought Xi'an to Xavier's Institute for help. There Xi'an joined his newest students as The New Mutants. She left the team when Leong and Nga disappeared. She rescued the children but discovered they had been used in genetic experiments. It took some doing, but Xi'an found a way to undo these experiments. She then took her siblings with her as she attended college to live a normal life, one which brought her back into contact with fellow Xavier's alum, Kitty Pryde. Xi'an had discovered much about herself in the time since seeing Kitty, including her own sexual preference. Xi'an was attracted to Kitty, but the feeling was ultimately not reciprocated.

When Xi'an graduated college, she was surprised to find former New Mutants teammate Danielle Moonstar (aka Mirage) waiting for her. The two friends reunited, and Xi'an helped Mirage track down a mutant and recruit him to the school. She brought the kids back to Xavier's and took a job as the school librarian. When the school reorganized into training squads, Xi'an became advisor to the kids too young for squads, which included her young siblings, who had not yet developed mutations. But the death of the hero Northstar left his squad without an advisor, and Xi'an has stepped in to help.

HEIGHT: 5'4"
WEIGHT: 119 lbs.
EYES: Brown
HAIR: Black

SUPERHUMAN POWERS: Karma has the psionic ability to take possession of others' minds. She can possess multiple minds at once, though her control is a bit fragmented when she does so. When possessing other minds, her own body stands still and is vulnerable. She has also been developing other telepathic abilities.

ABILITIES: Karma is fluent in Vietnamese, French, and English, and has studied a little Spanish, Japanese and Mandarin Chinese.

POWER GRID	1 2 3 4 5 6 7
INTELLIGENCE	
STRENGTH	
SPEED	
DURABILITY	
ENERGY PROJECTION	
FIGHTING SKILLS	

MAGMA

HISTORY: Magma grew up as Amara Aquilla, daughter of the First Senator of Nova Roma, a hidden city in the Rainforests of Brazil. The citizens of Nova Roma claimed a heritage directly descended from Ancient Rome. To save his daughter from being a potential human sacrifice to the Black Priestess Selene, Amara's father sent her to live in the jungles outside Nova Roma. She remained in hiding for years until discovered by the New Mutants. Both Amara and the New Mutants were soon captured by Selene, and Amara was readied for sacrifice. Selene used her powers to drain Amara's life force, but a distraction caused her to knock Amara into a nearby pit of lava. This awakened Amara's latent mutant powers, and she defeated Selene. Amara's father sent her to the United States with the New Mutants to learn more about modern civilization.

Amara learned to adjust to the outside world and was a valuable member of the New Mutants. Amara traveled back to Nova Roma to visit, but it was then that Amara's life was shattered, and she was told that life in Nova Roma was a lie. She learned that Nova Roma was not an ancient civilization, but a place populated by kidnapped and mind-wiped victims of Selene, who created the city. Amara was told her real name was Alison Crestmere, the mutant daughter of a British Ambassador. Amara left Nova Roma to find her real family, finally armed with her real life history. Or was it her real history?

After leaving Nova Roma, Magma ran into trouble on several occasions and was eventually captured by the Church of Humanity, then crucified on the lawn of the Xavier Institute along with several other mutants. Magma survived the attack, but the day after she awakened, she lapsed into a coma. She remained in the coma until two students at the school, Hellion and Elixir, snuck into the infirmary. Elixir healed Magma, and she woke with explosive fury, then fled the school. When she caught up with New Mutants teammate Cannonball, she was once again calling herself Amara. She claimed to "know" that the life she had been told was false was, in fact, true. She has not explained these claims, but for now, Amara has spent some time as a member of the X.S.E. before returning to Xavier's to teach.

REAL NAME: Amara Juliana Olivians Aquilla
KNOWN ALIASES: Alison Crestmere
IDENTITY: Secret
OCCUPATION: Teacher
CITIZENSHIP: Legal Resident of the U.S.A.
PLACE OF BIRTH: Nova Roma (disputed)
MARITAL STATUS: Single
KNOWN RELATIVES: Lucius Antonius Aquilla (father in Nova Roma), unnamed mother (deceased), unnamed ambassador ("father" in England)
GROUP AFFILIATION: Xavier Institute/Faculty Member, Advisor to the Paragons Training Squad, formerly X.S.E., New Hellions, Hellions, Gladiators, New Mutants
EDUCATION: High school equivalency, numerous college-level courses
FIRST APPEARANCE: New Mutants #8 (1983)

HEIGHT: 5'6"
WEIGHT: 131 lbs.
EYES: Blue
HAIR: Blonde

SUPERHUMAN POWERS: Magma has the ability to take on a fiery form in which she radiates heat and light. In this form, she can generate flames, cause seismic upheaval, and call molten rock to the earth's surface, generating lava or causing small volcanic eruptions. She can also send magma blasts at an opponent, projecting molten rocks through the air.

ABILITIES: Magma has received extensive training in hand-to-hand combat and swordsmanship, and possesses extensive knowledge of ancient Roman culture.

POWER GRID	1	2	3	4	5	6	7
INTELLIGENCE							
STRENGTH							
SPEED							
DURABILITY							
ENERGY PROJECTION							
FIGHTING SKILLS							

Art by Chris Bachalo

MERCURY

REAL NAME: Cessily Kincaid
KNOWN ALIASES: None
IDENTITY: Secret
OCCUPATION: Student
CITIZENSHIP: U.S.A.
PLACE OF BIRTH: Portland, Oregon
MARITAL STATUS: Single
KNOWN RELATIVES: Mark Kincaid (father), Jill Kincaid (mother)
GROUP AFFILIATION: Xavier Institute/Hellions Training Squad
EDUCATION: Currently in high school level classes
FIRST APPEARANCE: New Mutants #2 (2003)

HISTORY: Cessily lived a completely normal life and was a beloved only child, until her mutation developed. Her body changed to a metallic, mercury-like substance. Her parents did not know how to deal with this change. While they did not reject Cessily outright, they shipped her off to Xavier's, hoping the neighbors would never know about their mutant daughter. Whenever holidays came around, Cessily was asked to stay at school, and when she did go home, her parents never went out with her in public.

At Xavier's, Cessily was paired with Wallflower, a shy girl with uncontrolled pheromone powers. Cessily was immune to Wallflower's pheromones, but Wallflower ignored her roommate entirely, never speaking to her. Cessily eventually made her first friend at Xavier's in resident bad boy Hellion, who has been like an older brother to her ever since. Where Cessily always tries to change to please others, Hellion has tried to teach her to stand up for herself. When Cessily met Wither, an outcast at the school due to his death touch, she discovered she was immune to his powers as well. This forged a connection between them. Cessily is attracted to Wither, but his heart belongs to Wallflower. Still, Cessily stood up for Wither and got Hellion to welcome Wither into their Hellions clique and training squad.

Recently, the Hellions met with a powerbroker called the Kingmaker. When granted one wish by Kingmaker, Cessily asked to have her parents accept her. She journeyed to Portland and found her parents as open and loving as before she got her powers. When the Hellions realized Kingmaker's gifts came with a price, they tricked him and backed out of the deal. It was only then that Cessily realized her parents' love had been forced — they had been mind-controlled. Free of Kingmaker's influence, the Kincaids blamed Cessily and disowned her. The school is currently determining how to proceed with Cessily's family situation, but she has returned to Xavier's.

HEIGHT: 5'4"
WEIGHT: 114 lbs.
EYES: Silver with no pupils
HAIR: Red

SUPERHUMAN POWERS: Cessily's body is composed of a non-toxic form of Mercury. She is no longer a carbon-based life form and does not eat or breathe in the same ways as normal humans. Still, she consumes food out of habit and has not realized the scope of her change. Cessily's form is completely malleable, and she can change shape at will. Among many other abilities this grants her, Cessily can form a puddle to get under doors, can stretch and bend her body, and can turn parts of her body into weapons.

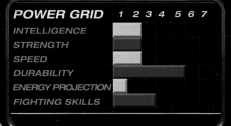

POWER GRID	1	2	3	4	5	6	7
INTELLIGENCE							
STRENGTH							
SPEED							
DURABILITY							
ENERGY PROJECTION							
FIGHTING SKILLS							

HISTORY: Dani Moonstar's mutant powers shattered her happy childhood as she began having uncontrollable nightmares, including one of the death of her parents. Shortly after the dream, Dani's parents disappeared and she believed them dead, haunted by dreams of a demon bear she thought was responsible. Her grandfather contacted Professor Xavier about Moonstar's powers, but when Donald Pierce murdered Dani's grandfather, Dani came to live at Xavier's school. Soon afterward, the school was attacked by the Demon Bear, and with the help of her New Mutants teammates, Dani discovered that her parents had transformed into the bear, and she was able to free them.

When the New Mutants were kidnapped and brought to Asgard (home of the Norse Gods), Dani was selected by a winged horse named Brightwind which then made her a Valkyrie, a legendary Chooser of the Slain. She returned home with Brightwind and her new abilities. Over time, her abilities began to change and grow, and life went on. She worked on several X-teams, served as a S.H.I.E.L.D. agent, and worked undercover in the Mutant Liberation Front. A battle with the reality-warper Arcadia broke Dani into various parts of herself and various powers. When she was put back together, she had regressed to her more limited powers. Since that event, Dani's powers have fluctuated, but seem to be on the wane, a situation that frustrates her.

Dani recently left the life of the various X-teams and attempted college. But she did not last long, as she got distracted by a young mutant who was arrested in Boulder. Dani got the girl, Wind Dancer, out of legal trouble and brought her back to Xavier's. Once there, Dani was offered a job by Xavier to recruit new students. She forged a bond with a group of students, and even became legal guardian to one, Elixir. When the school reorganized, Dani stayed and became advisor to a squad of students, Wind Dancer and Elixir among them, who carry the name of the team she holds dearest — the New Mutants. Showing how much her time at the school has calmed the once angry young teen, Dani has also started a relationship with a human federal agent named Justin Pierce, the heroic nephew of the villain who killed Dani's grandfather.

REAL NAME: Danielle "Dani" Moonstar
KNOWN ALIASES: Moonstar, Spellbinder, Psyche
IDENTITY: Known to U.S. Government
OCCUPATION: Teacher
CITIZENSHIP: U.S.A.
PLACE OF BIRTH: Boulder, Colorado
MARITAL STATUS: Single
KNOWN RELATIVES: Black Eagle (grandfather, deceased), William Lonestar (father), Margaret "Peg" Lonestar (mother), Joshua Foley (Elixir, legal ward)
GROUP AFFILIATION: Xavier Institute/Faculty Member, Advisor to New Mutants Training Squad, formerly X-Men, X-Force, S.H.I.E.L.D., Mutant Liberation Front, Valkyrie, New Mutants
EDUCATION: High school degree, some college courses
FIRST APPEARANCE: Marvel Graphic Novel #4 (1982)

HEIGHT: 5'6"
WEIGHT: 148 lbs.
EYES: Brown
HAIR: Black

SUPERHUMAN POWERS: Mirage has the ability to create illusions, most frequently using manifestations of the target's worst fears or greatest desires. She also can form telepathic bonds with animals. In the past she has been able to generate psionic arrows and make her illusions into solid matter. Both these abilities have faded. Mirage was also selected as a Valkyrie in the realm of Asgard. She thought the abilities this granted her faded when her winged steed perished, but has recently discovered she retains the ability to sense death.

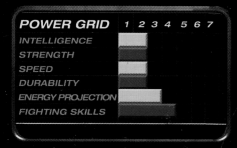

POWER GRID	1	2	3	4	5	6	7
INTELLIGENCE							
STRENGTH							
SPEED							
DURABILITY							
ENERGY PROJECTION							
FIGHTING SKILLS							

Art by Randy Green

PRODIGY

REAL NAME: David Alleyne
KNOWN ALIASES: None
IDENTITY: Secret
OCCUPATION: Student
CITIZENSHIP: U.S.A.
PLACE OF BIRTH: Chicago, Illinois
MARITAL STATUS: Single
KNOWN RELATIVES: Christopher (father), Dorothy (mother), Kim (sister)
GROUP AFFILIATION: Xavier Institute/New Mutants Training Squad
EDUCATION: Currently in high school, has taken college level classes
FIRST APPEARANCE: New Mutants #4 (2003)

HISTORY: David Alleyne has always been the smart one, but when he was a teenager, the answers just started appearing in his head — so long as he was in the same room as the teacher. He started to figure out that he was a mutant, and that he now had the ability to know anything that the people nearby knew. Feeling this made him a cheater, and knowing the knowledge would fade, David was driven to study even harder. He took college-level courses while finishing high school. But he kept his mutation a secret, until the hate group Purity outed him to his parents and attempted to attack him. David was rescued by the librarian at his school, the former New Mutant Karma, and her former teammate Danielle Moonstar. The two offered David a place at Xavier's.

David went to the school in order to learn at a place that would understand his unique learning situation, not so he could become an X-Man. He wants only to lead a normal life. He resented the formation of training squads, and only reluctantly agreed to share leadership duties of his squad when he realized that there were valuable things to be learned from training as junior X-Men. He also became close friends with his roommate, Elixir, overcoming an initial dislike based on Elixir's headstrong ways and his past as a member of an anti-mutant hate group.

David has recently attempted to become more useful by removing the mental block that keeps him from retaining the knowledge he absorbs after the target leaves the vicinity. With a combination of Moonstar and Emma Frost's powers, David was shown a vision of what it was his mind feared, and why it constructed the block. He saw himself becoming the smartest man on the planet, but with stolen intelligence and no sense of the cost of his actions. In his vision, he took over the world and had to be stopped by his friends, at the cost of all their lives. This vision also made him aware of a crush on Moonstar and a deeper romantic connection with teammate Surge. David opted to keep the mental block in place.

HEIGHT: 6'1"
WEIGHT: 187 lbs.
EYES: Brown
HAIR: Black

SUPERHUMAN POWERS: Prodigy has a subconscious form of telepathy which allows him to absorb the skills and knowledge of anyone around him. However, he is unable to retain that knowledge. When the person leaves the room, Prodigy no longer retains the information. This power is always on. In addition, Prodigy is always reading the attacks directed at him, and so long as he is not distracted, can see a direct attack coming and therefore has a much easier time dodging it. When focused, he can be almost untouchable by anyone without heightened speed.

POWER GRID	1	2	3	4	5	6	7
INTELLIGENCE							
STRENGTH							
SPEED							
DURABILITY							
ENERGY PROJECTION							
FIGHTING SKILLS							

Art by Randy Green

HISTORY: Bigger and stronger than other kids, Santo has always been something of a bully. He learned from his parents that the way to get respect was to remind everyone how strong you were. He was on several athletic teams at a young age, and his parents thought he could be a professional in any of numerous sports. When his mutation developed, he became even bigger and stronger and his body turned into a pile of rocks he could detach at will. His parents had no problem with his new rock-covered body, but suddenly the strength everyone respected was considered something bad, not good. He couldn't be on the wrestling team or the football team anymore, and the students who once looked at him as the strongest kid in school now looked at him as a freak.

Santo came to the Xavier Institute and became friends with his roommate Julian Keller. Julian was the school's resident troublemaker, and Santo took up a position as his strong right arm. Both boys joined Emma Frost's Hellions when the student body was broken into training squads. Always looking for a way to prove his strength, Santo stuck to Julian's side, knowing the trouble Julian made could lead him to a good brawl. He's had numerous run-ins with the New Mutants, a rival squad at the school, and in particular, tried to get into a good scrape with Prodigy, the leader of that squad. Prodigy's powers allowed him to see any move Santo made ahead of time, making him impossible to hit. Being able to land the one shot it would take to put Prodigy down became a long-term goal for Santo.

On a recent trip to California, the Hellions were offered their hearts' desires. Santo's wish was uncomplicated. He wanted a way for his strength to be respected. He became an instant contender in a wrestling league for super-powered individuals. But when the Kingmaker, the mysterious figure who granted these wishes, wanted the Hellions to commit crimes to earn their wishes, Santo was one of the first to stand against him, opposing even Julian. Santo lost his shot at glory, but took his first step towards heroism.

REAL NAME: Santo Vaccarro
KNOWN ALIASES: None
IDENTITY: Secret
OCCUPATION: Student
CITIZENSHIP: U.S.A.
PLACE OF BIRTH: Boston, Massachusetts
MARITAL STATUS: Single
KNOWN RELATIVES: Unnamed parents, unnamed younger sister
GROUP AFFILIATION: Xavier Institute/Hellions Training Squad
EDUCATION: Currently in high school level classes
FIRST APPEARANCE: New Mutants #3 (2003)

HEIGHT: 6'2"
WEIGHT: 482 lbs.
EYES: White (no visible pupils)
HAIR: None

SUPERHUMAN POWERS: Rockslide's body is made of rock, giving him enhanced strength, stamina and resistance to injury. He can also detach parts of his body, flinging them as heavy rock projectiles. He has no control over these body parts until he reattaches them manually. He has only learned to detach his limbs, and generally tends only to fire off his hands.

POWER GRID	1	2	3	4	5	6	7
INTELLIGENCE		2					
STRENGTH				4			
SPEED		2					
DURABILITY					5		
ENERGY PROJECTION	1						
FIGHTING SKILLS			3				

SURGE

REAL NAME: Noriko "Nori" Ashida
KNOWN ALIASES: None
IDENTITY: Secret
OCCUPATION: Student
CITIZENSHIP: Japanese Citizen, no criminal record
PLACE OF BIRTH: Tokyo, Japan
MARITAL STATUS: Single
KNOWN RELATIVES: Seiji Ashida (father), Suki Ashida (mother), Keitaro Ashida (brother)
GROUP AFFILIATION: Xavier Institute/New Mutants Training Squad
EDUCATION: Currently in high school level classes
FIRST APPEARANCE: New Mutants #8 (2004)

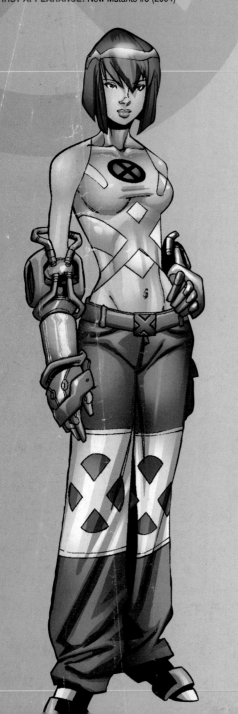

HISTORY: Noriko ran away from home when her mutation developed and her father loudly proclaimed that he "didn't believe in mutants." She came to America and lived on the streets using prescription drugs to help control the rate at which her body absorbed electricity. When her body was overloaded she would talk at an increased speed, move quickly and have trouble ordering her thoughts. The only way to combat this was to discharge the electricity in large dangerous bursts. Noriko tried to find help at Xavier's but was turned away by Hellion, who thought she was just some homeless girl. When Elixir saw her on the street one day in town, he organized his teammates to go looking for her and help her out. She was again overloaded on electricity, but by using Wallflower's pheromones, they calmed her down enough to bring her to the school. Beast made a pair of gauntlets for Noriko to wear that would control her electrical intake and discharge. Prodigy quickly befriended her, despite Nori's gruff exterior.

When a ghost was haunting the school, Noriko was the one who finally got through his angry façade and helped him make peace with his death. Missing her own brother back in Tokyo, she adopted a big sister role and took Jeffrey Garrett under her wing.

Noriko has had problems with teammate Prodigy since her arrival, with her rebellious nature clashing with his by-the-book thinking and occasionally judgmental attitudes. But despite this, he is the one she is closest to on her squad. When he recently saw a vision of his future that included a tragic romance between them, he responded by shutting Noriko out of his life, and she has been hurt enough by this to realize she has feelings for him.

HEIGHT: 5'7"
WEIGHT: 137 lbs.
EYES: Brown
HAIR: Electric Blue

SUPERHUMAN POWERS: Surge has the ability to absorb electricity from the air or from appliances and devices. This electricity builds in her body and causes her mind to race. It can either be channeled into her speed, making her a very fast speedster, or it can be discharged in offensive bursts. Her power gauntlets allow her to regulate intake and release, which minimizes her problems with her ability. It is unclear if she will ever gain enough control naturally to be able to remove them.

ABILITIES: Surge is a native Japanese speaker who speaks English fluently, with little trace of an accent.

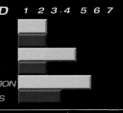

POWER GRID	1	2	3	4	5	6	7
INTELLIGENCE							
STRENGTH							
SPEED							
DURABILITY							
ENERGY PROJECTION							
FIGHTING SKILLS							

HISTORY: Brian Cruz was born in San Juan, Puerto Rico, but moved to the United States as a child. Like many immigrant children, his greatest desire was to fit in and be accepted in his new home. A mutation that developed during adolescence made things more complicated. Brian had a form of mind control that caused others to run away from him. He was brought to the Xavier Institute by Emma Frost who, as a gifted telepath, was resistant to his abilities.

Emma taught Brian control. She taught him to focus his ability, to turn it on and off by giving it a trigger. That trigger, being his touch. It became a game of "tag" and when he tagged himself, he was it, and everyone would flee. As he learned control, he also learned to transfer this pariah effect and, by tagging anyone or anything, make affected minds run away from them or it. He also learned how to focus the power and choose who would run and who would not. He soon made friends, quickly becoming a constant member of Hellion's bad-boy crowd. When the student body was divided into training squads, Brian followed his friends into Emma Frost's Hellions squad.

On a recent trip to California, the Hellions were each offered one wish. Worried his friends might no longer hang with him if they got their heart's desire, Brian wished for his friends to stay together as a group. The Kingmaker, who was granting the wish, convinced Brian he could do better, and showed Brian how to make his friends need him. Brian began training to be the next Kingmaker. He learned how to use contacts and favors to make people "it" for real. When the team learned their wishes required crimes to be committed on behalf of the Kingmaker, they tricked him and broke the deal. In the battle, Brian learned that he could use his power in a different way — making the target "it" and forcing everyone to race towards them, causing the target to be overwhelmed by nearby people.

REAL NAME: Brian Cruz
KNOWN ALIASES: None
IDENTITY: Secret
OCCUPATION: Student
CITIZENSHIP: U.S.A.
PLACE OF BIRTH: San Juan, Puerto Rico
MARITAL STATUS: Single
KNOWN RELATIVES: Unnamed parents, two unnamed siblings
GROUP AFFILIATION: Xavier Institute/Hellions Training Squad
EDUCATION: Currently in high school level classes
FIRST APPEARANCE: New Mutants #10 (2004)

HEIGHT: 5'9"
WEIGHT: 175 lbs.
EYES: Brown
HAIR: Brown

SUPERHUMAN POWERS: Tag has a form of mind control that allows him to "tag" a person or object, making them "it." This can have one of two effects. Either the target becomes a pariah, and all others run away from it, mindlessly trying to put as much distance as possible between them, or the target becomes a desirable "it" and all others try to get as close as possible, which can make the target buried under a pile of people. Tag decides which people view the tagged person or item as "it." This power has a limited range, and those affected by it can get out from under his control when they flee too far.

ABILITIES: Tag was raised with a bilingual education and is equally fluent in Spanish and English.

POWER GRID	1	2	3	4	5	6	7
INTELLIGENCE		2					
STRENGTH		2					
SPEED		2					
DURABILITY		2					
ENERGY PROJECTION			3				
FIGHTING SKILLS		2					

Art by Michael Ryan

WALLFLOWER

REAL NAME: Laurie Collins
KNOWN ALIASES: None
IDENTITY: Secret
OCCUPATION: Student
CITIZENSHIP: U.S.A.
PLACE OF BIRTH: Kent, Connecticut
MARITAL STATUS: Single
KNOWN RELATIVES: Sean Garrison (father), Gail Collins (mother)
GROUP AFFILIATION: Xavier Institute/New Mutants Training Squad
EDUCATION: Currently in high school level classes
FIRST APPEARANCE: New Mutants #2 (2003)

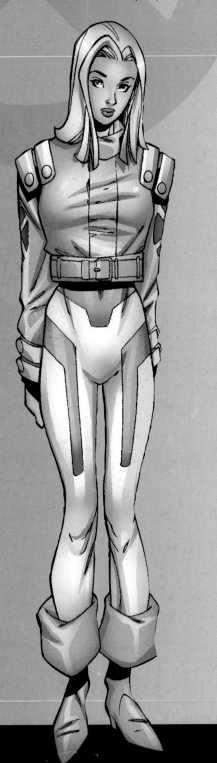

HISTORY: Laurie Collins does not know who her father is, but she knows she inherited her mutant abilities from him. Sean Garrison, a self-help guru, used his pheromone powers to make quite a few women love him. One of them was Gail Collins. When Gail became pregnant with his child, she became immune to his abilities. She soon realized she'd been manipulated and snuck off, leaving him unaware he had a daughter. Feeling violated, Gail withdrew socially and raised her daughter on her own. Laurie fed off her mother's isolation, and became a shy girl herself, a wallflower all through her younger years.

Laurie's mutation developed when she was a teen, and only made matters worse. She feared that any time she came out of her shell, she would manipulate those around her, and that she could never trust that anyone's feelings for her were real. When the Xavier Institute went public, Gail brought Laurie to attend. She moved to Salem Center to be near her daughter, but had Laurie room at the school. Laurie's powers and withdrawn behavior kept her alone until the arrival of Sofia Mantega (Wind Dancer). Sofia's wind abilities could keep Laurie's pheromones at bay, and the optimistic Sofia persisted until the two became friends. At Sofia's urging, Laurie started meeting other students, and they formed a group of friends, who would eventually become the New Mutants training squad.

But coming out of her shell has had negative effects on Laurie as well. She began a relationship with teammate Elixir, which ended when it was revealed that Elixir had briefly had a simultaneous romance with one of the faculty members. The hurt over this betrayal hardened Laurie, who used her pheromones aggressively as a response — first to chase off an apologetic Elixir and later to make their teammate Prodigy kiss her to make Elixir jealous. These manipulations have put some distance between Laurie and her friends, as well as between Laurie and Gail. They have also brought her that much closer to behaving like her father.

HEIGHT: 5'4"
WEIGHT: 118 lbs.
EYES: Blue
HAIR: Blonde

SUPERHUMAN POWERS: Wallflower can control emotions through the use of emitted pheromones. Initially she could not control when she released them, and could only match the emotion she felt. She has learned control in her time at Xavier's and can now keep her pheromones in check, emit them on command, and can induce a variety of emotional and physical responses, including fear, anger, lust, calm, happiness, and sleep.

POWER GRID	1	2	3	4	5	6	7
INTELLIGENCE							
STRENGTH							
SPEED							
DURABILITY							
ENERGY PROJECTION							
FIGHTING SKILLS							

HISTORY: Sofia grew up comfortable with her powers, using them openly and freely with the blessing of her mother, who raised her alone in Caracas. When her mother was killed during riots, Sofia was sent to Colorado to live with a father who she'd never met, an American businessman with little time for a daughter. Barrett kept Sofia at arm's length and left the raising of his daughter to his butler/driver, Derek Newton. Sofia was mocked at school for her cheerful attitude and strange accent. When her father failed to remember her sixteenth birthday, Sofia's optimistic facade crumbled and she went to one of his stores and trashed it with her wind powers. Barrett was ready to send her back to Venezuela before Danielle Moonstar arrived to offer Sofia a place at Xavier's.

At the Institute, Sofia was able to find friends and maintain her optimistic outlook on life. She befriended her roommate, Wallflower, and the two friends became the core of the training squad, the New Mutants. Given the codename Wind Dancer, Sofia stepped up to lead the New Mutants. But her headstrong ways, and her tendency to let the negative build up inside her until she exploded, made her a less than ideal candidate. She eventually asked Prodigy, her genius teammate, to take over as leader. But Prodigy recognized that Wind Dancer was the emotional heart of the team. The two agreed to lead the squad together.

The New Mutants had an up and down year. They lost out in squad competitions to the rival Hellions and were sunk by interpersonal problems within the squad. Sofia grew attracted to Julian Keller, leader of the Hellions. Their squads' rivalry has kept the two from becoming a couple, but Julian is certainly a key figure in Sofia's life.

REAL NAME: Sofia Mantega
KNOWN ALIASES: Briefly used a hyphenated last name "Mantega-Barrett" to honor both parents, but has since gone back to her mother's last name.
IDENTITY: Secret
OCCUPATION: Student
CITIZENSHIP: Venezuela, U.S. green card
PLACE OF BIRTH: Caracas, Venezuela
MARITAL STATUS: Single
KNOWN RELATIVES: Walter Barrett (father), Miranda Mantega (mother), Paolo Mantega (uncle), three unnamed cousins
GROUP AFFILIATION: Xavier Institute/New Mutants Training Squad
EDUCATION: Currently in high school level classes
FIRST APPEARANCE: New Mutants #1 (2003)

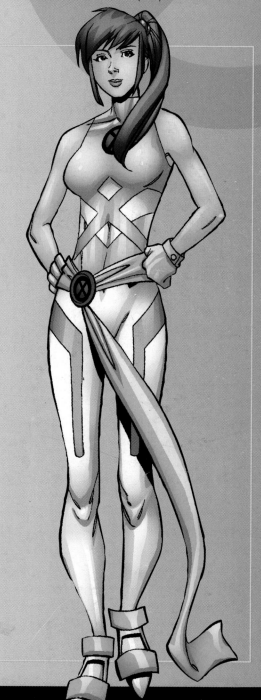

HEIGHT: 5'5"
WEIGHT: 122 lbs.
EYES: Brown
HAIR: Brown

SUPERHUMAN POWERS: Wind Dancer controls air. She has developed a wide array of powers mostly focused on her understanding of the wind. She can fly on wind currents, use the wind to bring her faraway sounds or create an area of silence. Offensively, she can generate intense winds or focused winds capable of slashing at an opponent. She can also fire compressed air into a target's ear, disrupting their sense of balance.

ABILITIES: Wind Dancer is a native Spanish speaker who has mastered English with an accent. She also knows some Portuguese.

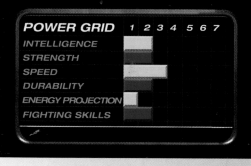

POWER GRID	1	2	3	4	5	6	7
INTELLIGENCE							
STRENGTH							
SPEED							
DURABILITY							
ENERGY PROJECTION							
FIGHTING SKILLS							

Art by Randy Green

WITHER

REAL NAME: Kevin Ford
KNOWN ALIASES: None
IDENTITY: Secret
OCCUPATION: Student
CITIZENSHIP: U.S.A.
PLACE OF BIRTH: Atlanta, Georgia
MARITAL STATUS: Single
KNOWN RELATIVES: Trevor Ford (father, deceased), Angela Ford (mother, deceased)
GROUP AFFILIATION: Xavier Institute/Hellions Training Squad
EDUCATION: Currently in high school level classes
FIRST APPEARANCE: New Mutants #3 (2003)

HISTORY: Kevin Ford's mutant ability to decay organic matter first manifested in a tragic way. When his father made contact with Kevin, Kevin's power started to kill him. As Trevor Ford collapsed, Kevin tried to revive him, continuing contact until his mutant power killed his father. Kevin fled and eventually took refuge in a junkyard where he found that his ability did not affect the metal that surrounded him. When he was attacked by a guard dog, it met the same fate as Kevin's father. The men at the junkyard tried to punish the dangerous mutant and would have beat him to death if not for the arrival of Danielle Moonstar, who brought Kevin to Xavier's.

When Kevin and his friends were attacked by Donald Pierce, an enemy of the X-Men, Kevin found that his body wanted to kill. Between his anger at an injury of teammate Wallflower and his power's hunger, he would not let go of Wallflower and almost attacked Moonstar when she tried to stop him. Moonstar was forced to use her illusion powers to show Kevin his worst fear — killing Wallflower and the rest of his friends. Kevin decided it was not safe for him to stay at Xavier's and left the school. Kevin returned some time later, but had trouble fitting in with his old friends in the New Mutants training squad, due to his attraction to Wallflower. This drove him to spend time with the rival Hellions squad. When the FBI arrested Kevin for the death of his father, the school handed him over so as not to give the message that mutants are above the law. The Hellions decided to rescue him, but the New Mutants went to stop the Hellions from getting in trouble with the law. A battle ensued, and the New Mutants won. Kevin had his day in court, but the charges were dismissed and the death ruled accidental. Kevin resented Moonstar and the New Mutants for not standing up for him and asked to be transferred to the Hellions, becoming part of their training squad.

Kevin also was briefly cured of his mutation via an illegal cure provided by the mysterious Kingmaker. But the Kingmaker demanded that Kevin and his fellow Hellions commit crimes in return for the favors he granted. Kevin was among the first to reject the Kingmaker's bargain, suggesting he is growing healthier in his acceptance of himself.

HEIGHT: 5'8"
WEIGHT: 146 lbs.
EYES: Brown
HAIR: Brown

SUPERHUMAN POWERS: Wither has the mutant ability to decay any organic matter he touches. His power affects anything carbon based, whether alive or already dead. The decay is quick and if the touch is prolonged he will reduce the matter to ash.

POWER GRID	1	2	3	4	5	6	7
INTELLIGENCE							
STRENGTH							
SPEED							
DURABILITY							
ENERGY PROJECTION							
FIGHTING SKILLS							

Art by Michael Ryan

THE OFFICIAL HANDBOOK OF THE MARVEL UNIVERSE
WOLVERINE
SALVADOR
¡SOTO!

except that he spent at least one winter below Monte Cassino in Italy, may have witnessed the aftermath of the British invasion of Dresden, and even encountered Hitler himself.

Following the war's end, Logan returned to Japan and battled Kimora, an extradimensional despot stranded on Earth. Perhaps remembering the lessons taught by Seraph, Logan chose not to kill Kimora when given the chance. Although details remain vague, it is possible that Logan also traveled to his earlier hunting grounds of Russia and China, where he was discouraged by the rise of totalitarian communism. It may have been during these years that Logan was temporarily enslaved by unknown parties, a part of his life that he later would keep secret from even his closest friends.

Discouraged by the war and its aftermath, but having retained a taste for intercontinental travel and adventure, Logan returned to Canada and to his earlier carefree attitude, entering freelance intelligence work in hopes of earning money and reputation. He contacted his friend Chang, who arranged for Landau, Luckman, and Lake to find work for Logan and handle his business affairs in exchange for Logan's occasional services. Operating mostly out of Ottawa and Calgary, with occasional forays into South America and Madripoor, Logan established a clientele that included various government agencies and a reputation as one of the intelligence field's deadliest free agents. In Calgary, he often worked with, and became romantically involved with, a woman named Cracklin' Rosa, proprietor of the Hotel St. Cecil. Although now over a half-century old yet retaining the strength and vitality of a much younger man, Logan was still unable to face his own mutant nature, and he subconsciously refused to recognize that his recuperative powers were superhuman in nature.

In the course of guarding a scientist named Carling on an assignment for Landau, Luckman, and Lake, Logan again clashed with Kimora, who sought Carling's expertise in establishing large-scale transportation between the Earth dimension and his own. Kimora

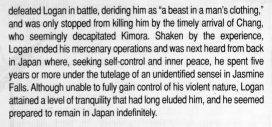

defeated Logan in battle, deriding him as "a beast in a man's clothing," and was only stopped from killing him by the timely arrival of Chang, who seemingly decapitated Kimora. Shaken by the experience, Logan ended his mercenary operations and was next heard from back in Japan where, seeking self-control and inner peace, he spent five years or more under the tutelage of an unidentified sensei in Jasmine Falls. Although unable to fully gain control of his violent nature, Logan attained a level of tranquility that had long eluded him, and he seemed prepared to remain in Japan indefinitely.

Logan's studies were interrupted by the arrival of Chang, who had tracked him down for assistance in opposing Kimora's efforts to conquer the Earth dimension via the secrets of the abducted Doctor Carling. Chang led Logan into Kimora's dimension, apparently Logan's first venture into such an environment, and joined by Carling's half-extradimensional daughter Rose they stormed Kimora's stronghold. Loath to resort to brute force after his years of meditative training, Logan proved adaptable in dealing with Kimora's non-human defenders but only managed to defeat Kimora himself at the cost of unleashing the animal savagery that he had spent the past few years repressing. Following their return to the Earth dimension, Chang offered Logan a position with Landau, Luckman, and Lake, who were now using Carling's interdimensional travel methods in their own affairs. Logan declined, but agreed to consider the offer further, recognizing a need to rethink his way of life. Returning to his freelance activities while contemplating his next move, Logan suffered a severe, near-fatal wound under unrevealed circumstances; however, despite the speed of his recovery, Logan still refused to admit to himself that he possessed superhuman powers, but it may be that this incident caused him to reconsider the notion of joining a team.

In the early 1960s, Logan joined the clandestine Weapon X Program, where he was assigned to Team X, a multinational intelligence unit overseen by the Black Ops Special Services Section of the Central Intelligence Agency. Discovering the full extent of Logan's mutant nature, the Weapon X Program duplicated his healing and age suppression factors for use in their other agents. Logan was stunned to find among his teammates both his nemesis Sabretooth and his former lover Silver Fox, revealed to have survived Sabretooth's attack decades earlier. The trio were able to work together with little if any recollection of their past encounters due to memory implants performed by the Program's telepathic ally Aldo Ferro, code-named Psi-Borg. Using the codename Wolverine, Logan worked alongside other agents such as Maverick, Wraith, Mastodon, Vole, and Wildcat.

In keeping with U.S. interests of the times, Team X was often dispatched to Cuba and Southeast Asia, although details of these missions are sparse. In 1963, Wolverine and Sabretooth were operational in Cuba when Silver Fox, possibly as a result of renewed memory of her attack at Sabretooth's hands, betrayed them to Cuban soldiers. Silver Fox subsequently deserted Team X and became a terrorist, eventually joining the subversive organization Hydra.

Later, in 1968, Wolverine and Sabretooth were sent to the Soviet Union to sabotage a Russian moon voyage by assassinating the Soviet super-agent Epsilon Red. The mission was called off before Wolverine could carry out his orders, although Sabretooth killed Epsilon Red's wife on a whim. Sometime later, Team X was sent to East Germany to sabotage a Berlin super-soldier program and retrieve experimental technology as well as a double agent named Janice Hollenbeck. During their escape, Sabretooth murdered Janice to prevent her from slowing the team's withdrawal, enraging Wolverine. In the aftermath of the escape, Wolverine's rapid recovery finally forced him to face his mutant nature. Disturbed by this realization and unwilling to continue working with Sabretooth, Wolverine resigned from Team X, which disbanded not long after. Wolverine's memories of his years with Team X later become fragmented as a result of the memory implants he received, which, coupled with his mind's own defenses, further confuse his memories.

Following at least one tour of military duty in the Vietnam War, Wolverine found work in the early 1970s as an espionage agent with Department K, a secret branch of the Canadian Defense Ministry that secretly maintained ties to the Weapon X Program. Operating out of Ottawa, Canada, he was partnered with fellow mutant Neil Langram, and he renewed his friendship with Cracklin' Rosa. Logan frequently worked with Nick Fury, now a high-ranking C.I.A. agent; in his later years he worked with such spies as Richard and Mary Parker, who on one occasion rescued him from a notorious criminal. At some point, Wolverine's healing factor was put to the test when a mission ended with him trapped under a glacier, forced to survive on strips of his own flesh for six months until finally rescued.

After Wolverine had been with Department K for many years, Langram was approached by representatives of the international elite organization the Hellfire Club, which sought mutant operatives to further their power-seeking goals. Langram turned down the offer and planned to publicly reveal the Club's activities, only to be slain by Sabretooth, then a mercenary in the Club's employ. Wolverine joined a young American spy, Carol Danvers, in investigating

Langram's death, which led them to the Hellfire Club's Canadian facility. Facing Sabretooth, he learned from his foe some of the details of the Club's operations, including its intent to, in cooperation with national governments, organize mutant operatives for an impending "war" between mutants and normal humans. Sabretooth detonated a bomb to destroy the facility, although he and his opponents survived. In the aftermath of their investigation, Danvers sought to bring matters to the attention of Senator Robert Kelly, but the results of her efforts, if any, were never revealed.

Wolverine's reports of the Hellfire Club's mutant conspiracy were dismissed by his superiors, who believed him to be paranoid and began to distrust him. For his part, Logan became obsessed with his own mutant nature. Disillusioned with himself and troubled by Sabretooth's revelations, he turned to drugs and alcohol, perhaps in an effort to test the extent of the healing factor which, he now came to realize, had played so important a role in his lifetime of adventure. He was ultimately dismissed from Department K after accidentally shooting a fellow agent on the firing range. Disgusted with himself, Wolverine planned to lose himself in the Yukon, hoping to avoid the mutant conflict predicted by Sabretooth.

However, before Wolverine could leave Canada, he was abducted by operatives of the Weapon X Program who sought to use him in experiments to create the perfect killing machine. The near-indestructible metal known as Adamantium was bonded to his skeleton, and in the course of the process his claws, whose

Art by Marc Silvestri

existence he had long forgotten, emerged from his hands, shocking the Weapon X scientists. Wolverine's personality was buried beneath implanted memories and brainwashing, and, reduced to a near-mindless state, he was forced by the Weapon X Program to slaughter every inhabitant of the small town of Roanoke. However, Wolverine eventually broke free of Weapon X's programming and fell into a berserker fury, slaying almost everyone at the facility before fleeing into the nearby woods of the Canadian Rockies. Living in the woods for at least several months, Wolverine formed a psychic bond with a supernatural feral being known as a Hunter in Darkness, and his bestial rage was somewhat calmed by a Lakota chief. During this time, Wolverine apparently dwelled in a cabin with a female Weapon X victim known only as the Native.

Wolverine eventually came upon a young honeymooning couple, James and Heather Hudson, whom he attacked, only to be downed by Hudson's rifle. While recuperating, Wolverine regained enough of his human persona to be horrified at the presence of his Adamantium claws, incorrectly believing them to have been implanted in his body, but any memory of his experience as a Weapon X test subject remained lost to him. Recovering his mental faculties with the help of the Hudsons, Wolverine joined Department H, the superhuman-oriented government agency that James Hudson had founded.

Not long after his recovery, Wolverine traveled to the U.S. to consult Adamantium expert Doctor Myron MacLain. Following his consultation, Wolverine found himself targeted both by Sabretooth

and, under the command of Silver Fox, by Hydra. He was aided against his assailants by several former allies including Nick Fury, Carol Danvers, and Natasha Romanova, now a Russian super-spy known as the Black Widow. Although Wolverine and his allies triumphed against his attackers, his full memories had not been restored and he recognized none of his former friends and enemies. At some point following this incident, Sabretooth took to his annual practice of stalking Wolverine on his birthday.

Under treatment from Department H, Wolverine eventually regained many memories of his past experiences, but mental manipulation by the Weapon X Program and his own healing factor still left certain areas of his life blank. He also underwent intense psychotherapy, which he continued to receive throughout his Department H tenure, to help him control his berserker rages.

As an operative of Department H, Wolverine returned to the espionage field and, by coincidence or by design, was given the codename Weapon X. As a spy, he was given deadly assignments that no other operative would touch. In this capacity, he served primarily in Siberia and the Western Pacific, notably the Pacific Rim of Asia and the islands along that coast, including his old stomping grounds of Japan. He eventually achieved the rank of Captain in the Canadian Armed Forces.

One of his earliest missions again allied him with Carol Danvers and pilot Major Ben Grimm on a special mission into Russian territory. In the course of this mission, Wolverine, still adjusting to his new situation, refrained from using his Adamantium claws, possibly in an attempt to prove to himself that he did not need them. On another mission, Wolverine spent four months in Hong Kong, where he clashed with the organized crime organization the Triads and the noted assassin McLeish, a.k.a. the White Ghost.

Nearly three years after the Hudsons found Wolverine, the first verified public team of super heroes in several years, the Fantastic Four, debuted to worldwide acclaim. Inspired by this, James Hudson oriented Department H toward the formation of a government-sponsored super-team that would operate in the public eye. Hudson nominated Wolverine for leadership of this team, which, in its early stages of development, was known as The Flight. In preparation for his career as a publicly known super hero, Wolverine was outfitted with a distinctive yellow-and-blue costume. Contemplating the wisdom of this new career, Wolverine took temporary leave from his Department H duties and returned to Madripoor, where he was reunited with his old friend Seraph. Wolverine helped Seraph and her new student, the mercenary called the Viper, in Seraph's ongoing activities against the Hand, adventures which are apparently the first that he undertook in his new costume. On one occasion, Seraph and the Viper rescued Wolverine from his old enemy Sabretooth, Seraph sacrificing her life in the process, but not before exacting from Wolverine a promise to help Viper in her stead. Moved by Seraph's example of heroism, Wolverine returned to Canada and agreed to work with The Flight and eventually become its leader, dividing his time between Canada-based Flight training and espionage missions abroad.

Despite Hudson's plans for a Canadian super-team, Wolverine remained his only candidate, and Logan lingered in Canada for months while Hudson continued the search for other suitable recruits. Still on leave, Wolverine was recalled to duty to confront D'Von Kray, a Canaanite warrior from the 40th Century in pursuit of the mutant time-traveler Cable. Wolverine wore his yellow-

and-blue costume on this occasion, evidently the first time he did so while in Canada. Wolverine defeated Kray, who was taken into Department H custody only to escape soon afterward and resume his tracking of Cable, with Wolverine in pursuit. Both Wolverine and Cable fought Kray, who was eventually defeated and recaptured. Shortly after this, Wolverine was partnered with Colonel Rick Stoner of the C.I.A. to retrieve an armored prototype invented by Hudson and stolen by Hydra. Again Wolverine refrained from using his claws in battle, perhaps to distance his espionage assignments from his eventual role as costumed hero, relying instead on a large dagger in battle, much as he did during World War II.

Under pressure to produce additional super-agents, Hudson subjected a convicted murderer to an experimental process designed to manifest any latent superhuman powers. Wolverine, perhaps subconsciously remembering his experience at the hands of the Weapon X Program, warned Hudson that his test subject, who had been codenamed Bedlam, might prove uncontrollable. Disturbed by Hudson's actions, Wolverine returned to his intelligence operations, although he remained on call for The Flight as necessary, training new recruits in combat at select intervals.

Wolverine worked with various intelligence operatives from other nations, most notably his friend Carol Danvers and her then-partner, Michael Rossi. While stationed in Japan, he befriended Asano Kimura of the Japanese Secret Service, who came to admire Wolverine's respect and love for Japan. On occasion, Wolverine observed the Japanese government's efforts against various gigantic monstrous creatures, many of them prehistoric life forms released from natural suspended animation. Wolverine's time in Japan also saw him reunited with Ogun, under whom he continued his samurai studies.

At times, Wolverine accompanied Danvers and Rossi to the U.S., where he worked with New York City government official Tarkington Brown and an unnamed superhuman captain. For a time, under the aegis of the Canadian military, Wolverine was stationed at Valhalla Base, part of the NORAD defense system. At some point, while visiting the Hudsons in Canada, he flew into a berserker rage and nearly killed his friends, an experience that forced him to face his lack of progress in controlling his bestial nature.

Some months after the debut of the American super-team known as the Avengers, Wolverine, again stationed in Canada, recruited Canadian Detective Sean Bernard for The Flight. Bernard was assigned the use of Hudson's Guardian armor under the code-name Groundhog. Over a month later, the American criminal Egghead led a team of superhuman mercenaries in an attempt to extort funds from Canada via the threat of a nuclear warhead. Wolverine, in his yellow-and-blue costume, led a team of Flight trainees against Egghead's superhuman forces. Although the mission was a success, the trainee Saint Elmo died, Groundhog resigned, and other trainees proved themselves unsuited for such missions. Based upon this lack of preparation, Hudson eventually divided The Flight into three divisions of increasing proficiency: Gamma Flight, Beta Flight, and Alpha Flight.

During his time with The Flight, Wolverine formed a romantic relationship with fellow member Narya, the half-human goddess code-named Snowbird, which ultimately ended badly. Among the other Flight trainees with whom he periodically worked was Gamma Flight's Wild Child, a young mutant with a buried berserker nature much like Wolverine's own. Wolverine also recruited a young superhuman with multiple personality disorder named Jeanne-Marie Beaubier, later code-named Aurora.

At some point, Wolverine's espionage work took him to Vladivostok in Russia where he worked with longtime ally Nick Fury just prior to the latter's appointment to the directorship of the Supreme Headquarters International Espionage Law-enforcement Division. Wolverine worked directly with S.H.I.E.L.D. on occasion during these years, even receiving S.H.I.E.L.D. identification, but did not formally join the organization. On one occasion he clashed with superhuman Russian operative Vladimir Zaitsev; in the course of this encounter he wore a brown-and-orange costume, presumably to prevent his activities on this occasion from being linked to his eventual public image as Alpha Flight's leader.

After Carol Danvers was captured on a mission behind Russian lines, Wolverine worked with Michael Rossi and others to break into Lubyanka Prison to free her, despite direct orders to the contrary. During the mission, Rossi was apparently slain and the other members of the team abandoned the effort, leaving Wolverine to smuggle Danvers out of Russia alone despite her insistence that he abandon her to save himself. Following these events, Danvers was recruited as Security Chief for Cape Canaveral; with his friend and

lover out of the intelligence field, Wolverine had less reason to remain in it himself, further steering him toward full-time leadership of Alpha Flight.

As the preparation for Alpha Flight's debut continued, Wolverine traveled to Japan to seek the advice of his longtime sensei Ogun, only to be shocked to learn that Ogun, his former instructor in honor and moral codes, had given himself over to dark magic to become an assassin, intending to enslave Wolverine to his will. Wolverine escaped this fate and, deeply disturbed by this meeting, vowed never to return to Japan. Returning to Canada, he discarded the bladed weapons he had used on occasion, symbolizing his break with Ogun. Accepting his fate, he came to depend more upon his Adamantium claws in battle.

Eager to avoid dwelling on his confrontation with Ogun, Wolverine, ready to make his debut as a publicly known super-agent, was sent to disrupt terrorist activities in Ontario. However, James Hudson informed him that the "assignment," Wolverine's first public Canada-based mission since battling Egghead's forces years earlier, was actually a Department H test. During the course of this test, Wolverine was abducted by the mutated genius known as the Leader, as were the Greek demigod Hercules and the Deviant Karkas, all of whom the Leader intended to use in a campaign against the gamma-spawned powerhouse named the Hulk. Wolverine escaped his restraints and freed his fellow captives, although the Leader fled the debacle. By coincidence, the Hulk himself arrived in Canada shortly before Wolverine's return. The Canadian military mobilized to oppose the Hulk, but Wolverine, relishing the challenge, asked to be given the opportunity first. In the course of this assignment, Wolverine fought both the Hulk and the mystic creature called the Wendigo, but despite his best efforts, he failed to defeat the Hulk. Wolverine nevertheless remained ready to assume leadership of Alpha Flight, spending a few last months to complete his roster of espionage missions, including one in communist territory where he worked with the female espionage agent Charlemagne, a long-time friend and lover.

Upon his return to Canada, Wolverine assisted James Hudson in containing Bedlam, who had resisted all efforts to control him and was finally placed in suspended animation. As a result, Wolverine began to question the wisdom of continuing to work for Department H. Moreover, he realized that he was developing romantic feelings for Heather Hudson, further complicating his situation. When the team of American mutant adventurers the X-Men were captured by the sentient island Krakoa, the team's founder, Professor Charles Xavier, sought out other mutants, including Wolverine, to aid him in their rescue. Disillusioned with his Canadian work, interested in resuming the life of a free agent, and intrigued by Xavier's offer, Wolverine resigned from Department H to join Xavier's new team of X-Men who successfully rescued their predecessors from Krakoa. Following this incident, most members of the first team resigned from active service, leaving Wolverine and his fellow recruits to carry on the X-Men's mission of protecting a world that hated and feared them. The only founding members who remained, along with Xavier himself, were the telepathic Jean Grey, to whom Wolverine developed an immediate attraction, and team leader Cyclops, with whom Wolverine, never much for authority figures, would soon find himself at odds.

Early in his tenure with the X-Men, Wolverine explored New York City and became subject to one of Sabretooth's annual stalking efforts, reminding Wolverine that even in his new life the dangers of the past would not be easily forgotten. Although initially brusque and distant to his new teammates, as if leery of becoming too attached to them, Wolverine soon formed a close friendship with the teleporting Nightcrawler and began pursuing his attraction to Grey, much to her annoyance. Soon after, Grey was replaced by the cosmic entity known as the Phoenix, fooling even Wolverine's heightened senses.

During Wolverine's early membership in the X-Men he faced a wide variety of threats which would recur many times throughout the years, from the demonic N'garai and giant robot Sentinels to the near-unstoppable Juggernaut and the X-Men's oldest enemy, the mutant master of magnetism, Magneto. The team even ventured into outer space (as far as is known, Wolverine's first such experience) to oppose a threat to the universe itself. However, Wolverine was soon brought back to earth both figuratively and literally, for on the heels of the X-Men's cosmic experience, he found himself confronted by James Hudson, who, in Wolverine's absence, had been tapped for the role of Alpha Flight leader himself. Hudson wore his super-powered battlesuit as Weapon Alpha in an attempt to capture Wolverine and return him to Department H. Wolverine's teammates helped drive Hudson off, but Logan knew that a future fight with his former allies was inevitable.

After being captured in a clash with Magneto, Wolverine and the X-Men escaped to the Savage Land, a prehistoric jungle hidden deep in the Antarctic to which Wolverine took an immediate liking. From the Savage Land the team made its way to Japan, Wolverine's first visit since severing ties with Ogun. Filled with mixed feelings over his return, Wolverine chanced to meet a young woman named Mariko Yashida, cousin to the former X-Man Sunfire. Initially frightened of the formidable mutant, Mariko was soon set at ease by Wolverine, who found himself strongly attracted to her beauty and gentle demeanor. The two spent much time together during the X-Men's stay in Japan. However, while Wolverine contemplated his new feelings for Mariko, older emotions arose when the team's return flight to the U.S. was diverted to Canada, where Hudson, now known as Vindicator, led the finalized Alpha Flight team in another failed attempt to capture their former would-be leader.

Shortly afterward, the Phoenix, whom the X-Men still believed to be Jean Grey, seemingly perished. Sobered by the loss, Wolverine took to wearing the brown-and-orange costume he had once worn battling Vladimir Zaitsev, perhaps as a reminder that his life among the X-Men was no less dangerous than his earlier career in Department H and elsewhere. Accompanied by Nightcrawler, Wolverine returned to Canada to make his peace with Alpha Flight, joining the team against the revived menace of the Wendigo. Later, when Mariko visited New York, she and Wolverine continued to explore their relationship. The two soon realized they were in love, giving Wolverine new ties to the land he had loved for so long.

Months later, Wolverine learned that Mariko's father, the crimelord Shingen Harada, had forced her to marry one of his criminal associates. Wolverine tried to convince Mariko to leave with him, but she felt duty-bound to obey her father's wishes, despite the shame her father's criminal activities caused. Shingen manipulated Wolverine in an attempt to drive a further wedge between him and Mariko, but Mariko remained true to her feelings. When Wolverine was forced to slay Shingen in a savage duel, Mariko declared Wolverine to be her champion, presenting him with the honor sword of the Clan Yashida.

Wolverine and Mariko announced their engagement, but Mariko called off the wedding while being manipulated by of one of the X-Men's old foes, the psionic mutant Mastermind. While under his control, Mariko strengthened the ties between Clan Yashida and the Japanese underworld. Feeling honor-bound to divest her family of these ties, Mariko vowed to prove her own worth by accomplishing this task without Wolverine's help; Wolverine, respecting her wishes, agreed to postpone their marriage until her self-appointed mission was complete.

Later, when the X-Men were teleported to Japan after an adventure in outer space, Wolverine and his teammates sought to aid the victims of an attack by a giant dragon. Unable to save a dying woman, Wolverine vowed to protect her daughter Amiko whom he came to regard as a foster daughter. Realizing his life was not one to be shared with Amiko, he left her in Mariko's care. Not long afterward, Wolverine's teammate Kitty Pryde fell under the control of Ogun, forcing Wolverine to again confront his former sensei and ultimately kill him, although Ogun would return years later as a spirit to bedevil both Wolverine and Pryde.

As one piece of his past was seemingly laid to rest, Wolverine found himself confronted with another when, following the apparent death of James Hudson, his widow Heather sought Wolverine's advice on how to carry on her husband's heroic legacy as Vindicator. Wolverine agreed to advise her, only for both to be attacked by Lady Deathstrike, who believed that Wolverine's Adamantium skeleton was a legacy of her father's stolen work. Deathstrike and her forces were defeated, but she subsequently had herself transformed into a cyborg and continued her vendetta against Wolverine.

When the X-Men responded to a brutal attack on the subterranean mutant community known as the Morlocks, Wolverine found himself, for the first time since joining the X-Men, in combat with his oldest enemy Sabretooth, who had joined the assassins called the Marauders in the service of enigmatic geneticist Mister Sinister. Wolverine fought Sabretooth several times during the so-called "Mutant Massacre," setting the stage for many more battles in the future. However, a more powerful menace awaited the X-Men when they fought the would-be world destroyer called the Adversary. Defeating their godlike enemy, in the aftermath the X-Men were believed dead by the world at large, and the team chose to use that belief to operate more covertly.

Perhaps made introspective by recent events, Wolverine began to spend more time away from his fellow X-Men, returning to Madripoor for the first time in years. There he befriended the nascent crimelord Tyger Tiger and helped her against the forces of her rival, Roche. In memory of his dead mentor Seraph, Wolverine became part-owner of her one-time establishment, the Princess Bar, and he re-established the Madripoor reputation of "Patch," acting to keep the peace between Madripoor's criminal factions. Wolverine also spent weeks living in the Savage Land, where he romanced a native woman named Gahck who, unbeknownst to Wolverine, bore him a son.

Returning to the X-Men's then-headquarters in Australia, Wolverine was ambushed by the Reavers, a team of cyborgs that included many of his old enemies, including Lady Deathstrike. The Reavers tortured and crucified Wolverine, who was freed by the young mutant Jubilee, and the two escaped to Madripoor. Jubilee subsequently accompanied Wolverine on several adventures, and Logan came to regard his unlikely sidekick as a surrogate daughter.

During one adventure, Wolverine was rendered amnesiac by a chemical attack, and he briefly found contentment in the island village of Rumika before it was decimated by soldiers involved in the mysterious Lazarus Project. Wolverine's memory was soon restored, but this incident may have triggered memory implants and/or suppressions left in place long ago by the Weapon X Program, because Wolverine, who had for years demonstrated a clear memory of most of his life, soon found himself troubled by gaps in his knowledge of his past.

As if in response to his renewed interest in his past, Wolverine's former commanding officer, Silas Burr, surfaced in Madripoor. Now known as the mutant mercenary Cyber, Burr possessed Adamantium-laced skin to match Wolverine's claws. Seized by an innate terror of the man who had so sorely wounded him so many decades ago, Wolverine nevertheless overcame his fear and put a stop to Cyber's efforts to control Tyger Tiger's operations. Perhaps encouraged by this triumph, Wolverine soon investigated the abandoned Weapon X facility where Adamantium had been bonded to him years before. Perhaps in an attempt to reconnect to his definite memories of Department H, Wolverine took to again wearing his yellow-and-blue costume.

Circumstances then again led Wolverine to Japan, where Clan Yashida was besieged by both internal dispute and attacking Hand ninjas. These proceedings were observed by Silver Fox, who, in cooperation with the Hand's leader, Matsu'o Tsurayaba, sent an operative to poison Mariko with blowfish toxin. With the prospect of a slow and painful death before her, Mariko asked Wolverine to grant her a quick and merciful death, which he reluctantly did. Blaming Tsurayaba for Mariko's death, Wolverine promised his enemy a slow death in return, with Wolverine returning each

anniversary of Mariko's death to periodically disfigure Tsurayaba.

After the former Team X member Mastodon died when his age suppression factor seemingly reversed, Wolverine found himself allied with his former teammates in Team X, including Sabretooth and, surprisingly, Silver Fox. Opposing Psi-Borg, revealed to be the orchestrator of their plight, Silver Fox was killed by Sabretooth, leaving Wolverine to mourn another lost love.

Soon after these tragedies, Wolverine joined the X-Men in another attack on Magneto, who used his magnetic powers to forcefully remove the Adamantium from Wolverine's body. The shock overloaded Wolverine's healing factor, nearly killing him. He ultimately recovered with the help of his X-Men teammates, but was shocked to discover that his claws, which he had long thought to be

implants, were actually a part of his natural skeleton. Only later would he realize that the Adamantium in his body had partially repressed the berserker nature that had plagued him for so long, with its absence heralding a return to a more animalistic mindset.

Months later, Wolverine faced Sabretooth under much different circumstances, as his longtime foe was being held at the X-Men's mansion while Professor X attempted to cure him of his bloodlust. Sabretooth subsequently escaped confinement, and in the ensuing battle Wolverine sank one of his claws into Sabretooth's brain, nearly lobotomizing him. Disturbed by his behavior and concerned that future loss of control might make him a danger to his friends, Wolverine left the X-Men for a time. His return to Madripoor proved no less disturbing, for many of his friends had been killed in an attempt by his enemies to frame him for murder.

Wolverine was next kidnapped by the time-traveler Genesis, who sought to remake him as one of his Horsemen. Slaying Cyber for his Adamantium, Genesis attempted to once more bond Wolverine's skeleton with the near-unbreakable metal. Wolverine's body rejected the procedure, in the process regressing him to a more animalistic state than he had been in since the Weapon X experiment itself. With the help of the ninja Elektra, Wolverine again managed to overcome his bestial impulses and reclaim his humanity.

Months later, Wolverine faced yet another specter from his past when the Viper, now one of the world's most feared terrorists, invoked Wolverine's promise to Seraph years before. Bound by the debt he owed, Wolverine agreed to marry Viper, giving her the status necessary to become ruler of Madripoor and banish Wolverine. In the course of challenges to Viper's authority by Hydra and the Hand, Wolverine fought both against and alongside Sabretooth, who had had Adamantium bonded to his own skeleton in imitation of Wolverine's former state. Driven from his former home, Wolverine next faced the loss of his very identity when he was captured by the eternal mutant Apocalypse. While a member of the alien race of shapeshifters known as the Skrull impersonated Wolverine in the X-Men's ranks, Apocalypse succeeded where Genesis had failed, removing Sabretooth's Adamantium and bonding it to Wolverine, transforming him into the Horseman Death. Fortunately, Wolverine's service to Apocalypse proved brief, as he ultimately regained his true persona and rejoined the X-Men once more.

Wolverine's exile from Madripoor was short-lived, as he was invited back by Viper to aid her against Ogun, still active as a possessing spirit and hoping to claim the body of Wolverine himself just as he had hoped to corrupt his spirit years before. Injured in the ensuing clash, Viper agreed to divorce Wolverine in return for medical treatment, freeing him from his bond to her. Yet Wolverine was not so lucky at remaining free of the control of the Weapon X Program. Revived by Malcolm Colcord, one of the few survivors of Wolverine's slaughter years ago, the Program used Wolverine as a stalking horse for other former Weapon X operatives via the same technology that had been used to force him to slaughter the inhabitants of Roanoke years before. Weapon X also recruited Sabretooth, restoring the Adamantium that Apocalypse had stripped from him, but the murderous mutant pursued his own agenda against Wolverine, temporarily stripping him of his mutant powers and almost killing his foe before Weapon X reined him in.

Wolverine recovered from Sabretooth's attack and became an instructor at the X-Men's school following its exposure as a sanctuary for mutants and the subsequent swelling of the student body. Wolverine also continued to embark on periodic solo adventures, eschewing his costumed identity to interact with mainstream humanity and fight more mundane but no less deadly foes.

Determined to learn the full truth of Weapon X's experiments on him, Wolverine sought the aid of Cyclops and fellow experimentee

Fantomex in invading the so-called World, the base of Weapon X's parent project, the Weapon Plus Program. Wolverine was horrified to learn of the Roanoke massacre and other Weapon Plus secrets, but his perusal was interrupted by the attack of Weapon Plus's latest subject, Weapon XV. Wolverine defeated his experimental successor, only to find himself stranded in space. His teammate Jean Grey arrived in a shuttle to rescue him, only for both to be trapped on Magneto's former space station, which Magneto sent hurtling into the sun. The pair were saved when Grey accessed the cosmic power of the Phoenix entity who had impersonated her years before; they returned to Earth to find Magneto had taken control of Manhattan and threatened to reverse the Earth's magnetic poles. In the ensuing battle, Magneto callously killed Grey with a lethal electromagnetic pulse, an act that sent Wolverine into a rage. He decapitated Magneto, not knowing that it was actually a mutant impersonator and not the true master of magnetism.

Following Grey's death, Wolverine has been more at odds with Cyclops than ever, disgusted by Cyclops's apparent disregard of his wife's fate and the solace he found with the White Queen. Wolverine himself has recently had a relationship with Alcohol, Tobacco and Firearms agent Cassie Lathrop. He has also pursued the daunting goal of exposing the activities of the Weapon X Program.

A recent encounter with the former test subject called the Native, as well as a clash with the Weapon Plus Program's director Sublime, has once more underscored the questionable nature of some of his memories; it is clear that Wolverine still has many secrets about himself to discover.

HEIGHT: 5'3"
WEIGHT: (without Adamantium skeleton) 195 lbs., (with Adamantium skeleton) 300 lbs.
EYES: Blue
HAIR: Black
DISTINGUISHING FEATURES: Animal-like canine teeth, hirsute physique, unique hairstyle

SUPERHUMAN POWERS: Wolverine has the ability to regenerate damaged or destroyed areas of his cellular structure far more rapidly than an ordinary human. His healing factor's speed is in proportion to the wound's severity; for example, he can fully recover from an ordinary gunshot wound within minutes, but it took him several weeks to fully recover from injuries sustained in a duel with Lord Shingen, including one wound from a sword that completely pierced his trunk. However, Wolverine's healing ability has dramatically increased in recent years, enabling him to fully recover from even the most devastating injuries, including brain damage, in a matter of days, if not hours.

Wolverine's natural healing also affords him virtual immunity to poisons and most drugs, as well as an enhanced resistance to diseases. For example, it is nearly impossible for him to become intoxicated from drinking alcohol. He also has a limited immunity to the fatigue poisons generated by bodily activity, and hence has greater endurance than an ordinary human. His agility and reflexes are similarly enhanced.

In addition, Wolverine's healing factor provides him with an extended lifespan by slowing the effects of the aging process. Although over a century old, Wolverine is as healthy and physically fit as a man in his prime.

Wolverine also possesses superhumanly acute senses, allowing him to see things at a maximum distance greater than a normal human's. His hearing is enhanced in a similar manner, and he is able to recognize people and objects by scent, even if that person or object is hidden. Wolverine can use these enhanced senses to track any creature with an impressive degree of success.

Wolverine's skeleton includes six retractable one-foot-long bone claws, three in each arm, that are housed beneath the skin and muscle of his forearms. Wolverine can, at will, release these slightly curved claws through his skin beneath the knuckles on each hand. The skin between the knuckles tears and bleeds, but the blood loss is quickly halted by his healing factor. Wolverine can unsheathe any number of his claws at once, although he must keep his wrists straight at the moment his claws shoot from his forearms into his hands. When unsheathed, the claws are fully within his hands, and thus Wolverine can still bend his wrists. The claws are naturally sharp and tougher than that of normal human bone structure, allowing Wolverine to cut through most types of flesh and natural materials.

Wolverine's entire skeletal structure, including his claws, has been artificially bonded to the nearly indestructible metal Adamantium. As a result, Wolverine's bones are virtually unbreakable, and his claws are capable of cutting through almost any substance depending on its thickness and the amount of force he can exert. Due to his healing factor, the presence of Adamantium in his body does not interfere with his bones' normal function of generating blood corpuscles. The reinforcement of his skeleton enables Wolverine to withstand high levels of physical pressure, giving his muscles sufficient force to briefly lift/press several hundred pounds.

SPECIAL LIMITATIONS: Despite the extent of his healing factor, Wolverine is not immortal. If the injuries are extensive enough, especially if they result in the loss of vital organs, large amounts of blood, and/or loss of physical form, such as having flesh burned away by fire or acid, Wolverine can die.

SPECIAL SKILLS: Due to his extensive training as a soldier, a C.I.A. operative, a samurai, a spy, and a member of the X-Men, Wolverine is an exceptional hand-to-hand combatant, having mastered virtually every fighting style on Earth. He is also a trained expert in multiple types of weapons, vehicles, computer systems, explosives, and assassination techniques. Wolverine is fluent in many languages, including Japanese, Russian, Chinese, Cheyenne, Lakota, and Spanish; he has some knowledge of French, Thai, and Vietnamese.

PERSONAL WEAPONRY: Throughout his life, Wolverine has used a variety of bladed weapons, most frequently daggers and, at times, swords. He has also wielded many different types of firearms throughout his careers as a soldier, a mercenary, and a spy.

POWER GRID	1	2	3	4	5	6	7
INTELLIGENCE							
STRENGTH							
SPEED							
DURABILITY							
ENERGY PROJECTION							
FIGHTING SKILLS							

LADY DEATHSTRIKE

REAL NAME: Yuriko Oyama
KNOWN ALIASES: None
IDENTITY: Secret
OCCUPATION: Assassin, CEO of Oyama Heavy Industries
PLACE OF BIRTH: Osaka, Japan
CITIZENSHIP: Japanese, with criminal record in Canada
MARITAL STATUS: Single
KNOWN RELATIVES: Kenji Oyama (Lord Dark Wind, father, deceased), two unnamed brothers (deceased)
GROUP AFFILIATION: Ally of Reverend William Stryker, former employee of Sabretooth, formerly Reavers
EDUCATION: Privately tutored
FIRST APPEARANCE: (as Yuriko Oyama) Daredevil Vol. 1 #197 (1983), (as Lady Deathstrike) Alpha Flight Vol. 1 #33 (1985)

HISTORY: Yuriko Oyama is the daughter of Kenji Oyama, a former Japanese kamikaze pilot during World War II, whose face was horribly scarred in a failed suicide attack on an American battleship. Later becoming the head of Oyama Heavy Industries, Kenji had Yuriko and her two brothers privately tutored by Marcy Stryker, wife of an American soldier named William Stryker. Kenji felt much shamed by his failure decades earlier, and as a result he ultimately scarred the faces of his three children in a ritual design. Becoming the criminal scientist Lord Dark Wind, Kenji developed a means for bonding the virtually indestructible metal Adamantium to human bone, a procedure he hoped to use in creating an army of super-soldiers for Japan. However, his notes were stolen and it took him years to rediscover the process.

Growing to despise post-war Japanese civilization, Lord Dark Wind had the then-crippled assassin Bullseye brought to his island off the Japanese coast. There, Dark Wind replaced some of Bullseye's broken bones with Adamantium substitutes, hoping that in return Bullseye would assassinate Japan's minister of trade for him. Arriving in Japan intent on recapturing Bullseye, the blind costumed crimefighter Daredevil encountered Yuriko, who sought vengeance on her father, both for scarring her and for the deaths of her brothers, who had perished in Lord Dark Wind's service. Moreover, the young man Yuriko loved, Kira, served in Dark Wind's private army, and she did not want her father to cause him harm. After Yuriko guided Daredevil to her father's private island, Bullseye escaped and Yuriko herself slew Lord Dark Wind just as he was about to kill Daredevil.

Following Daredevil's departure, Kira committed suicide in despair over Dark Wind's death. The shock of Kira's death radically altered Yukio's outlook on life, and she resolved to carry on her father's work. Yuriko became convinced that the mutant adventurer Wolverine had gained his Adamantium-laced skeleton by means of the process stolen from her father years earlier. Garbed as a female samurai and calling herself Lady Deathstrike, Yuriko led a number of her father's warriors to Canada where they confronted Wolverine, seeking to retrieve his Adamantium skeleton for study. She was defeated by Wolverine's long-time friend Heather Hudson, who had adopted the costumed identity of Vindicator in her role as leader of the Canadian super-team Alpha Flight.

Having failed to defeat Wolverine, Lady Deathstrike resolved to better fight him on his own terms and so struck a deal with Donald Pierce, the renegade White King of the elitist Hellfire Club, who had formed a band of cyborg mercenaries named the Reavers. Pierce had the extradimensional being named Spiral transform Deathstrike into a cyborg, healing her facial scars in the process. Now possessing superhuman strength and Adamantium claws to rival Wolverine's own, she led three other cyborgs in Pierce's employ — former Hellfire Club soldiers Cole, Macon, and Reese — in an attack on Wolverine, only to again meet defeat. Now interested only in vengeance, Deathstrike later joined Pierce and his Reavers in an ambush on Wolverine in a remote town in the Australian outback. Capturing him, they crucified him on an X-shaped cross and left him to die. Wolverine was rescued by the young mutant Jubilee, and after a brief clash with the Reavers, the pair escaped. Believing Wolverine had fled to the mutant research facility on Muir Island, the Reavers arrived and clashed with both a ragtag group of X-Men and the U.S. government-sponsored Freedom Force team. After both sides suffered casualties, the tide of battle began to turn against them and the Reavers retreated.

Later hoping to succeed alone after her failures with a team, Deathstrike had the Reavers' former ally, the mutant aborigine Gateway, teleport her to Wolverine's location. At that moment, Wolverine had traveled back in time to Spain in 1937, so Deathstrike was also sent into the past. Caught in a skirmish during the Spanish Civil War, the pair subsequently fought their way through temporal distortion to return to the present, their battle unresolved. In a subsequent confrontation, Deathstrike learned that the self-styled mutant master of magnetism, Magneto, had forcibly removed the Adamantium from Wolverine's body. As a result, she lost interest in her quest and returned to the Reavers in search of purpose.

After an attack on the Reavers by giant robotic Sentinels summoned from the future by the time-traveling mutant villain Trevor Fitzroy, Pierce rebuilt the Reavers and led them in capturing Milo Thurman, a former government employee who possessed incredible natural prophetic abilities. Pierce intended to transform Thurman into a cyborg Reaver under his control, but his plan was opposed by Thurman's former lover, the mutant mercenary Domino. As Deathstrike battled Domino, Pierce downloaded almost 60% of Thurman's consciousness into his own mind before the Reavers' base was destroyed.

Later striking out on her own, Lady Deathstrike once again clashed with Wolverine but was possessed by the spirit of another of his nemeses, Ogun. Eventually abandoned by the spirit once it had learned from her how to infiltrate cybernetic systems, Deathstrike subsequently allied with the Japanese terrorist group Strikeforce Ukiyoe and they clashed with the super-soldier Captain America following his return from an extradimensional exile. She next found herself targeted by Prime Sentinels, mutant-hunting cyborgs under the command of the time-traveling villain Stryfe. Although not a mutant herself, Deathstrike unknowingly carried within her cybernetic programming the control codes for the more powerful Omega-class Sentinels. With the help of Wolverine and his teammates in the X-Men, Deathstrike defeated Stryfe and his forces. Despite their shared victory, Deathstrike's dislike for Wolverine endured, and she was subsequently recruited by Wolverine's arch-nemesis, the feral mutant Sabretooth, to assist him in striking at Wolverine's loved ones in exchange for valuable information. Deathstrike, alongside the Russian super-soldier Omega Red, crippled Wolverine's friend Yukio and abducted his ward, Amiko. Having obtained what he wanted, Sabretooth subsequently double-crossed Deathstrike and Omega Red, cheating them out of the information he had promised them.

Lady Deathstrike later went to the aid of her former associate William Stryker, who had since become a minister and led an anti-mutant crusade that resulted in his imprisonment due to the murderous actions of his Purifier soldiers. Breaking him out of government custody, Deathstrike gave him access to the resources of Oyama Heavy Industries. In the course of aiding Stryker in his

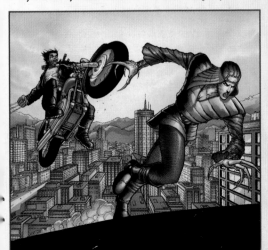

efforts, she fell under the control of Paul, a sentient computer entity who sought to protect the community of mutants living in Mount Haven. Under Paul's control, Deathstrike fought both Stryker and the X-Men, once more dueling with Wolverine and, ironically, meeting more success under Paul's control than she ever had on her own. In the course of one clash, Deathstrike was buried beneath collapsing rubble, but when the X-Man Bishop investigated he found only her severed cybernetic arm. Deathstrike's current whereabouts and activities are unknown.

HEIGHT: 5'9"
WEIGHT: 128 lbs.
EYES: Brown
HAIR: Black
DISTINGUISHING FEATURES: Cybernetically enhanced body, clawed hands, left side of face scarred in a ritual design (surgically repaired when transformed into cyborg)

SUPERHUMAN POWERS: Lady Deathstrike is a cyborg with augmented strength, speed, agility, endurance, and reflexes. Her skeleton has been artificially laced with molecules of the metal Adamantium, rendering her bones virtually unbreakable. Deathstrike is able to cybernetically interface her consciousness with external computer systems, allowing for direct data access to her brain's memory centers and granting her the ability to remotely operate such systems.

Deathstrike's cybernetic systems also include a self-repair and reconfiguration program, allowing her to automatically repair damage to her cyborg body. The more damage she endures, the longer her reconfiguration program will take to repair her body.

Lady Deathstrike's fingers have all been replaced with one-foot-long Adamantium claws, which she is capable of telescoping to twice their original length.

SPECIAL SKILLS: Lady Deathstrike is a supremely skilled martial artist, considered an expert in the art of Kenjitsu and other samurai warrior skills. She is an accomplished pilot of various aircraft and seacraft, and is fluent in both Japanese and English.

PERSONAL WEAPONRY: Prior to her transformation into a cyborg, Lady Deathstrike wielded a five-foot-long electromagnetically tempered steel katana. The weapon was destroyed after it shattered against Vindicator's personal force field. She subsequently used a high-powered, long-range blaster that fired armor-piercing explosive bullets, and has also used grenades of great explosive force.

OTHER ACCESSORIES: Lady Deathstrike formerly wore a wristband that contained instrumentation capable of detecting Adamantium.

POWER GRID	1	2	3	4	5	6	7
INTELLIGENCE							
STRENGTH							
SPEED							
DURABILITY							
ENERGY PROJECTION							
FIGHTING SKILLS							

SABRETOOTH

REAL NAME: Victor Creed
KNOWN ALIASES: Der Schlächter ("The Butcher" in German), Slasher, El Tigre, others
IDENTITY: Secret, known to various government officials
OCCUPATION: Mercenary, former government agent, possibly others
PLACE OF BIRTH: Unrevealed
CITIZENSHIP: Unrevealed, numerous international criminal records
MARITAL STATUS: Unrevealed
KNOWN RELATIVES: Zebadiah Creed (father, presumed deceased), unnamed mother (presumed deceased), Graydon Creed (Tribune, son, deceased)
GROUP AFFILIATION: None; formerly Weapon X, Brotherhood of Mutants, Hound Program, Marauders, X-Factor, Team X, former agent of Tribune, Foreigner, Montenegro and others, former partner of Constrictor
EDUCATION: Unrevealed
FIRST APPEARANCE: Iron Fist Vol. 1 #14 (1977)

HISTORY: Little is known about the early life of the feral mutant named Victor Creed, although it is believed that he suffered an abusive childhood at the hands of his father who, disgusted by the boy's mutant nature, frequently beat him and chained him up in the darkened basement of their home. As an adult, Creed took the name Sabretooth, and by the 1910s he was known by this name in a small Canadian frontier community where he intimidated almost everyone. One of the few exceptions was a young man named Logan, whom Sabretooth sensed had superhuman abilities similar to his own. Hating the love that existed between Logan and a young Indian girl named Silver Fox, Sabretooth brutally assaulted her, apparently raping her and leaving her for dead. The enraged Logan then forced Sabretooth into a pitched battle, which ended with Sabretooth victorious. Unbeknownst to either combatant, Silver Fox survived the attack and soon departed from the community.

Little is known about Sabretooth's subsequent activities until the early 1960s when he served in Team X, a special intelligence unit run by the Central Intelligence Agency for the subversive Weapon X Program. In Team X, Sabretooth was reunited with both Logan, now known as Wolverine, and Silver Fox; however, due to false memory implants provided by Weapon X's ally Psi-Borg, it is unclear how much of their shared past the three recall.

Sabretooth had a falling out with Wolverine during a mission in East Berlin in Germany during the early 1960s, exacerbating the already tense animosity between the two. During that same mission, Sabretooth met and romanced Leni Zauber, an operative for another unnamed government agency. Unbeknownst to Sabretooth, Zauber was actually the shape-shifting mutant known as Mystique. Sabretooth remained with Zauber for a month before returning to his Team X duties and stayed with the team until its disbandment. He then set out on his own as a hired assassin, earning a worldwide reputation. At some point in the subsequent decades he became a student of the enigmatic Foreigner, head of the assassin guild known as the 1400 Club and one of the few men that Sabretooth respected. Sabretooth was also again manipulated by Mystique, who, for reasons of her own, seduced him in order to become pregnant with his child. However, the resultant son had no mutant potential and was abandoned by Mystique, growing up to become the anti-mutant activist Graydon Creed.

While working for the elitist Hellfire Club, Sabretooth clashed with Wolverine in the latter's capacity as an agent of the Canadian government's Department K. Months later, an amnesiac Wolverine, having recently been subjected to experiments which bonded the unbreakable metal Adamantium to his skeleton, sought the advice of Adamantium creator Doctor Myron MacLain. Sabretooth, hired by unidentified parties, interrupted the consultation and attempted to kill his former foe and teammate, only to be stopped by Wolverine's allies. At some point, Sabretooth began annually stalking Wolverine on the day Logan believed to be his birthday.

In recent years Sabretooth, although always a violent man, gradually began developing a psychotic bloodlust that overcame his admittedly heartless human persona. As a result of this further mutation, Sabretooth's features became more animal-like, a condition which eventually corrected itself. He first came to attention in recent years when he abducted noted attorney Jeryn Hogarth, who was rescued by his client, the martial artist known as Iron Fist. Later, Sabretooth formed a partnership with the costumed criminal the Constrictor on an assignment for the crimelord Montenegro. However, driven by his hunger for violence, Sabretooth disguised himself and slew several people in New York City, resulting in reports of a mysterious "Slasher." When Sabretooth was exposed as the Slasher, he and the Constrictor found themselves fighting not only Iron Fist, but his allies as well -- the super-strong Power Man, the cyborg detective Misty Knight, and the mutant adventurer El Aguila. Sabretooth and the Constrictor were forced to retreat; however, the pair later sought revenge on Knight, only to again meet defeat at the hands of Power Man and Iron Fist.

Later, in an effort to prove himself to the Foreigner, Sabretooth tracked down the costumed adventurer the Black Cat, who had clashed with some of the Foreigner's agents. The effort led to battles with both the Black Cat and the costumed crimefighter Spider-Man, with Sabretooth ultimately being hospitalized under guard. Soon escaping, he was subsequently recruited by an old acquaintance, the mutant thief Gambit, to join a cadre of mutant assassins, the Marauders, in the service of the enigmatic geneticist Mister Sinister. The Marauders were sent to slaughter the underground mutant community of Morlocks, leading to a clash with the Morlocks' allies, the X-Men, who counted Wolverine among their ranks. In the course of the so-called "Mutant Massacre," Sabretooth and Wolverine fought several times, with Sabretooth ultimately being defeated.

As his bloodlust increased, Sabretooth hired the telepathic Birdy to help him keep his urges in check, only for Birdy to be murdered by his son Graydon, now an avid anti-mutant activist with a deep hatred of his parents. Sabretooth then slipped into a killing spree, but was captured by his former Team X teammate Maverick and the X-Men. The X-Men's founder, the telepathic Professor Charles Xavier, tried to help Sabretooth overcome his bloodthirsty impulses, just as the X-Men had helped Wolverine deal with his own berserker rages. Sabretooth played along at first, although doing little to hide his contempt for the X-Men, but when the opportunity presented itself he escaped from his holding cell in Xavier's mansion. Confronted by Wolverine, the two fought savagely and Sabretooth was nearly lobotomized when Wolverine thrust one of his claws into Sabretooth's brain. Following this attack, Sabretooth seemed unusually passive, and one of the X-Men's allies, the young mutant called Boomer, became fond of the seemingly peaceful prisoner and tried to help him reform. However, Sabretooth soon regained his true personality and turned against Boomer and the X-Men, almost killing the X-Man Psylocke during his escape.

Not long after, Sabretooth was recruited by the U.S. government to pursue the malfunctioning mutant tracker known as the Hound. To that end, Sabretooth was made a member of the government-sponsored mutant team X-Factor, much to the chagrin of X-Factor's leader, Forge. Unknown to his supposed teammates, Sabretooth was actually a sleeper agent of the government's Hound Program, under orders to kill the members of X-Factor should they be deemed uncontrollable. He was forced to wear an inhibitor collar that administered a severe shock to his nervous system if he became overly aggressive towards any of his teammates or if he tried to remove the collar. After joining his teammate Mystique in opposing the terrorist organizations Hydra and A.I.M., Sabretooth obtained pills to help him overcome the pain and, after succeeding in removing the collar, he savagely assaulted several other members of X-Factor before escaping. Rejecting the government's authority, Sabretooth also killed several potential members of the Hound Program, setting back the government's efforts to control mutants. Sabretooth also clashed with the Russian super-soldier Omega Red who sought to capture the feral mutant and bring him to the Russian telepath Elena Ivanova, whose mother Sabretooth had killed years earlier while Elena was still in-utero.

Under unrevealed circumstances, Sabretooth had the near-unbreakable metal Adamantium bonded to his skeleton and claws, much as the Weapon X Program had done to Wolverine many years

Art by Joe Jusko

before. Sabretooth then attacked Wolverine during his wedding to the Viper on the island nation of Madripoor. Wolverine was forced to cooperate with his foe to save Madripoor from an attempted invasion by the ninja clan the Hand and the terrorist organization Hydra. In a later encounter, Sabretooth and Wolverine were set against each other by the eternal mutant Apocalypse, who sought to transform one of them into a Horseman in his service. After a savage battle, Wolverine defeated Sabretooth, tearing out his heart, and Apocalypse removed the Adamantium from Sabretooth, bonding it to Wolverine's skeleton instead. Left for dead, Sabretooth was found in an extremely weakened state by Gambit and the mutant shapeshifter Courier. The trio broke into one of Mister Sinister's bases, and, after some haggling, Sabretooth received treatment to kickstart his healing factor. Gambit subsequently secured enough Adamantium from Sabretooth's former partner, the Constrictor, to keep him alive.

Restored to his former self, Sabretooth joined Mystique's restructured Brotherhood of Mutants in an effort to release a virus that would infect the normal human population. However, after an attack on the Muir Island research base, Sabretooth was defeated by the X-Man Bishop.

Sabretooth was subsequently captured by the re-formed Weapon X Program, and Adamantium was once more bonded to his skeleton. Sabretooth was used as the Program's key operative, responsible for recruiting other former Weapon X members back into the fold. Sabretooth recruited the mercenary Deadpool, but failed to recruit his former Team X teammates Maverick and Wraith. Sabretooth was then assigned as backup on Deadpool's mission to kill the shapeshifting mutant Copycat, Deadpool's former lover. When Deadpool refused to kill her, Sabretooth performed the deed instead.

Sabretooth soon betrayed Weapon X by stealing its data on the world's known mutants, data he used as a lure to recruit two more of Wolverine's enemies, Omega Red and the cyborg Lady

Deathstrike, to attack Wolverine's friends and family, capturing Logan's young ward Amiko. Sabretooth quickly betrayed these allies as well, teleporting himself and Wolverine to the original and long abandoned Weapon X facility where he taunted his nemesis with the revelation that some of Wolverine's amnesia about his life was due to his own healing factor, which repressed overly painful memories. Using command codes stolen from the Weapon X project's Director, Sabretooth utilized a device that stripped Wolverine of his mutant powers. Sabretooth then challenged Wolverine to a supposed final battle during which his own mutant abilities were negated by the same device. Both mutants seemingly died of wounds sustained in the ensuing fight, but once their powers were reactivated both were revived by their mutant healing factors.

Sabretooth next set about using his stolen data to murder several mutants under consideration by the Weapon X Program, which soon recaptured him and subjected him to the hypnotic power of the mutant Mesmero to keep him in line. However, Mesmero soon lost his powers, leaving Sabretooth a threat once again. Sabretooth escaped Weapon X a second time with the help of Mister Sinister, then disguised as the project's lead scientist, Doctor Charles Windsor. Returning to his former mercenary ways, Sabretooth accepted employment from an offshoot of Weapon X to track down an escaped test subject called the Native. Outfought by the Native, Sabretooth manipulated Wolverine into tracking her for him, only to be turned on by his employers as they recaptured their quarry. Seeking vengeance, he allied with Wolverine to raid the facility where the Native was being held. After killing his employers and watching Wolverine and the Native escape, Sabretooth swore to finish the job he had started, tracking down and killing the Native after subduing Wolverine. Sabretooth was then recruited into the latest incarnation of the Brotherhood, led by Magneto's former Acolyte Exodus.

HEIGHT: 6'6"
WEIGHT: 275 lbs.
EYES: Amber
HAIR: Blond
DISTINGUISHING FEATURES: Large, pointed, animal-like canine teeth, clawed hands and feet

SUPERHUMAN POWERS: Sabretooth is a mutant who possesses superhumanly acute senses of sight, hearing, smell, and taste — although perhaps not of touch — comparable to those of certain animals, allowing him to track prey similar to the way dogs and wolves do. His night vision is preternaturally sensitive, containing twice the average human being's area of light-gathering retina, and extends into the infrared portion of the electromagnetic spectrum. His hearing is extraordinarily acute, able to detect light breathing in a cave at 200 feet. His sense of taste can detect one part of foreign matter in 10,000. His highly developed olfactory sense and memory allow him to detect and track a scent over eight hours old, possibly a concentration of 20 parts per million, which he had not been exposed to for up to several months previously. Dilute, common odors of perspiration, perfumes, cigarettes, candies, and food are beacons to his senses.

Sabretooth also possesses the ability to regenerate damaged or destroyed areas of his cellular structure at a rate far greater than that of an ordinary human being. This healing factor makes him virtually immune to poisons and to most drugs. In addition, Sabretooth has a limited immunity to the fatigue poisons generated by bodily activity, giving him greater endurance than any ordinary human being. His healing factor contributes to his superhuman senses via extremely rapid cellular regeneration, and also slows his aging process, meaning he is far older than he appears.

Sabretooth has claws on his hands and animal-like canine teeth which, unaugmented, are strong enough to tear through substances as durable as bone. Since having his skeleton bonded with the nigh-unbreakable metal Adamantium, his claws can tear through almost any substance known to man.

SPECIAL SKILLS: Sabretooth is a formidable hand-to-hand combatant, having been trained by the Foreigner, the C.I.A., and many others. Sabretooth is also an extraordinary hunter and tracker.

Art by Darick Robertson

POWER GRID	1	2	3	4	5	6	7
INTELLIGENCE							
STRENGTH							
SPEED							
DURABILITY							
ENERGY PROJECTION							
FIGHTING SKILLS							